STRUCTURAL GEOLOGY
FOR PETROLEUM GEOLOGISTS

Structural Geology
for Petroleum Geologists

WILLIAM L. RUSSELL

Professor of Geology
Texas Agricultural and Mechanical College

McGRAW-HILL BOOK COMPANY, INC.

New York   Toronto   London

1955

STRUCTURAL GEOLOGY FOR PETROLEUM GEOLOGISTS

Library of Congress Catalog Card Number 55-6169

II

THE MAPLE PRESS COMPANY, YORK, PA.

PREFACE

The purpose of this book is to present the structural data and information which petroleum geologists and students of petroleum geology need in order to practice their profession. Petroleum geologists are naturally interested in many aspects of structural geology which are not related to prospecting for or producing petroleum. However, limitations of space prevent discussion of those aspects of structural geology which have no bearing on oil finding.

Although petroleum geologists are in a profession with a practical objective, too great an emphasis on what is immediately useful would make any treatment of structural geology less valuable. In writing the chapters which follow, the author has kept in mind that the main objective is to give a thorough understanding of the subject. In many cases this may be achieved by forgetting for the moment the practical applications.

This book is intended to be used with the author's previous publication, "Principles of Petroleum Geology," and each of the two books is designed to cover subject matter which the other omits. It is hoped that this planned treatment of two related subjects may permit a better integration of courses in petroleum geology and structural geology.

Acknowledgments are due to Travis J. Parker for a critical reading of the manuscript. The author would like to express especial gratitude to his wife, Leonore K. Russell, for a critical reading of the manuscript and for aid in preparing the references.

WILLIAM L. RUSSELL

CONTENTS

CHAPTER 1

INTRODUCTION

Uses and Value of Structural Geology

There is no need to argue about the value of structural geology. Geologists appear to be unanimous in stressing its usefulness both in pure science and in industrial applications. It is, moreover, an essential part of the education of a geologist even in such diverse fields as mining geology, petrology of igneous and metamorphic rocks, and petroleum geology. Petroleum geologists, for whom this text is primarily written, make continued use of structural geology during the course of their professional activities. In fact, petroleum geology is based essentially on structural geology and stratigraphy.

Scope of This Book

This book is designed to give petroleum geologists the structural knowledge they will need for their profession. The structures of sedimentary rocks are naturally emphasized, and particular attention is given to structures which are important in the discovery or development of oil and gas fields.

In this volume the relations of structural geology to stratigraphy have been stressed, for it appears that this will make the work more useful. The stratigraphic aspects of structural geology have come to be recognized fairly recently, and it appears that they are a promising field for investigation. Furthermore, it is generally recognized that promising traps for oil or gas accumulation which are of purely structural origin are steadily becoming scarcer compared to those produced wholly or partly by stratigraphic causes. Since the stratigraphic-type fields are likely to become of increasing importance in petroleum geology, it is desirable to understand thoroughly their structural features and relations.

This text is designed to be used with the writer's previous book, "Principles of Petroleum Geology."[1] In order to avoid unnecessary repetition, subjects treated thoroughly in one book have in general not been discussed at length in the other. When it is necessary to treat the same subject in both books, as in the case of unconformities and salt domes,

---

[1] William L. Russell, "Principles of Petroleum Geology," McGraw-Hill Book Company, Inc., New York (1951).

1

an effort has been made to arrange the subject matter so as to avoid duplication.

This volume is intended to be used as a textbook for graduate and undergraduate courses in structural geology, and as a reference book for petroleum geologists. It is assumed that the course in structural geology will precede the course in petroleum geology. It might be supposed that professional geologists have such a thorough knowledge of structural geology that they would have no use for a textbook on the subject. However, most petroleum geologists are specialists, many of whom do not have time to keep up with developments outside their special field. For this reason an up-to-date treatment of the subject should be useful to them, to refresh their memory and to acquaint them with the new evidence, developments, and interpretations. In this book the emphasis is on structural types and processes, rather than on detailed descriptions. The individual structures are used as examples to illustrate the types.

DEVELOPMENT OF STRUCTURAL GEOLOGY

Sources of Data. Three aspects of the growth and development of structural geology are the collection of field data, the development of generalizations, and the testing of theories. The essential data on which the science is based are obtained in the field. In their raw state, these data are field observations, well logs, and geophysical measurements. These isolated facts are assembled and combined by geologists to form interpretations of local structure. The interpretations of local structure are in turn accepted as known facts and used in developing principles. The correct interpretation of local structure is aided by all the available information from wells, surface geology and geophysics, and a thorough knowledge of the stratigraphy. It is also helpful to have a knowledge of the types of local structures that have been found in the region and their changes with depth and other habits. Interpretation continually improves as new knowledge becomes available. This information may come from new wells, from new surface work, from geophysical surveys, or from data on distant areas that have a bearing on the case. Structural interpretation in areas of sedimentary rocks is based on an accurate knowledge of the stratigraphy. Usually it is necessary to work out the stratigraphy before interpreting the structure, and the accuracy of the structural interpretation depends in a large part on the accuracy of the stratigraphic knowledge.

Making Generalizations. A vast amount of information about local structures has now accumulated in maps, sections, and written reports, some published and many unpublished. Generalizations made from this descriptive material constitute the main body of structural geology. The study of great numbers of anticlines, faults, unconformities, and other structural features yields reasonably accurate conceptions of typical and exceptional structures, the relations of structures to each other and to depth, and the like. These generalizations are likely to be geometrical and statistical. They have to do with the sizes, shapes, frequency of occurrence, behavior with depth, and relations to oil and gas fields and other mineral deposits.

Testing Theories. Theories are needed to explain the observed structures and relations. Some theories become practical guides in deciphering the structure and in applying the structural knowledge to find mineral deposits. Theories may be of great value because they explain the modes of formation, show the relations between seemingly unrelated observations, or result in new discoveries. Naturally, poor theories retard the progress of a science, while good theories promote progress. The best method for testing theories seems to be to list all explanations and hypotheses which are even remotely possible, and then compare each carefully with the evidence. It appears that the best progress is made if new theories are eagerly welcomed but critically evaluated.

It is unfortunate that a general textbook inevitably discusses so many subjects and theories that there is generally not sufficient space to discuss in detail how the various theories of the science were suggested, developed, criticized, tested, and finally accepted or rejected, or still considered unproved. Because of the limitations of space, it is frequently necessary to make categorical statements without presenting the evidence, or to select only one out of many possible theories for discussion. This is apt to give an erroneous idea of the difficulties and the complex problems involved in proving or disproving a theory. In particular, it may influence the student to forget to use the method of multiple hypotheses in solving the theoretical problems which arise during the course of his work. Lack of space also prevents giving a correct idea of the degree of certainty of many theories which are now considered established. Actually, the theories of structural geology should be perpetually under scrutiny to detect defects in them, and new evidence should be carefully considered to determine its bearing on the theories which are assumed to be proved.

Another important point is that the method of multiple hypotheses should be used to test the correctness of the various interpretations of structure made as the evidence is assembled. The interpretation of the presence of an anticline or a fault in a given locality should be treated in the same manner as unproved theories—that is, all possible explanations should be devised and the evidence for and against each interpretation carefully weighed. This method of procedure is especially desirable for a beginning geologist, or for any geologist working in unfamiliar territory.

DEFINITIONS OF STRUCTURAL GEOLOGY

The definition of structural geology involves two concepts. Clearly structural geology deals with the effects of forces on the rocks of the earth, and this type of subject matter is ordinarily considered to comprise the science. However, structural geology also deals with geometrical shapes of the various geologic features, or with the geometrical arrangement of their parts. It is evident that there is a dynamic and a static or geometrical phase of structural geology. The first phase is clearly the more important; in fact, some geologists may possibly consider that the shapes and geometrical relations of geologic features are not part of the subject matter of structural geology at all. However, the common use of such expressions as the "structure" of a limestone reef or a concretion, as well as the usage of the term in ordinary speech, shows that the concept of structure also involves shapes and geometrical relations. Moreover, sedimentary structures, such as cross-bedding and stratification, are commonly considered part of the subject matter of structural geology, although they are geometrical features not produced by the action of forces.

In a book on structural geology for petroleum geologists, it is very desirable to emphasize the geometrical aspect of the science. This is because the traps which localize commercial oil accumulations are in part produced by the deformation of the strata and in part by the configuration of the reservoir rock, which has nothing to do with deformation. The most important application of structural geology to finding oil and gas is in locating and studying the traps which determine the place of formation of commercial accumulations of oil or gas. To leave out some of these traps because they were not produced by tectonic forces would clearly be a glaring omission.

NOMENCLATURE

Anyone writing a book on structural geology is forced into a consideration of problems of nomenclature. There is a remarkable lack of agreement on the names which should be given to the important structural features and processes. In some cases the same name is given to two entirely different things, and in others there is more than one name for the same thing. At times geologists, disturbed by this confusion, have appointed committees to establish the correct usage, or have written books or papers in which they proposed an entirely new terminology. These efforts have in some cases only served to increase the confusion, for many geologists have ignored the proposed changes. It might be supposed that the meaning of the terms could be established by looking up the definitions in the publications in which they were first used. Unfortunately, this often does not help matters, either because the usage has changed since the terms were first used, or because the original definitions were not sufficiently clear.

The general policy used in this book is to follow the commonest usage, and to define how each term is used. The introduction of new terms has been avoided if possible, because previous experience has shown that these new terms merely add to the confusion. The terminology adopted is selected primarily for its usefulness in petroleum geology. Problems in nomenclature are also discussed on pages 50 and 108–109.

QUALIFICATIONS AND DUTIES OF A STRUCTURAL GEOLOGIST

Qualifications. The characteristics of a successful structural geologist change with the times. In the nineteenth century and in the first two decades of the twentieth century, structural geologists were engaged primarily in surface field work, and they naturally needed the physical stamina and other qualities required for field work. At present the structural work of oil companies is carried on chiefly in the office, and it is no longer necessary for a geologist who works for them to have the qualifications of a field geologist. A very essential part of the mental equipment of a structural geologist is his ability to visualize structural features in three dimensions and to express his conceptions accurately by graphic methods. In other words, he should have facility in making maps, cross sections and the like. He also needs the ability to express his ideas clearly, both orally and in written reports.

Duties. Structural geology differs from other branches of geology in that there is no large, organized group of persons who call themselves structural geologists. Outside the teaching profession, few geologists refer to themselves as structural geologists. Even though a geologist may use structural geology continually in his work, he is generally known by some other appellation, such as "petroleum geologist" or "mining geologist."

The structural work of petroleum geologists consists in making structure maps, cross sections, geologic maps, and isopach maps, in detecting and mapping faults, correlating well logs, writing reports, making recommendations based on structural data, conferences, research, furnishing information to other departments of the company, and interpreting geophysical surveys. Work which involves making graphical representations of structural features, such as maps and cross sections, is likely to be given to a geologist soon after he joins a company, and reports and recommendations are frequently written by more experienced geologists. However, both types of work are likely to be given to structural geologists at any time.

Types of Instruction Needed in Structural Geology

It has been generally recognized that a student who has definite plans to become a petroleum geologist needs three types of education in structural geology: theory, field work, and laboratory training. What is here called theory consists in listening to lectures and reading books and periodicals on structural subjects. Mapping of structural features in the field is an important part of the training of a petroleum geologist, even if he never expects to do field work after graduation. In fact college courses involving field work are more needed now than they were a generation ago, for petroleum geologists at the present time rarely get training in surface field mapping after being employed. The best areas for geology students to secure field training in structural geology are those in which varied types of structures are well exposed. Regions of undeformed strata and gentle dips are not satisfactory for this purpose.

Laboratory training in structural geology is considered to consist in practice in constructing maps, cross sections, block diagrams, and the like. It is clear that this type of work is an essential feature of the training of every petroleum geologist. For some time after a geologist joins an oil company his structural work is likely to consist in making structure maps and cross sections or in similar activities in which laboratory training rather than theoretical knowledge is needed. A geologist whose laboratory training is defective will be handicapped in securing a job and in giving satisfaction after he is employed.

The amount of mathematical training a student in structural geology needs depends somewhat on what field he will enter. Those who will become petroleum engineers or geophysicists need a good deal of mathematics and physics. There has been a tendency for some phases or problems of petroleum geology to become more quantitative and more mathematical with time. The interpretation of electrical well logs is an example of this. Furthermore, some research problems or investigations of subjects related to structural geology require extensive knowledge of higher mathematics and physics for their solution. An example of this is the dimensional analysis of scale models, which is mentioned in Chap. 3. During their ordinary structural work, petroleum geologists frequently need to use trigonometry, but they rarely need a knowledge of higher mathematics. Structural problems of great complexity frequently arise in the work of a petroleum geologist, but their complications are geometrical or geological. In this age of specialization it may be better to leave problems involving extensive knowledge of physics and mathematics to the geophysicists.

Petroleum geologists could study with profit the special branch of mathematics which deals with probabilities, random errors, and correlation coefficients, and in general with the application of the laws of chance. Some problems in this field are the prediction of the chances of success of a given number of wildcat wells, determining the effects of various structural and stratigraphic conditions on the chances of success, studying the relations of oil and gas fields to structural and stratigraphic conditions, deciding whether geophysical anomalies of various types show any significant relation to structural or stratigraphic features, and deciding whether the variations in the hydrocarbon content of soils show any significant relation to oil and gas fields.

Opinions differ as to the amount of specialized training needed by a petroleum geologist, as to the time when he should begin to specialize, and as to the nature of his special studies. A geologist tends to look with favor on the type of education he has himself received, and on the type needed for his speciality. Some universities change their curricula slowly in response to changing needs, and subjects which have been taught for a long time tend to acquire a certain amount of prestige in academic circles. On the one hand there is danger of dealing too much with subject matter of general interest but no actual usefulness in prospecting for oil, and on the other hand there is danger of concentrating so intensively on the immediately practical that the instruction degenerates into a trade course.

The subject matter of structural geology comprises a number of somewhat disconnected fields, such as structural problems related to mining, studies of the major structural features of the earth and their origin, and structures important in petroleum geology. A geologist entering the petroleum industry is benefited by a course dealing primarily in the structures of oil fields and sedimentary rocks, just as a geologist entering mining geology would benefit most from a course emphasizing the types of structure he will encounter in his future work. It does not appear practicable to cover all phases of structure thoroughly in a single-semester course, or in a textbook of ordinary length.

The studies of Levorsen[1] regarding the percentages of graduates in geology entering various types of geologic work afford a means of estimating the relative numbers of geology students needing different types of courses. About half of all graduates in geology who become professional geologists of some type enter the petroleum industry. This is about ten times as many as enter the mining industry. It therefore appears that about two-thirds of all geology students need a course and textbook emphasizing the structural problems of petroleum geology and sedimentary rocks.

[1] A. I. Levorsen, Survey of College Students Majoring in Geology, *A.A.P.G. Bull.*, vol. 34, p. 1375 (1950).

CHAPTER 2

MAPS AND CROSS SECTIONS

The most important single technique which needs to be acquired by a structural geologist is the ability to express his structural concepts graphically and to interpret accurately the graphic representations of others. These representations, which generally take the form of maps or cross sections, indicate the nature of the structural features much better than any amount of verbal description. It would be difficult to exaggerate the importance of maps and cross sections in petroleum geology. They summarize the results of geological and geophysical investigations costing millions of dollars. They are extensively used both for estimating the value of untested prospects and for planning the development of oil and gas fields after their discovery. A major part of the work of petroleum geologists consists in gathering data from which maps and cross sections will be constructed. The value of a petroleum geologist to his company depends to a considerable degree on his ability to express graphically his ideas about structure and stratigraphy.

General Features of Maps

Maps and map making constitute a subject of considerable complexity; it would require many volumes to treat it adequately. In this chapter only geological maps are discussed in detail, and other types are referred to only briefly.

A map is a projection on a plane surface of features whose real occurrence is on a much larger scale. The maps most people are familiar with are small-scale representations of large-scale features on the surface of the earth. However, the maps most important in petroleum geology frequently represent conditions far below the surface of the earth. The various real features are represented on the maps by symbols; this means that a legend is needed to explain the meaning of the symbols. On maps which cover a very large area, such as a state or a continent, the method of projection is important. The projection is the method of representing on the geometric plane of the map the curved surface of the earth. The larger the area, the more the earth's surface departs from a geometrical plane, and the more distortion is needed to represent it on a plane surface. If the area represented is only a few miles square, no important errors will be introduced in geologic mapping if the distortion is neglected and the earth's surface is assumed to be flat.

Of course every map should have an indication of the orientation and a scale. The orientation is generally given by an arrow pointing north, and north is generally at the top. However, if the shape of the map makes it inconvenient to place north at the top, it is permissible to depart from this custom. The scale is the ratio between the distance between two points on the map and the distance between the same two points in the field. There are three ways of expressing scale. One is to state that so many inches, or centimeters, on the map represent so many feet, miles, or kilometers in the field. A second method is to give a fraction of which the numerator is the length of a given feature on the map and the denominator the length of the same feature in the field. Thus a scale of 1 in. to the mile would be represented as the fraction 1/63,360. The scale 1/62,500 is commonly used by the United States Geological Survey for many topographic maps. The third type of scale is graphic. That is, the actual lengths of certain units in the field, such as feet, miles, or kilometers, are plotted graphically on the maps. This graphic scale is generally the best, because no errors are introduced if the scale is changed in photographic reproduction, or if the prints shrink on drying.

The selection of the scale to be used in mapping is determined by the necessity for keeping the map a reasonable size, by the amount of detail that needs to be plotted, and to some extent by the size of the errors. It is naturally desirable to keep the features shown on the map from being too crowded or too small, and it is also advisable to choose a scale small enough so that any errors will appear small.

Base Maps

The map on which a geologist plots his data is generally referred to as a base map. Base maps may be ordinary geographic maps showing culture and streams, or they may be topographic maps or airplane photographs. In areas where the land is sectionized, it is very desirable to secure base maps which show the boundaries of the sections, townships, and ranges. If no suitable base map is available, the geologist has to make one. This, of course, adds greatly to the expense and time involved in geological mapping. The best base maps are those which show many points which can be identified in the field and used for locating wells and outcrops. If elevations are to be used, as in the drawing of structure contours, it is desirable to use base maps showing numerous elevations at bench marks and road corners. Accurate base maps make possible accurate and detailed geologic maps, and one of the best ways to promote geologic work is to provide satisfactory base maps.

METHODS OF OBTAINING LOCATIONS

The method used in geologic mapping to obtain locations depends on the nature of the available base maps and on the type of geological work being done. Usually it is possible to obtain extremely accurate locations on airplane photographs without moving from one spot. Generally the arrangement of trees, gullies, streams, and roads will indicate the exact spot whose location is wanted. In case the base map shows only roads and streams, it may be necessary to determine the distance and direction to these by pace and compass traverse. This takes time and may involve appreciable errors. If the land is sectionized, section corners can generally be found in the field by the characteristic configuration of the fence lines. Where the methods mentioned above do not give sufficiently accurate locations, it is necessary either to abandon geologic work or to go to the expense of obtaining greater accuracy. The plane table and telescopic alidade are commonly used to make maps and obtain locations in oil work. If properly used, they give sufficiently accurate results for all geologic purposes.

METHODS OF DESIGNATING LOCATIONS

The location of every point on the earth may be designated accurately by giving its latitude and longitude. However, oil companies and petroleum geologists rarely use this method to indicate the location of wells and other features on land. If the land is sectionized, it is customary to use the land-classification grid for giving the locations of wells and often of geological features also. In sectionized areas the section lines should be shown on the structure or geologic maps made for oil development, because maps showing land ownership are based on the section lines, and it is very desirable to know the relation between the land ownership and the structure. In the New England and Atlantic coastal states north of Florida and in Kentucky, Tennessee, and most of Texas, the land is not divided up in any orderly or systematic manner, and the location of particular tracts is difficult. In the Texas Panhandle and the states of the United States other than those mentioned, the land is sectionized, and the accurate designation of locations is easy.

The method of subdividing the land according to the Federal land-classification scheme is illustrated in Figs. 2-1, 2-2, and 2-3. Points are located by subdivisions within a section, by the number of the section within a township, and by the township and range number. In the description of a location, the order is always from smaller units to larger. Thus the sixty-fourth part of the section is given first, then the sixteenth, and then the quarter of the section, the section number, the township, and finally the range. An example is "nw se ne, sec. 16, T. 34, N.,

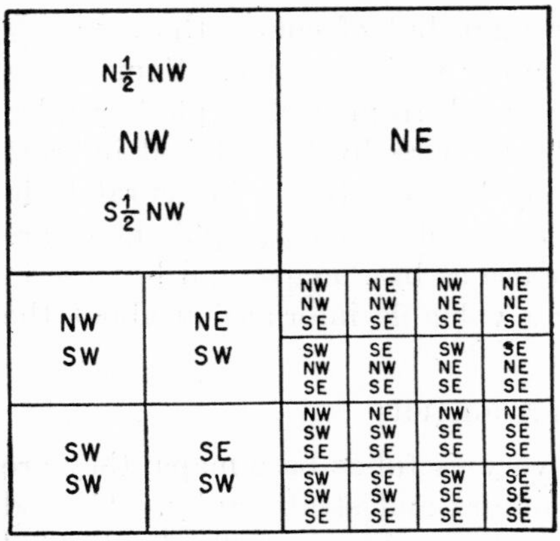

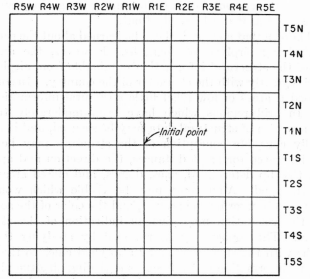

FIG. 2-1. Method of describing locations within a section.

6	5	4	3	2	1
7	8	9	10	11	12
18	17	16	15	14	13
19	20	21	22	23	24
30	29	28	27	26	25
31	32	33	34	35	36

FIG. 2-2. Numbering of sections in a township.

FIG. 2-3. Numbering of townships and ranges.

R. 14 W." In Kentucky and Tennessee oil men and geologists have devised a method, known as the Carter Coordinate System, for indicating locations. It is somewhat similar to the Federal land-classification scheme.

TOPOGRAPHIC MAPS

Topography may be indicated on maps by shading or coloring the areas according to their elevations, by hachures, by relief maps, and by topographic contours. It is theoretically possible to estimate the elevation of every point on a topographic map, but of course the accuracy of the elevations estimated in this manner varies greatly. Some topographic maps, especially those which are made from airplane photographs, are highly accurate; but generally the topography is sketched in from traverses made along roads, and it may be shown very inaccurately in the areas which cannot be seen from the roads. Topographic maps are of value to geologists because of their use as base maps, and because in some cases the topography itself gives valuable information about the structure.

AIRPLANE PHOTOGRAPHS

Airplane photographs are not only very useful as base maps; they are also a great help in working out structure and stratigraphy. If good airplane photographs are available, points may generally be located rapidly and accurately. In wooded areas it may be necessary to pace from the nearest open spot, but in open country the geology can generally be located as fast as it can be worked out.

It is well known that a great deal can be learned about the geology of an area by studying airplane photographs. However, the amount and reliability of the structural information obtainable from airplane photographs varies greatly with the character of the country. In some humid, densely wooded areas of low relief little structural information may be obtained. In arid regions which have been moderately to strongly deformed, a wealth of structural data may be secured, and in some cases a practically complete conception of the structure may be obtained. Beds may be traced for great distances, the direction and approximate amount of the dip determined, axes, domes, and closed areas outlined, and faults mapped. Alignments may be visible which would not be detected by an observer on the ground, and the color of the soils and the nature of the vegetation may give an indication of the structure or stratigraphy. The topography as revealed by studying the airplane photographs with the stereoscope may also yield clues to the structure. Papers giving information and references regarding airplane photographs have been published in *Photogrammetric Engineering*[1] and by the American Geological Institute.[2]

So much may be discovered by studying the photographs that there is a tendency to assume that there is no need for a geologist to go into the area at all. Office studies of airplane photographs may indicate

[1] Symposium of Information Relative to Uses of Aerial Photographs by Geologists, compiled by H. T. U. Smith, *Photogrammetric Engineering*, vol. 13, no. 4, pp. 531–628 (1947).

[2] Outstanding Aerial Photographs in North America, *Am. Geol. Inst. Rept.* 5, National Academy of Science–National Research Council (May, 1951).

which regions have sufficient promise to justify visiting in the field. Many promising anticlines and other structures have been discovered by studying airplane photographs, but it is generally advisable to study the area on the ground before commencing a test. It is possible to determine from a study of the airplane photographs something about the continuity of the units of sedimentary rocks, their structure, and also their resistance to erosion. The vegetation may offer clues to the lithologic nature of the sediments. However, it is obvious that a much more complete and detailed conception of the stratigraphy could be obtained from observations in the field. In some areas relatively minor features, such as fossils, concretions, textures of sedimentary rocks, narrow zones of fracturing and slickensiding, and local dips along fault planes, may give the clue to the true structural interpretation. These features may be too small or too much covered by vegetation to be seen on the airplane photographs.

Maps made up of airplane photographs are also called aerial maps, or aerial mosaics. The term "airplane maps" is used in this book because "aerial" sounds too much like "areal."

Geologic Columns and Stratigraphic Sections

It is frequently advantageous to present a summary of the stratigraphy of an area in the form of a column, with the oldest rocks at the base. The descriptions of formations may be given in words, or the nature of the rocks may be shown by graphic symbols. Since a detailed knowledge of the stratigraphy is essential for making an accurate structure map, it is frequently desirable to show the geologic column used in making the structure map plotted graphically along one side. "Geologic column," "geologic section," "stratigraphic column," and "stratigraphic section" are terms used to describe stratigraphy listed or plotted in this manner. The graphic symbols given on the right-hand side of Fig. 2-4 may be used to show the formations graphically. It is advisable to give the thickness of all formations and members. If the stratigraphic column is shown graphically, the thickness may be given by a graphic scale, as in a well log.

Geologic and Areal Maps

Symbols Used. The symbols used in geologic maps to designate the same geologic features vary a good deal. With the exception of dip and strike symbols and the designation of the axial traces of anticlines and synclines, there are no symbols whose meaning is absolutely invariable. Because of this variation in usage, it is desirable to study the legend of a map in order to be sure what the author intends the symbols to mean. All symbols shown on a map should be explained in the legend.

Some of the common symbols used on geologic maps are shown in Fig. 2-4.

The symbols used to indicate areas covered by certain formations or by strata of certain ages are also given in Fig. 2-4. In general, the symbols used on maps tend to have the same lithologic significance as those used in plotting geologic columns and graphic well logs. Small dots are commonly used to indicate sandstones, large dots or circles, conglomerate,

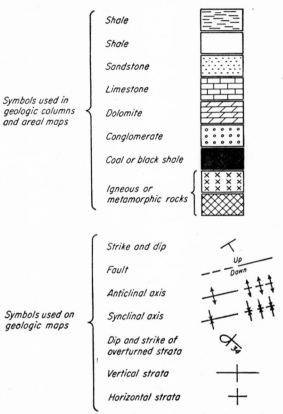

FIG. 2-4. Symbols used on geologic maps and geologic columns.

horizontal lines or blank spaces, shales, "brick-wall" pattern, limestones, and "brick-wall" pattern with inclined lines, dolomite. The symbols used to designate particular formations on areal maps may be a definite black and white pattern, a color, or simply a letter or number. If a color is used to indicate lithology, it is desirable to use orange, red, or yellow for sandstones, blue for limestones, and purple or violet for dolomites. Igneous dikes and intrusions, if small in area, are commonly shown in shades of red. It should be understood that the usage of these symbols varies somewhat, and the meaning may vary considerably from that indicated above. Nevertheless it is desirable to follow this usage, for departures from it are likely to be misinterpreted. Colors are also used to indicate the age of rocks.

Definitions. An areal map shows the areas where the various geologic formations crop out, each formation being indicated by a particular color, pattern, or symbol. A geologic map is very much the same as an areal map; however, important structural features, such as faults and anticlinal axes, are generally shown on geologic maps. For purposes of laboratory training, an areal map may be defined as one which shows only the areas of outcrop of the formations, with faults and other structural features omitted. The student can then be asked to make areal maps that show these structural features. To avoid confusion, the term "areal map" will be used in this book to indicate a map showing formation boundaries only. In the geologic literature, the terms "areal map" and "geologic map" are used more or less interchangeably, and some structural features are generally indicated on the published areal maps.

Regional Areal Maps. Geologic or areal maps of large regions, such as countries or states, indicate at a glance the regional structural relations. Areal and geologic maps are very useful in petroleum geology, and geologists should know how to obtain from them as much useful information as possible. In addition to showing the general or regional structural relations, the small-scale maps of large areas indicate what formation a well will start in, and give some indication of the formations likely to be encountered in drilling. The direction of the regional dip and strike may be estimated from these maps, and the amount of the regional dip may also be estimated if the thickness of the formations is known. The variations in the widths of the outcrops show where the dip is steep and where it is gentle. Angular unconformities are shown by the truncation or elimination of certain formations. Usually the larger folds are indicated, and in some cases the height of the larger folds and the closure may be roughly estimated.

The methods of interpretation just described are based on the assumption that the variations in the elevation of the surface are too small to affect the results. The effects of topography are less important where the dip is steep, the area covered by the map large, and the relief small. Where there is considerable relief or where the scale of the map is large, the effects of topography have to be carefully considered in making interpretations.

Local Areal Maps. Local structural features, such as folds and faults, may show up on areal maps of areas of limited extent, such as individual counties. In regional areal maps the effect of topography is relatively

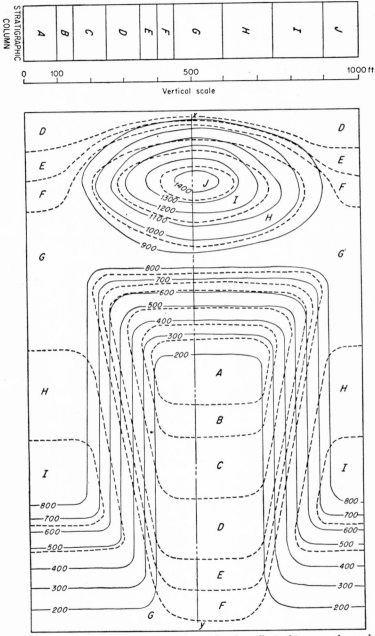

Fɪɢ. 2-5. Combined areal and topographic map showing effect of topography and outcrop pattern.   Solid lines are topographic contours, dashed lines formation boundaries.

slight, because the regional structural features indicated are large compared to the topographic relief. In local areal maps the effect of the topography must always be considered in interpreting the structure. If the topography is not known, the effects of the topographic relief may be confused with the effects of structure. Older formations tend to crop out in valleys; older formations also crop out along the crests of anticlines where there is little topographic relief. If nothing were known about the topography, it would be difficult to distinguish between the effects of topography and of structure on areal maps. Thus a circular area of younger formations surrounded by older could be interpreted either as a syncline or structural basin on a flat surface or as a circular mountain or plateau in an area of flat-lying beds. Figs. 2-5

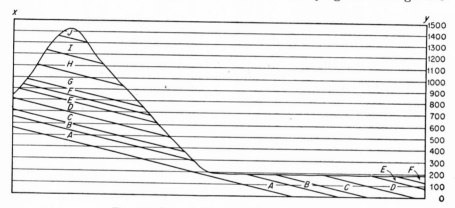

FIG. 2-6. Cross section from *X* to *Y* in Fig. 2-5.

and 2-6 illustrate a condition of this nature. If accurate and detailed areal and topographic maps are both available in an area, a structure map may be constructed from them, as explained below.

Topographic Expression of Structures on Areal Maps. A fundamental point to remember while studying the expression of structural features in topographic and areal maps is that the original topographic features produced by direct structural uplift or depression have generally been largely or completely removed by erosion. Fault scarps are deeply scarred by erosion before they reach considerable heights, and anticlines are eroded as they rise. Moreover, it is only where deformation has taken place late in geologic time that there are still topographic remnants of the original uplifts or depressions. It is more common to find that the deformation took place so long ago that the original topographic features which it produced have long since been eroded away. If in such cases the rocks of the area are all of the same resistance to erosion, there will be no effect of the structure on the topography. If the formations differ in their resistance to erosion, the resistant rocks will tend to occupy the topographic elevations. Thus there will be an effect of structure on topography, but it may be entirely different from that produced by the original direct uplifts and depressions. This subject is discussed further on pages 351–352.

The Use of Areal Maps in Training Geologists. Areal maps furnish excellent means for training students in structural geology. In most of the problems in areal maps given in the Laboratory Supplement to this book, the interpretation is simplified by assuming that the ground surface is flat. In such cases the features shown on the areal map are produced by the intersection of the three-dimensional structural features with the plane represented by the earth's surface. The best way to learn how to make and interpret areal maps of various structural features is to visualize them and their intersection with the plane of the earth's surface in three dimensions.

PROBLEMS RELATING TO DIP AND STRIKE

Definitions. Dip, strike, and the plane of stratification are perhaps the most fundamental concepts in structural geology. The plane of stratification is simply a plane surface parallel to the stratification. In other words, it is parallel to the layers or laminations in the sedimentary rocks. If the layers are wavy or irregular, the plane of stratification is considered to be as nearly as possible parallel to the average attitude of all the strata. The dip of the strata is the angle between the plane of stratification and a horizontal plane. The strike is the direction of a line along which the plane of stratification and a horizontal surface intersect.

The Measurement of Dip and Strike. It is commonly supposed by geologists that the measurement of dip and strike in the field is a simple problem which is mastered by geology students in elementary courses. Actually this measurement is not always as simple as it seems; certainly geologists with years of experience may be found who have not yet mastered it.

The strike is always given as so many degrees east or west of north. If the actual measurement is a bearing east or west of south, this is reversed to give the corresponding bearing from north. Thus if a geologist sights along the strike and reads S. 32° E. on his compass, he records the strike as N. 32° W. The dip is measured in such a direction that the angle between the plane of stratification and a horizontal plane is at a maximum. This means that it is measured at right angles to the strike. If the plane of stratification is imagined to be a flat inclined surface, the dip is measured in the direction in which water would run if poured out on this surface. If the flat surface formed by the plane of stratification is partly covered by water, the direction of the shore line or edge of the water is the strike. In surface geological work the measurement of the strike is frequently aided by finding such shore lines on exposed layers of rock along the edges of puddles, streams, and lakes.

If the dip is at a high angle, it may be measured with a clinometer. Usually the geologist holds his compass so that it is in a vertical plane at right angles to the strike, and tilts it until the straight edge is parallel to the plane of stratification. The clinometer is turned until the bubble is in the middle of the tube, and the dip read off. In order to avoid errors, it is necessary to keep the eyes of the observer at the same level as the point at which the dip is being measured. Dips measured in this way are generally subject to errors of one or two degrees, and in some cases the unavoidable error may be much larger. It varies considerably with the nature of the deposits. Uneven bedding, cross-bedding, channeling, initial dip, delta formation, slumping, crumpling, and the presence of small folds may render such measurements worthless. Beginning students should bear in mind that it requires three statements to describe the dip accurately. One is the direction of the strike, the other the angle of dip, and the third the quadrant toward which the strata dip. The statement that the strike is N. 60° E. and the dip 40° is ambiguous; it is also necessary to state whether the strata dip northwest or southeast.

The Three-point Problem. Where the dip is not more than one or two degrees, it is generally necessary to measure the dip by taking elevations on the same stratum at three separated points not in a straight line. If the exposures are not continuous, this involves correlation between the points. In other words, there must be some stratum, contact, or key horizon which extends between the three points and which can be readily recognized at all three. It is desirable that the three points be at least 100 ft apart, and the measurements are more reliable if they are several hundred feet apart.

One method for solving the three-point problem is illustrated in Fig. 2-7. Plot the positions of the three points, and let A be the point of lowest elevation, B the point of highest elevation, and C the point of intermediate elevation. Draw a line from A to B, and let P be the point on the line AB having the same elevation as point C. It is assumed that the three points lie in a plane whose dip is uniform. Accordingly,

$$\frac{PB}{PA} = \frac{\text{elevation of } B - \text{elevation of } C}{\text{elevation of } C - \text{elevation of } A}$$

From this proportion the distance of point P from A and B may be determined, and point P plotted. Draw the line CR through point P, and drop a perpendicular from point A or B to CR. The direction of line *CR* is the strike, and the dip is the difference in elevation between point *A* or *B* and the line *CR*, divided by the map distance from point *A* or *B* to the line *CR*. This gives the tangent of the dip angle. It may be converted to per cent slope by multiplying by 100.

Determining Dip and Strike from Two Components of the Dip. In some cases it may be possible to measure the component of the dip in two directions, the strike being unknown. This may occur in surface work when the dip along the sides of two cliffs may be measured, but the dip at right angles to the face of the cliff cannot be determined. One measurement may be along the face of a cliff, and the other the slope from an outcrop on the ground to the outcrop of the same key horizon

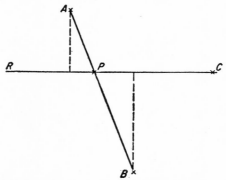

Fɪɢ. 2-7. A method for solving the three-point problem.

in an inaccessible point. The same problem may occasionally occur in subsurface work. The dip and strike may be determined by plotting on a sketch map to a convenient scale two intersecting lines parallel to the two directions in which the component of the dip is known. A point on each line a convenient distance from the intersection is selected. The relative elevations of the intersection and of the other two points may now be determined from the distances and angle of slope. Thus we have the three-point problem, the solution of which was described above.

The solutions of the two problems given above are preferred because they do not involve memorizing formulas.

Maps Showing Conditions in Geologic Past

Paleogeologic or Paleoareal Maps. Maps which show conditions in the geologic past are designated by the prefix "paleo" attached to the name of the type of map. Perhaps the best-known of these are paleogeographic maps, which show geographic conditions, such as the distribution of land and sea, in the geologic past. Paleoareal or paleo-geologic maps show the distribution of the geologic formations and structural features at various times in the past. The first step in constructing a paleoareal map is to select an angular unconformity. The geologic formation which lies immediately beneath this unconformity is plotted on the map at all points where sufficient information is available. The formation boundaries which constitute the paleoareal map are then sketched in from these data. The reason an angular unconformity is chosen is that under ordinary conditions it is only at angular unconformities that a number of different formations will underlie a contact. Where the contacts are conformable or where a disconformity is present, each contact is generally underlain by a single formation over great areas. Changes in facies from one area to another may cause the type of rock underlying a given contact to vary greatly, but these variations are not what is shown on paleoareal maps. Maps showing changes in facies are known as lithofacies maps. They are discussed in Chap. 11.

Where great local relief is present beneath a disconformity, the formations immediately beneath it may vary without structural deformation. Thus a paleoareal map may be influenced to some extent by the buried topography beneath the unconformity. However, in general the configuration of the formation boundaries shown on paleoareal maps is due to structural deformation and not buried topography. What is shown on paleoareal maps is the area of outcrop of the formations at the time just before the deposition of the basal beds above the angular unconformity.

Paleoareal maps show the underground distribution of the formations beneath the angular unconformity, and this may be a great help in correlation, in determining where promising reservoir rocks are present, for deciding where good reservoir rocks are likely to be associated with good source rocks, and for locating traps formed by truncation. Another use is for determining how the structure beneath angular unconformities will vary from the known structure above them, and particularly for determining how the size and closure of anticlines will be affected by the angular unconformity. One of the most important uses of paleoareal maps is for dating the formation of folds and faults. Folds and faults on paleoareal maps are interpreted in the same manner as on areal maps. Any structural feature which shows up on a paleoareal map was already in existence at the time when the oldest beds above the angular unconformity were laid down. If an anticline found in the strata above the angular unconformity appears on the areal map showing the distribution of the strata just beneath the angular unconformity, this anticline must have been partly formed before the beds just above the angular unconformity were deposited. If the accumulation of oil occurred before the time represented by the angular unconformity, only those anticlines which show up on the paleoareal map may be productive.

Paleotectonic and Palinspastic Maps. According to Eardley,[1] paleotectonic maps show structural features that were formed during the period covered by the map. Thus a paleotectonic map of the Devonian period would show structures that developed during the Devonian in the area covered by the map, and no others.

Kay[2] states that palinspastic maps show rocks and structural features in their interpreted position prior to thrust faulting, folding, and flowage. These maps are evidently very difficult to construct, because accurate knowledge would be needed of the amount of shortening produced during deformation. This is a subject about which the opinions of geologists differ greatly. Palinspastic maps have not been used extensively by petroleum geologists.

CROSS SECTIONS

Definitions. Cross sections show the geologic formations and structures intersecting an imaginary plane surface, which constitutes the plane of the cross section. Generally cross sections are drawn to illustrate the structural and stratigraphic relations and are in a vertical plane, but they do not have to be vertical. Special reasons may make it advisable to show inclined or horizontal cross sections. If the cross section is vertical, its top is generally the intersection of the plane of the cross section with the ground surface, and its base is set at any convenient depth. If a great trench is imagined to be cut through the earth's surface, cross sections show the formations as they would appear on the vertical sides of this trench. The structure shown in the cross section is generally best known near the surface, where the conditions may be actually observed, and becomes increasingly uncertain downward. The base of the cross section should be placed above the depth at which the interpretation of the structure becomes so uncertain that it is untrustworthy.

Construction. *Plotting Formations and Dips.* Cross sections are so useful that every geologist should know how to construct and interpret them. The representation of the topography on the cross section is very simple. The intersection of each topographic contour with the plane of the cross section is plotted as a dot, and the dots are connected as a smooth curve. The geologic formations or members of formations present along the surface trace of the cross section are plotted, and any surface dips or subsurface well data are projected into the plane of the cross section. The observed dips along the course of the cross section

[1] A. J. Eardley, "Structural Geology of North America," Harper & Brothers, New York, pp. 1–2 (1951).

[2] Marshall Kay, Paleogeographic and Palinspastic Maps, *A.A.P.G. Bull.*, vol. 29, pp. 426–450 (1945).

may be plotted as short straight lines, and these lines are used to draw the subsurface formation contacts. In sketching in the course of the formation contacts at depth, the lines should be parallel to the observed dip lines where near them, but should show folds which are rounded and not angular.

Cross Sections Diagonal to the Strike. It is desirable to choose the course of the cross section so that it is as nearly as possible at right angles to the strike of the strata. A section at right angles to the strike is not only easier to construct but shows the structural features more nearly

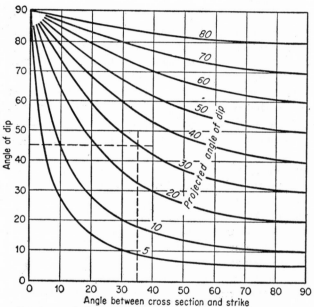

Fig. 2-8. Correction for angle between plane of cross section and strike of strata. If the true dip of the strata is 45°, and the angle between the cross section and the strike 35°, the dip of the strata as projected in the cross section would be 30°. (*After Foley and Herald, published by permission of the American Association of Petroleum Geologists.*)

as they actually are. However, in spite of these precautions, some dips are likely to be found which make a considerable angle with the plane of the cross section. It is obvious that dips will appear in their true magnitude only where the plane of the cross section is at right angles to the strike. The greater the angle between the direction of the dip and the plane of the cross section, the smaller the dips will appear on the cross section. If the cross section is parallel to the strike and at right angles to the direction of the dip, all dips less than 90° will be reduced to zero. The easiest way to correct the dips for the angles between the direction of the dip and the direction of the cross section is to use a diagram. Fig. 2-8, from a paper by Foley and Herald,[1] shows a diagram for use in making this correction.

If a geologist has to make these corrections when the diagram is not available, he can obtain the corrected dips by expressing all dips as per cent slope and multiplying the observed dips by the cosine of the angle between the direction of the true dip and the plane of the cross section. The corrected dips to be shown on the cross section may also be calculated by expressing all dips as per cent slope and multiplying the observed dips by the sine of the angle between the strike and the plane of the cross section.

The Projection of Dips and Structural Features. If the strike of the strata and the trend of the anticlines and synclines are at right angles to the direction of the cross section, the observed dips may be projected to the plane of the cross section along lines which are perpendicular to it. The position of a fault on the cross section is shown by projecting the strike of the fault until it intersects the cross section. Where the folds do not intersect the cross section at right angles, the individual dip measurements are projected to the cross section not along lines perpendicular to it but along lines parallel to the axes of the anticlines and synclines.

The Construction of Cross Sections from Areal Maps. It is possible to construct cross sections from areal maps, though areal maps cannot be made from cross sections. In making cross sections from an areal map, the boundaries of the formations are indicated where they intersect the surface in the plane of the cross section. The positions of the contacts at depth must be determined from the thicknesses of the formations given in the stratigraphic column. If the vertical scale of the cross section is not exaggerated, the formation thicknesses should be plotted at right angles to the formation contacts or planes of stratification.

If the dips are only 5° or less, no serious error is involved in assuming that where the elevation of the top of a formation is known, the elevation of the base may be determined by simply subtracting the thickness. In areas of high dips, however, a different method must be used to determine the elevation of the base at a point immediately below the outcrop of the top. This problem is involved in making cross sections based on areal maps, drawing structure-contour maps based on areal maps, and changing the horizons on which structure contours are drawn. The nature of the problem is shown in Fig. 2-9, which is a cross section at right angles to the strike. *A* is the outcrop of the base of the formation, *B* the outcrop of its top, and *BE* the thickness. The problem is to determine the dip and the elevation of the base of the formation at a point

[1] Lyndon L. Foley and Stanley C. Herald, Projection of Dip Angle in Profile Section, *A.A.P.G. Bull.*, vol. 17, pp. 740–742 (1933).

directly below *B*. Using the thickness *BE* as a radius, swing an arc toward *A*. The line *AD*, tangent to this arc, shows the dip of the base of the formation, and *BC*, the depth of the base at point *B*, is calculated by multiplying the width of the outcrop *AB* by the tangent of the dip angle. These relations hold only if the effects of topography are negligible. Where the elevations differ appreciably, the depth of point *B* cannot be calculated in the manner described. However, if the differences in elevation are known, the method for obtaining the dip from the width and thickness of the outcrop can be used even in areas of marked relief. It is merely necessary to plot the elevations correctly on the cross sections.

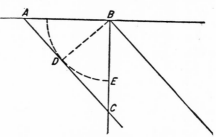

Fig. 2-9. Determination of dip from the thickness and width of outcrop of a formation.

Selection of Vertical Scale. In some cross sections the vertical scale is the same as the horizontal. In others the vertical scale may be very much greater. The question of whether or not to exaggerate the vertical scale is an important one, and the advantages and disadvantages of this procedure should be understood. The vertical scale should never be exaggerated if the structures are so sharp and the dips so steep that the important structural or stratigraphic features to be shown are brought out clearly without exaggeration. On the other hand, if the important structures do not show up when the vertical and horizontal scales are the same, it is necessary to exaggerate the vertical scale, in spite of the disadvantages of doing so. The exaggeration of the vertical scale should in these cases be sufficient to show the structures plainly. In areas where the dips are low, it is common to use vertical scales which are 5 or 10 times the horizontal scales. The disadvantages of doing this are that the thicknesses of the formations appear to vary abnormally and sedimentary strata and fault planes seem to dip much more steeply than they do, since their dips are also exaggerated. In sections where the vertical scale is exaggerated, the formations appear to thin out on the flanks of the folds and to thicken where the dip is gentle. The formations may actually thicken and thin in this manner, but exaggerating the vertical scale also greatly exaggerates this thinning and causes a marked thinning to appear where none actually exists.

The Interpretation and Uses of Cross Sections. The interpretation of cross sections is generally a simple matter. In fact, one of the greatest values of cross sections is that they show at a glance relations which would be very difficult to interpret from areal or structure maps. In areas of complex structure it is always advisable to present some structure sections, as is done on the folios of the U.S. Geological Survey. Where the dips are low and the structure is simple, structure-contour maps may give all the available information. It is important to bear in mind that in cross sections in which the vertical scale is exaggerated, the true thickness of the formations is shown only where they lie flat.

One of the most important uses of cross sections is for dating the time of origin of the structural features. This is explained in detail in Chap. 17, and will not be discussed further here. Cross sections illustrate angular unconformities, truncations along which there may be traps for oil, igneous intrusions, the structure of reefs, facies changes, and lenticularity or persistence of deposits; they also show whether or not the folds become steeper and show larger closure with depth. Oil-producing zones and fluid contacts may be shown as well. If lithologic variations are indicated, it is possible to determine whether or not they are related to the structure. Buried hills and ridges and the facies changes related to them may also be depicted. Another use of cross sections is for training geology students in visualizing the structural features in three dimensions. Problems involving cross sections will be found in the Laboratory Section.

THREE-DIMENSIONAL MODELS

Instead of representing such three-dimensional features as geologic structures on plane surfaces, it is possible to construct three-dimensional models on a reduced scale. These representations may be solid block diagrams showing structure sections on the sides and areal maps and relief on the top, or they may be peg models of oil fields, in which each well is represented by a rod or stick on which the formations may be shown by colors. Strings may be stretched to rods to show the correlation, and producing zones may be indicated by a special color. A disadvantage of these models is that they are inconvenient to carry around and take up a great deal of room in storage. They have a limited usefulness, however, in offices, museums, and other show places. Certainly they show the structural and stratigraphic features simply and clearly, in such a way that even a person without training in geology can generally understand them.

BLOCK DIAGRAMS

Types. Block diagrams are representations on a plane surface of three-dimensional block models. However, these representations are not drawn with the intention of making the solid models appear exactly as they would in a photograph. On the contrary, some short cuts and simplifying assumptions are made in the methods of construction, which make the block diagrams easier to make and interpret. All block diagrams show the upper surface of the block and two of the vertical sides. These two sides are geologic cross sections.

Perspective block diagrams are drawn so that the far sides of the blocks, which actually are rectangular, are shorter in the diagram than the near sides. Since this is the way actual blocks would appear, an illusion of perspective is given. Unfortunately perspective diagrams require more labor in drafting than some of the other types. In cabinet block diagrams one of the vertical faces is shown on true scale without any distortion. Vertical distances, and horizontal distances parallel to this cross section, are also shown to true scale. Horizontal lines in the other

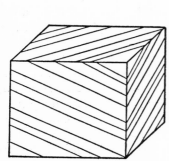

FIG. 2-10. A cabinet block diagram.

FIG. 2-11. An isometric block diagram.

side shown are inclined at an angle of 45° to the horizontal, and the horizontal lengths are reduced by one-half. Horizontal distances on the upper surface of the block diagram which are parallel to this vertical face are also reduced by one-half. A cabinet block diagram is shown in Fig. 2-10. Still another type is the isometric, the construction of which is described below.

The Construction of Isometric Block Diagrams. The construction of block diagrams has been discussed by Lahee,[1] Greenly and Williams,[2] Johnston and Nolan,[3] Ives,[4] Secrist,[5] Brown and Debenham,[6] and Lobeck.[7] In isometric block diagrams, horizontal lines on the two

[1] Frederic H. Lahee, "Field Geology," 5th ed., McGraw-Hill Book Company, Inc., New York, pp. 679–687 (1952).

[2] Edward Greenly and Howard Williams, "Methods in Geologic Surveying," Thomas Murby & Company, London, pp. 315–317 (1930).

[3] W. D. Johnston, Jr., and T. B. Nolan, Isometric Block Diagrams in Mining Geology, *Econ. Geology*, vol. 32, pp. 550–569 (1937).

[4] Ronald L. Ives, Measurements in Block Diagrams, *Econ. Geology*, vol. 34, pp. 561–572 (1939).

[5] Mark H. Secrist, Perspective Block Diagrams, *Econ. Geology*, vol. 31, pp. 867–880 (1936).

[6] C. Barrington Brown and F. Debenham, "Structure and Surface," Edward Arnold & Co., London (1929).

[7] A. K. Lobeck, "Block Diagrams," John Wiley & Sons, Inc., New York (1924).

vertical faces shown are inclined 30° to the horizontal. On the upper surface of the block, horizontal lines parallel to these two surfaces are also plotted inclined 30° from the horizontal. All vertical measurements and all measurements parallel to the two vertical faces shown are drawn to true scale. If, for example, the isometric block diagram shows the upper surface and the west and south sides of the block, vertical measurements and measurements along east-west and north-south lines are the same as in the original. Measurements along north-south and east-west lines in the original are now plotted along lines making an angle of 30° with the horizontal and 120° with each other. Hence measurements in other directions than vertical, north-south, and east-west, are not shown to true scale. Angles are, of course, distorted. Fig. 2-11 shows an isometric block diagram.

The vertical scale of block diagrams may be the same as the horizontal scale. The advantages and disadvantages of exaggerating the vertical scale are about the same as in the case of cross sections. However, if the topography is shown on the upper surface of the block diagram, the effect of the exaggeration of the vertical on the appearance of the topography must be taken into consideration.

The upper surface of the block shown in the diagram may be assumed to be flat, or the topography may be represented as viewed diagonally from a great height. The topography may be omitted if the land surface is nearly level, or if the area shown is so large that the topography would be minute or inconspicuous on the vertical scale used. If the topography is not shown, the upper surface of the block in the block diagram is merely an areal map plotted according to the method of projection.

The topography of the upper surface may be sketched in as it would appear if seen obliquely, but considerable skill would be required to sketch the contours in their correct positions on the projection. Topographic contours may be shown by transposing the topographic map to the isometric projection, but this does not give the illusion of three dimensions. The following method may be used to give an illusion of relief. The original topographic map is divided into small squares by two series of parallel lines. These squares are then shown in isometric projection on the upper surface of the block diagram, and the topographic contours sketched between the boundaries of the squares. The topographic contours are now in isometric projection, as are the other features shown on the top face of the block diagram. A point, which will be called point A, is marked or selected on this topographic map in isometric projection. Tracing cloth or paper is placed over this map, and point E is marked on the tracing paper immediately over point A. The lowest topographic contour is then traced off. A vertical line is drawn upward from A on the original map, and as many horizontal lines are marked off on the vertical line as there are topographic contours on the map. The interval between these horizontal lines is the same as the topographic contour interval, expressed in the vertical scale of the block diagram. Each of these horizontal lines is numbered to correspond to a topographic contour on the map, with the lowest topographic contour at the bottom, and the highest on top. The lowest topographic contour is traced off with point E overlying point A. To trace off the next higher topographic

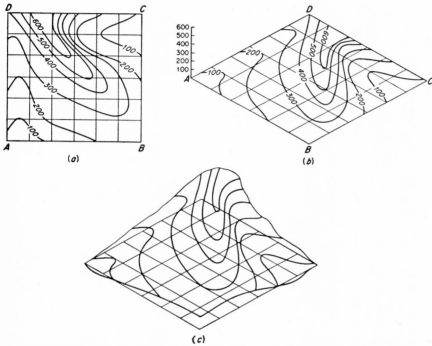

Fig. 2-12 (*a*), (*b*), and (*c*). Method of constructing an isometric block diagram showing topographic contours in relief.

contour, the tracing paper is shifted so that point E on the tracing paper is over the corresponding mark on the vertical line on the original map. The process is illustrated in Fig. 2-12*a*, *b*, and *c*. The points where the topographic contours terminate should be connected. The lines thus drawn mark the edges of the map and the upper edges of the vertical sides.

Uses. Block diagrams are useful for showing the relations of complex structure to areal geology and topography. They indicate very clearly the manner in which resistant formations produce topographic elevations at their outcrops, and they are valuable for demonstrating how structure may be interpreted from the topography. Block diagrams are also valuable for training students visualize the structures in three dimensions.

EQUAL-VALUE MAPS

One general class of maps, called equal-value maps, consists of lines connecting points at which some quantity has an equal value. The names of many of these maps are preceded by the prefix "iso," meaning "equal." Among this group are topographic, structure-contour, isocarb, isogam, isogal, and isonomaly maps. Since this type of map is important in structural geology, as well as in stratigraphy and geophysics, it seems worth while to mention a general criticism of the methods of making these maps before considering the various types.

With the exception of topographic maps, these equal-value maps are all likely to be based on data which are in some places accurately controlled by known values, and in other places highly uncertain because of lack of observations or wide spaces between them. Clearly these maps may vary greatly in accuracy in different parts of the same map, and where the data are scanty the features shown may be merely one of a number of possible interpretations. Since each map may vary so greatly in accuracy from place to place, the value of the whole map is lessened if there is no way of determining where the data are complete and accurate and where they are scanty or unreliable. Yet in many cases there is no way of determining from the maps how much control was available for drawing the equal-value lines.

The reliability of the data on which the maps are based may be shown in several ways. One way is to use different types of line to show accurate and poorly established values. Where this is done the general practice is to show solid lines where the control is good, and dashed or dotted lines where the information is incomplete. If there is sufficient space, it is very desirable to place on the final map the figures on which the equal-value lines are based. Where there is no room for the figures, dots or crosses can in many cases be placed on the maps to indicate the position of the control points.

The practice of presenting accurately controlled interpretations and guesswork without distinguishing between them may be severely criticised. Unfortunately this practice is followed by many of the best geologists and by some surveys and similar organizations of the highest repute. This reduces the value of the maps and may cause entirely erroneous conclusions to be drawn from them. In some cases there may be few quantitative values on which to base the interpretations. A geologist may then sketch in the equal-value lines over the whole map, using his own theories as a guide. If these maps are presented in such a manner as to suggest that they are based on definite evidence, they may give a false impression of conclusive proof whereas they merely embody the theories of those who make them.

STRUCTURE-CONTOUR MAPS

Definitions. The structure of areas which may have important oil prospects is generally shown by structure-contour maps. Since the accurate representation of structure is the objective of a large part of the work of a petroleum geologist, the extreme importance of the structure map in oil geology may be realized. Every petroleum geologist should be able to interpret structure maps accurately and rapidly, and to express his interpretations of structure adequately by means of structure maps.

A structure contour is a line drawn through points on the same stratigraphic horizon which have the same elevation. These lines are parallel to the strike and at right angles to the dip. The stratigraphic bed or layer on which the lines are drawn is generally called a key horizon or key bed. The terms "datum" and "datum horizon" are also used with the same meaning. This key horizon may be a thin layer, such as a coal seam, a bed of volcanic ash, a thin limestone, the contact of two formations, or a change in lithologic character within a formation, such as a color change. If the bed or formation used has appreciable thickness, the general practice is to use the top of it, but the bottom may be used instead if it is more suitable. In fact, any layer or stratum which may be recognized over a large area may be used as a key bed. The word "datum" as applied to structure maps may mean the base to which the elevations shown on the structure map are referred. Usually elevations above or below sea level are given wherever possible. However, in an area where accurate levels have not yet been run to determine the sea-level elevation, it is necessary to assume a datum—that is, it is necessary to start with an assumed elevation. Where this is done it is advisable to state the fact plainly on the map. Occasionally a geologist who desires all the elevations to be positive will assume a datum or zero elevation some distance below sea level. This should also be clearly announced on the map. Thus the statement "datum 3,000 ft below sea level" would mean that 3,000 ft has been added to all sea-level elevations.

Choice of Scale. The first step in making a structure map is to decide the scale and the structure-contour interval. The scale is determined in part by the desire to make the map a convenient size, in part by the need to make the scale large enough to show the important details, and in part by the accuracy of the surveying methods. The map can be split up into several sections if it is too large for convenience. The scale should certainly be large enough to show all important structures without crowding. Thus the steepness of dip and the area covered by the structures have a bearing on the scale used.   Larger scales may be needed to show steep dips and complex structures.   The type and accuracy of the mapping enter into the choice of scale because some maps are made with great accuracy on the assumption that large scales will be used. Other maps are made rapidly, and less accurate methods may result in comparatively large horizontal errors.   It is desirable to plot such maps on a small scale so that the errors will not appear large on the map. Even if the errors of a map are actually large, they may be made insignificant, or even invisible, by the choice of a sufficiently small scale.

Choice of Structure-contour Interval.   The choice of the structure-contour interval to be used has an important bearing on the value of the map.   The size of the errors in elevation, the types of structure present, and the purpose for which the structure map will be used all have a bearing on this choice.   Where the dips are steep and the scale fairly small, a large interval is needed to avoid too close spacing of the structure contours.   The size of the folds is also an important factor. If the anticlines rise only 30 ft or so above the adjacent synclines, a 50-ft structure-contour interval would clearly be too large to show them, and a 10-ft interval would probably be needed.   If, on the other hand, the crests of the anticlines rise thousands of feet above the adjacent synclines, an interval of 10 or 50 ft would be too small.   It would result in unnecessary drafting, and would clutter up the map with lines that would not be needed.   In such cases 100-, 200-, or 500-ft intervals would be likely to be satisfactory.

Still another important factor in determining what structure-contour interval should be used is the size of the various errors which affect the results.   A geologist or geophysicist who has completed a structure map of an area generally has some idea of the accuracy of the elevations of the control points.   Errors in the accuracy of these elevations may result from geological causes, from mistakes in mapping, or from the nature of the instruments used to get elevations.   The important point to remember is that the structure-contour interval should be larger than the average error due to all causes in the elevations of the control points. However, it is not necessary that it be many times the average error. A structure-contour interval two or three times the probable error is generally sufficiently large to eliminate most of the random errors in measurement.   A 10-ft interval should never be used where the average error is 20 ft, nor a 50-ft interval where the average error is 100 ft.   If the interval is not larger than the average errors of the elevations of key horizons, the map will show many apparent structures which are due merely to errors.   Such a map may be worse than no map at all, because it may cause those who do not know of its inaccuracies to waste large sums of money drilling or leasing the apparent structures shown.   Moreover, a geologist who presented structure-contour maps of this type would be discredited if it were found on checking that the structures he showed did not exist.

If the primary purpose of the structure-contour map is to determine the locations of wells to test prospective reservoirs far below the horizon contoured, it is generally inadvisable to use a structure-contour interval smaller than 10 ft. This is because there are generally irregular variations in intervals between the beds on which the structure is mapped and the formations in which production is sought. Since these variations in interval are generally greater than 5 ft, there are generally errors of more than 5 ft in projecting the structure of the shallower key horizon to the deeper prospective producing formations. In some cases, however, structure-contour intervals of less than 10 ft are justified. They may be needed where small anticlines at the surface are underlain by much larger anticlines at depths, or where the intervals between the contoured horizon and the prospective reservoir rocks are unusually constant. If the map shows the configuration of the reservoir rocks of producing oil or gas fields, or if it is intended for use in developing mineral deposits other than oil or gas, smaller intervals may be needed.

Reconnaissance and Detail Maps. Detail maps are made on a large scale, and the area covered by an individual map is generally limited. Detail maps are generally made of areas of high value, such as oil fields or structures or prospects which may become oil fields. The vertical and horizontal errors are kept to a minimum and minor structural features are shown. The structure-contour interval may be small, and is on the average smaller than in the case of reconnaissance maps.

Reconnaissance maps cover a large area, take less time per unit area to make, and tend to show the larger or regional rather than the small-scale features. The accuracy of the vertical and horizontal measurements is less, and the scale is generally smaller. Thus the horizontal errors, though larger in feet than those of the detail maps, may appear smaller when drawn to scale on the map. The vertical errors may be small compared to the large-scale or regional structure shown. Hence under some conditions the larger errors inherent in reconnaissance mapping are not a serious defect.

A number of conditions determine whether detail or reconnaissance types of structure maps should be made. The time factor, the accuracy of the methods of surveying, the types of instruments available, and the types and accuracy of the base maps all influence the choice. Frequently a reconnaissance-type map is made of an area to determine whether it is worth mapping in detail, or to decide which parts justify detailed maps. Sometimes a geologist finds it desirable to make a reconnaissance map of a region he expects to cover later in detail, in order to estimate how long the detailed survey will take, to learn the stratigraphy and structure, or to decide which areas will require the most careful work.   In some areas the distances between wildcat wells are large, but these wells furnish the only available means of mapping the subsurface structure.   In such cases a reconnaissance-type map may be most suitable for showing the subsurface structure.   Such maps are, however, generally called regional maps rather than reconnaissance maps.

Because of the methods used in making them, reconnaissance structure maps may show only the larger or more readily found structural features. Furthermore, many of the structural and stratigraphic interpretations shown on reconnaissance maps may turn out later to be in error.   For this reason a reconnaissance map should always be labeled as such, to prevent too much confidence being placed in it.

Permissible Errors.   A geologist who interprets a structure map should know the size of the errors that affect it, in order that he may know to what extent it can be trusted.   The relation of the permissible errors to the scale and the structure-contour interval has been discussed on pages 32–33.   In order to plan structure mapping efficiently, it is necessary to have a working knowledge of the amount of accuracy needed under various geological conditions and the size of the errors likely to result from the use of different methods of surveying.   On general principles, small errors are better than large ones.   However, under ordinary conditions the greater the accuracy the greater the cost and the longer the time needed to make the map.   In deciding on the accuracy required in a given case, the geologist must balance the extra cost of the more accurate methods against the advantages they give, and decide whether they are worth the cost.

Among the factors which must be considered in deciding what accuracy is needed are the time and money available for the work, the type of structure present, and the size of the unavoidable error in picking the key horizon.   Clearly the errors in elevation should be much smaller than the height or closure of the structures present.   If the closure of the anticlines is only 20 to 30 ft, the errors in elevation should be only a few feet, and the elevations must generally be obtained by telescopic alidades or Y-levels.   If, on the other hand, the anticlines have thousands of feet of relief, errors in elevation of 20 or 30 ft would not seriously affect the quality of the map, and the elevations could probably be determined by barometer or altimeter.

Some key horizons may be so definite in their nature or so nearly parallel to the strata below that practically no stratigraphic error is involved in their use.   The tops of coal beds, thin persistent limestones, beds of volcanic ash or bentonite, zones of concretions, and thin fossil zones are frequently of this nature. The use of certain types of key horizons results in unavoidable errors owing to uncertainty as to the exact position of the contact chosen or to irregularities in the intervals to the underlying beds. Errors of this nature would be likely to result from using as key horizons gradual transitions from one rock to another, formations which are affected by marked changes in facies, strata of which the exact correlations are uncertain, or surfaces which follow buried topography. Naturally, a geologist does his best to choose a key bed which involves minimum errors of this type. However, in some places no ideal key beds are present, and it is necessary either to use the inaccurate key bed or to make no structure map at all. In such cases, what determines whether it is worth while to make a structure-contour map on the inaccurate key horizons is the size of the structures. Structure-contour maps made on key horizons of this type may still be useful if the vertical relief of the folds is much larger than the unavoidable errors. Thus a key bed with an unavoidable stratigraphic error of 50 ft could be used in structure mapping where the anticlines rose hundreds or thousands of feet above the adjacent synclines.

The accuracy of the surveying methods should be related to the size of the unavoidable stratigraphic errors due to the nature of the key horizon. If this error is 50 ft, there is no need to keep the vertical errors in surveying below 5 ft, and the elevations may be obtained by altimeters or similar methods which give less accuracy.

Where the dips are gentle, the horizontal errors can be much larger than the vertical errors without seriously affecting the structural interpretation. For example, let it be supposed that the structural relief of an anticline is 50 ft and that the dip is about 50 ft per mile. An error of 50 ft in determinations of elevation would render the structure map worthless. However, a 50-ft error in horizontal distances would make a difference of only 0.5 ft in the elevation of the key horizon. In other words, moving a point 50 ft horizontally would not make it appreciably more or less favorable from a structural viewpoint. The locations of wildcat wells with reference to property lines must always be determined accurately, but in low-dip areas great accuracy in horizontal measurements is not necessitated by structural conditions.

On the other hand, the measurements of horizontal distances should be much more accurate in areas where faults and steep dips are present. In such cases, horizontal errors of a few hundred feet might place a location for a well on the wrong side of a fault or too far down the dip for production. Furthermore, in areas of steep dips the production of oil or gas may closely follow the crests of the anticlines, and it is therefore necessary to indicate these crests accurately on the structure maps.

Where the dips are steep a larger horizontal scale is needed, and this in itself implies greater accuracy in horizontal measurements.

Surveys of the areas covered by producing wells naturally require maps of larger scale and greater horizontal and vertical accuracy than maps of wildcat areas. Accurate measurements must be made to tie in the wells to each other and to all property lines in the vicinity. Vertical measurements should be accurate to within one foot. The greater value of producing leases justifies the greater expense needed to obtain this accuracy.

Characteristics of Good Key Bed. The selection of a good key horizon is another factor affecting the final value of a structure map. If a number of stratigraphic horizons can be traced through the area mapped, some of them may be much better suited for mapping structure than others. A good key bed should be readily recognizable, and it is desirable that no similar beds be present with which it is likely to be confused. If the key horizon is to be used in surface work, it should crop out in many places and be exposed over a large area. If it is to be used in subsurface work, it is most useful if it is found in many wells over a wide area. It should be a definite contact, and not a gradual transition. Since it is to be used to map structure, it should be free from the effects of purely stratigraphic variations. This means that it should not be affected by changes in facies or by buried topography. Perhaps the most important quality of a good key bed is that it should be parallel to the strata above and below, especially to those below. This is because the commonest use of structure maps is to determine the structure of formations at considerable depths below the contoured horizons. If the key bed and the deeper formations are parallel, the structure of the deeper strata may be accurately determined by the structure-contour map on the shallow bed. Any departure from parallelism which cannot be determined and allowed for will produce corresponding errors in the interpretation of the structure of the deeper horizon. Progressive regional variations in the thicknesses of intervals, generally called convergence or divergence, usually do not produce large errors in interpreting the structure of the deeper beds, provided that the rate and direction of the convergence are known and can be allowed for. This is explained on later pages.

In many cases the ideal key horizon sketched above will not be present in the area which is to be mapped. When this is the case, the geologists must select the best key horizon available and try to determine whether the unavoidable errors produced by using it are so large that the resultant structure map will be valueless. As explained above, it may happen that the errors, though large, are not serious because the structures are much larger.

Drawing of Structure Contours. Every geologist should realize how much may depend upon his interpretations of structural data which become embodied in structure-contour maps. A large part of the time of petroleum geologists is spent in securing data which will be used in making structure-contour maps. These maps summarize the structural information secured by expensive and prolonged geological and geophysical work and by even more expensive drilling. Furthermore, the future prosperity of an oil company may depend to a large degree on the dependability of its structure-contour maps.

It might be supposed that because of the importance of structure-contour maps a large part of the training of a petroleum geologist should be spent in practicing how to draw them. This, however, is not the case. The routine or mechanical operation of drawing in structure contours from closely spaced points is essentially a problem of drafting; at any rate, it could presumably be picked up by a draftsman without much knowledge of geology. What makes a geologist's knowledge and experience of value in drawing structure-contour maps is not his facility in placing each structure contour in its exact position between control points, but his skill in interpreting geological conditions from the available information. This involves his knowledge of sedimentary rocks in general, his familiarity with the local and regional structure habits which may influence the interpretation, and especially his ability to visualize structures in three dimensions. A geologist on joining an oil company may get more training in sketching structure contours in a few weeks than he could get if he spent all the laboratory periods of one semester on it. It is far more important to give a geological student training in general structural problems and fundamental concepts, which he will not get from his company work, than to spend a large part of his time sketching structure contours.

Nature of the Problem. It is evident that two entirely different problems are involved in making structure-contour maps. In one type of problem, the control points are closely spaced and the structure is simple. All that is necessary is to sketch in the structure contours so that they curve smoothly around the control points and at the same time maintain their proportionate distances from them. In the other type of problem, either the control points are few and far apart, or there are so many complications in the structure that the problem is one of interpretation of the structural features rather than sketching in the structure contours in a routine manner. Even where there are numerous control points the structure may be so complicated that a high degree of structural knowledge and experience is needed to interpret it. An example of this is found in the highly faulted strata over certain salt domes.

Contouring in Areas of Adequate Control. If the control points are closely spaced and the structure is simple and uniform, the problems of structure contouring are naturally greatly simplified. In such cases, the first step is to mark the spots where the structure contours would intersect the lines connecting the control points, on the assumption that the dip is uniform along these lines. With these spots and the control points as a guide, an accurate conception of the area may be built up. The structure contours are then drawn in to express this conception of the structure. Experienced geologists are able to dispense with these preliminaries and can sketch the structure contours in rapidly. In an oil field the wells are generally spaced sufficiently close so that the structure can be accurately mapped. However, even in oil fields faults, small folds, and various minor structural irregularities may make the interpretation of the structure uncertain. If the key bed is lenticular or variable, or if the horizon contoured is a transition or is interbedded with the overlying strata, there are likely to be unavoidable errors in structure mapping. These may show up as irregular peaks and depressions on the structure maps. The upper surfaces of many reefs are so irregular that large differences in elevation are found between adjoining wells. Structure contouring in such areas is subject to large uncertainties.

Accuracy Needed. The accuracy required in structure contouring varies somewhat with the field conditions. More accuracy is needed in contouring the top of a producing reservoir than in mapping the structure of a shallow horizon for use in determining the structure of deeper formations. In mapping the top of a producing formation, differences of a single foot in elevation may be important. On the other hand, since there are nearly always irregular variations in interval between two widely separated stratigraphic horizons, variations in elevation amounting to a foot or two would not be important if the structure map is to be used for deeper drilling. In the latter case, it is the structural interpretation that must be accurate rather than the minor details.

The expense of securing the data on which structure-contour maps are based warrants care and thought in preparing these maps. If the structure contours are sketched in carelessly, important structural features may be misrepresented. Fig. 2-13, from a paper by Low,[1] illustrates inaccurate and accurate methods of drawing the structure contours.

Where the producing zone is underlain by a level oil-water or gas-water contact, the thickness of the producing zone may be equal to the difference between the elevation of the top of the reservoir and that of the top of the water zone. Moreover, under such conditions structure contours indicate the limits of the producing area. Obviously, great accuracy in structure contouring is needed in fields of this type.

[1] Julian W. Low, Subsurface Maps and Illustrations, in Subsurface Geologic Methods, *Colorado School of Mines Quart.*, vol. 44, no. 3, fig. 348, p. 638 (July, 1949).

The Use of Arbitrary Rules and Mechanical Devices. In areas of complex folding and faulting the use of mechanical devices or arbitrary rules in plotting the structure contours is of little value. In areas of simple, uniform regional dip or very broad, gentle folds, structure contouring becomes so simple that the operation is more or less mechanical. Nevertheless, it does not seem that there is any substitute for an accurate conception of the structure in making the structure-contour maps.

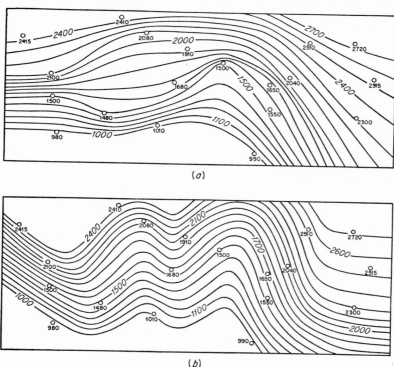

FIG. 2-13. Inaccurate and accurate methods of drawing structure contours. (*After Low, published by permission of the Colorado School of Mines.*)

Mechanical aids and arbitrary rules are likely to result in introducing unnatural features, such as sharp bends in the structure contours and a change in their direction at each control point.

Structure Contouring in Areas of Poor Control. It is in contouring the structure of areas where the structural control points are widely scattered that the training and experience of a geologist are especially valuable. Inexperienced geologists are likely to allow their imaginations to run away with them under these conditions, with the result that they show features which are geologically improbable or for which there is little evidence. A thorough knowledge of the structures present in the region is also very useful in such cases. If a geologist is familiar with the sizes and shapes of such structures and with the frequency of their occurrence, he can use this information as a guide in interpreting the data given by the structural control points.

Oil and gas fields found by subsurface methods alone are generally discovered in areas of widely scattered control points. If the control points are based on drilled wells, they are likely to be widely scattered except in the producing oil or gas fields. Thus by the time closely spaced control points are available, the oil and gas fields are already discovered. A geologist who waited for the accurate knowledge furnished by closely spaced control points before recommending drilling would never discover any new fields. It is hardly necessary to mention that there is a great advantage in being the first to recognize the presence of a favorable structural feature. Frequently only the company whose geologists first recognize the promising character of an area can get leases on it on reasonable terms. Obviously the geologist who is most valuable to his company is the one who can make correct structural interpretations from meager data.

In regions where the control points are far apart, it is customary to place a good deal of stress on whether a well is running high or low. If it is running high, it encounters the key horizons at an elevation higher than would be expected if only regional dip were present. If it runs low, it finds formations lower than expected. As an example of how the structural habit of a region is used in guiding the structural interpretation of geologists, it is worth while to consider how wells running high would be contoured in various areas. In the salt-dome region of the Gulf Coast a salt dome would naturally be assumed to be present, and the structure contours would be drawn to indicate a circular uplift. Along the Luling-Mexia-Talco fault zone of Texas a high well would be interpreted as an uplift on the upthrown side of a fault trending east or northeast, and the structure contours would be drawn to indicate a long, narrow structural feature. In the large structural basins of the Rocky Mountain region, the uplift would probably be considered a sharp anticlinal fold. Clearly something may be inferred about the character of structural features when the only evidence available is the fact that a well runs high or low.

Criteria of Interpretation. As new control points become available owing to drilling, the structure maps must be modified to agree with the new data. The best interpretations are those which require the least modification as the new evidence comes in. However, it should not be supposed that every modification means a mistake. New data generally require redrawing the structure contours even where the structure was interpreted as well as could possibly be expected.

Changing Structure Contours to Dip and Strike Readings and Vice Versa. Every geologist should be able to make a structure-contour map from dip and strike measurements, and he should also be able to determine the dip and strike from structure-contour maps. The need for making these transformations arises frequently in practical work. Furthermore, the training a student receives in solving problems of this nature gives him a further insight into the meaning of structures and how they are drawn.

It is quite a simple matter to determine the dip and strike at any point on a structure-contour map. The strike is parallel to the structure contours, and the dip is determined by their spacing. To determine the rate of dip between any two points, divide the difference in elevation between the two points given by the structure contours by the map distance between them. The result is the tangent of the dip angle. If this tangent is multiplied by 100, the per cent slope or grade is obtained.

The need to change a map in which the structure is shown by local dip measurements to a structure-contour map arises fairly frequently. In one part of an area there may be exposures of the key beds, while in another no key horizons may be present and the structure must be mapped by taking local dip and strike measurements. It may then be desirable to extend the structure-contour map which may be made in the area where the key horizons are exposed to the region where only dip and strike measurements are available. A structure-contour map is much easier to read and understand at a glance than a map showing many scattered dip and strike measurements. Seismic dip surveys commonly yield a large number of dip and strike measurements, and it is generally desirable to change these to structure contours drawn on a phantom horizon, as is explained in the next section.

The first step in making a structure-contour map based on dip and strike measurements is to sketch in the anticlinal and synclinal axes. These axes indicate where the structure contours bend most sharply in passing around the folds. If any faults are known, they should also be sketched in. It may also be desirable to construct a series of cross sections at right angles to the strike. The elevations of the key horizons at the points where they intersect the structure-contour levels on the cross sections can be transferred to the map. The structure contours may be sketched in between these cross sections. Two rules which may be helpful in this operation are that the structure contours are everywhere parallel to the strike and that the distance between the structure contours is inversely proportional to the dip, expressed in per cent slope. The distance between the structure contours may be determined for each dip by dividing the structure-contour interval by the tangent of the dip angle.

Phantom Horizons.   Phantom horizons are imaginary key beds which are used in making structure-contour maps from local dip and strike measurements where it is not possible to draw the structure contours on real key horizons.   It may be impossible to use real key horizons either because none are present or because the relation of the dip and strike measurements to the real key horizons is not known.   The results of seismic dip shooting are a large number of local dip and strike measurements made at various locations and various depths.   Frequently the structure varies with depth.   It is quite common, for example, to find that the folding becomes sharper with increasing depth.   Where this occurs, it is desirable to map the configuration of a horizon as close as possible to the formations which are most promising for oil and gas production.   It is also desirable that the horizon selected be close to the level at which most of the dip measurements were made.   Accordingly, the phantom horizon is assumed to have a definite elevation at some point at considerable depth, and the structure contours are sketched in as explained in the preceding section.   Although this key horizon is imaginary, the structure it shows is real except for the errors made during the surveys.   Aside from these errors the structure map on the phantom horizon shows the same structure as a real key horizon at the same depth. In many cases faults are very difficult to map accurately by seismic dip shooting, and this fact should be kept in mind in using structure maps on phantom horizons.

Representation of Uncertain Structure.   In many cases the value of a structure map may be determined to a large degree by the way in which the structural conditions are represented in areas where the control points are widely scattered or where more than one interpretation of the structure is possible.   The situation with respect to expressing structure contours in areas of poor control is very similar to the problem of showing any other type of equal-value map in areas of poor control, as has been explained on pages 39–40.   Other things being equal, the accuracy of the interpretation of the subsurface structure increases with the density of the drilling.   In many producing fields, it is a simple matter to contour the producing horizon or other key beds which are easily recognized on the logs.   On the other hand, the structure of other fields, such as highly faulted salt domes, may be so complicated that the structural interpretation is uncertain in spite of the close spacing.   Where the wells are closely spaced and the structure is simple, it is customary to omit elevations of the control points from the final structure maps. In such cases this omission is justified, because the inclusion of the elevations of the control points would clutter up the map with many figures, and would not add any important information if they were shown.

Where the control points are widely scattered, or where more than one interpretation of the structure is possible, the situation is entirely different. If the drilled wells are widely scattered, as they generally are outside of producing oil and gas fields, any structural interpretation should be considered as merely a report of progress. It is obvious that the drilling of additional wells in the future will give new control points, and this new information may cause considerable revisions of the structural interpretation. Even if no radical changes in the interpretation are made as a result of the new information, it is likely that the structure contours will need to be redrawn in the vicinity of the new wells. If the elevations of the key beds at the control points are indicated on the structure maps, they may be combined with the new data to make a more accurate structure map. If, on the other hand, the elevations of the control points are omitted from the structure maps, there is no way of accurately combining the old and new information. In such cases a map showing the elevations of the key beds at the control points and no structure contours at all would be much more valuable than a map showing structure contours and no elevations of the control points.

In structure maps based on elevations of key horizons exposed at the surface, it is sometimes desirable to show the outcrops of the key horizons between the control points. A surface-structure map giving this information inspires confidence and may be more easily checked by other geologists.

The arguments against the inclusion of the elevations of the key beds at control points on final structure maps are that showing a larger number of figures causes the maps to look cluttered up or messy, increases the cost and labor of drafting, and in many cases requires a map on a larger scale. The use of a larger-scale map would of course increase the cost of printing and publishing. In regional structure maps covering states or large structural basins, the wells might be so close together that there would be no room for elevations at each well if the scale were to be kept within reason. These practical considerations should be given due weight in deciding what to include. Nevertheless, the fact remains that much valuable structural information is being lost by omitting the elevations of the structural control points from final maps. Moreover, even where there is no room to show the figures giving the elevations, something may be gained by indicating the control points by dots or crosses.

Strike Lines and Form Lines

Strike lines and form lines are used to indicate the structure of an area where something is known about the structure, but not enough to justify drawing ordinary structure contours. Strike lines and form lines are like structure contours in being parallel to the strike; they also resemble structure contours in that they are closer together where the dip is steeper. They differ from structure contours chiefly in the absence of elevations; they are frequently shown dashed to indicate uncertainty as to the structure.

In some cases strike lines or form lines are used to represent the structure in areas where the chief source of information is measurements of local dips. If the local dips were shown without strike lines the map would be difficult to interpret. On the other hand, the structure as indicated by strike lines may be read at a glance. It should be noted, however, that strike lines and form lines alone make no distinction between anticlines and synclines, since no elevations are given. In order to make this distinction it is necessary to show at least one dip.

Isopach Maps

General Characteristics. Isopach (or convergence or isopachous) maps show variations in the thickness of some stratigraphic unit from place to place. The isopach lines which compose the map are drawn through points of equal thickness of a unit. Isopach maps may show variations in the thickness of a formation, member, or group, a single bed such as a coal seam, the strata belonging to a given geologic period or epoch, or a lithologic unit such as a sandstone or limestone; or they may simply show the variations in the interval between any two key beds or horizons that may be correlated. The area covered by an individual isopach map may be small, such as a single lease, concession, or oil field, or it may be very large, such as a regional structural basin hundreds of miles across.

It might be supposed that the stratigraphic units chosen for representation would be of uniform thickness, in which case the isopach maps would consist merely in a blank. This, however, is very rarely the case. In some cases the variations are irregular and are apparently caused by the local folds, buried topographic elevations, or stratigraphic changes. In other cases there may be a persistent increase in thickness over great distances, a feature that may be called regional thickening. Regional thickening is generally related to the great structural basins or geosynclines. There is usually a general tendency for all stratigraphic intervals to thicken toward the original bottoms of these regional structural basins. Strata are said to diverge in the direction of thickening, and to converge in the opposite direction.

Construction. Isopach maps are constructed in much the same manner as structure-contour maps. The known thicknesses are plotted on the map, and isopach lines are drawn through points of equal thickness, avoiding sharp angles. The isopach lines should be dashed where the information is incomplete. Where the rate of thickening is uniform and the control good, the isopach lines may be drawn by marking off proportional distances from the control points, and then connecting the positions determined in this manner by the isopach lines in flowing curves. However, different methods may be required near folds, faults, and other features, if they developed during the deposition of the strata whose thickness is shown on the map. For this reason, all variations in thickness near structural features should be examined with particular care. Isopach maps have been most useful in areas of slight to moderate deformation. Where the strata are so tightly folded that there is thinning on the flanks of the folds and thickening at the crests and troughs, isopach maps obviously do not indicate original variations in thickness before deformation.

Changing the Key Horizons of Structure-contour Maps. One of the most important uses of isopach maps is for changing the key horizon or datum on which the structure contours are drawn. It frequently happens that the only available structure maps of an area are made on key beds exposed at the surface or lying at relatively shallow depths. However, what controls the oil and gas production is of course the structure of the particular reservoirs in which production is obtained. It is therefore advisable, before using the existing structure maps for locating wells to test deeper horizons, to determine as accurately as possible the structure at the horizons at which oil or gas production is expected. If the intervals between the shallow key beds and some key horizon near the prospective producing section are known from wells in several directions from the area mapped, an isopach map may be constructed. This isopach map may be used to transpose the structure from the shallow to the deeper horizon. The structure map of the shallow horizon gives its elevation at all points on the map. Similarly, the thickness of the interval between the two key horizons may be estimated at all points on the isopach map. By subtracting the thickness of the interval from the elevation of the upper key horizon at each point, the elevation of the lower key horizon at that point may be obtained. Usually it is convenient to obtain the elevation of the lower key horizon at points where the isopach lines intersect the structure contours on the upper key horizon. If, however, the control points on the lower key horizon obtained in this manner are not sufficiently numerous, more may be obtained where needed.

Estimating Volumes or Reserves of Economic Minerals. In planning the development of any mineral deposit it is useful to have accurate estimates of the reserves. If the valuable mineral or deposit is a sedimentary rock, or is in a sedimentary rock and roughly parallel to the strata, the reserves may be estimated most accurately by means of isopach maps. Isopach maps are commonly made of deposits of coal, sedimentary iron ore, limestone, gravel, bentonite, and clay. In many maps both structure contours and isopach lines are shown, and this combination is especially useful in planning development. The isopach lines indicate the reserves, and the structure contours indicate how the quarries or mines may be placed so as to obtain the best drainage.

Isopach maps of the producing zones of oil and gas fields are used extensively in estimating reserves. If a reservoir produces either oil or gas but not both, the isopach map may show the thickness of the producing zone above the contact of the water and hydrocarbons, which is generally approximately level. If oil and gas are produced from the same reservoir, it is customary to make separate isopach maps of the gas and oil zones. The thickness of unproductive portions of the producing zones should of course be deducted from the total in making estimates of the volume of the producing reservoirs. These estimates are commonly expressed in acre-feet. One acre-foot is one foot thick and extends over an acre. It therefore comprises 43,560 cu ft, or 7,758 oil barrels of 42 gal. Petroleum engineers and petroleum geologists may know from the production histories of reservoirs of similar lithologic types approximately how many barrels of oil will be produced per acre-foot. There are, of course, other methods of estimating oil and gas reserves.

ADDITIONAL REFERENCES

Chalmers, R. M.: "Geological Maps; the Determination of Structural Detail," Oxford University Press, New York (1926).

Dake, C. L., and Brown, J. S.: "Interpretation of Topographic and Geologic Maps," McGraw-Hill Book Company, Inc., New York (1925).

Desjardins, L.: Measurement of Dip Angles on Aerial Photographs, *A.A.P.G. Bull.*, vol. 27, pp. 1534–1538 (1943).

Eardley, A. J.: "Aerial Photographs, Their Use and Interpretation," Harper & Brothers, New York (1942).

Earle, K. W.: "Dip and Strike Problems Mathematically Surveyed," Thomas Murby & Co., London (1934).

Elles, G. L.: "Study of Geological Maps," Cambridge University Press, New York, 2d ed. (1931).

English, W. A.: Use of Airplane Photographs in Geologic Mapping, *A.A.P.G. Bull.*, vol. 14, pp. 1049–1059 (1930).

Fenneman, N. M. "Physiography of Eastern United States," McGraw-Hill Book Company, Inc., New York (1938).

————: "Physiography of Western United States," McGraw-Hill Book Company, Inc., New York (1931).

Harker, A.: "Notes on Geologic Map Reading," Heffer & Sons, Cambridge, England, 3d ed. (1938).

Harrington, J. W.: The Elementary Theory of Subsurface Structural Contouring, *Am. Geophys. Union Trans.*, vol. 32, pp. 77–80 (1951).

Krumbein, W. C.: Lithofacies Maps and Regional Sedimentary-stratigraphic Analysis, *A.A.P.G. Bull.*, vol. 32, pp. 1909–1923 (1948).

Krumbein, W. C., and Sloss, L. L.: "Stratigraphy and Sedimentation," W. H. Freeman & Co., San Francisco, stratigraphic maps, pp. 393–422 (1951).

Levorsen, A. I.: Convergence Studies in the Mid-Continent Region, *A.A.P.G. Bull.*, vol. 11, pp. 657–682 (1927).

————: Studies in Paleogeography, *A.A.P.G. Bull.*, vol. 17, pp. 1107–1132 (1933).

Ley, H. A.: Structure Contouring, *A.A.P.G. Bull.*, vol. 14, pp. 103–105 (1930).

Mertie, J. B., Jr.: Graphic and Mechanical Computation of Thickness of Strata and Distance to a Stratum, *U.S.G.S. Prof. Paper* 129(c), pp. 39–52 (1922).

Nugent, L. E., Jr.: Aerial Photographs in Structural Mapping of Sedimentary Formations, *A.A.P.G. Bull.*, vol. 31, pp. 478–494 (1947).

Rich, J. L.: Simple Graphical Method for Determining True Dip from Two Components and for Constructing Contoured Structural Maps from Dip Operations, *A.A.P.G. Bull.*, vol. 16, pp. 92–94 (1932).

Smith, H. T. U.: "Aerial Photographs and Their Application," Appleton-Century-Crofts, Inc., New York (1945).

Spurr, J. E.: "Geology Applied to Mining; A First Book of General Geology and Metallogeny," McGraw-Hill Book Company, Inc., New York, 2d ed. (1926).

Swesnik, R. M., and Wheeler, R. R.: Stratigraphic Convergence Problems in Oil-finding, *A.A.P.G. Bull.*, vol. 31, pp. 2021–2029 (1947).

Wharton, J. B., Jr.: Isopachous Maps of Sand Reservoirs, *A.A.P.G. Bull.*, vol. 32, pp. 1331–1339 (1948).

CHAPTER 3

PHYSICAL PRINCIPLES AND MODEL STUDIES

The importance of a knowledge of physical principles varies greatly among the different branches of geology and geophysics. To geophysicists and to geologists who work on structural petrology and metamorphism, this subject is obviously extremely important. It is also more important to "hard-rock" geologists than to petroleum geologists. Petroleum geologists interpret the structural conditions from field relations, and not by analyses of forces and stresses. However, petroleum geologists occasionally attempt to show graphically on maps or cross sections the stresses which have caused field structures, and they also occasionally attempt to interpret the results of model experiments on structural features. An elementary knowledge of physical principles would be of aid in both these activities.

The basic information on physical principles and the interpretation of model studies is obtained from studies of the mechanics of three-dimensional stress distribution in solids, and from dimensional analysis of model experiments. The exposition of these subjects involves considerable mathematics and is not given in this book.

PREVIOUS WORK

Investigations of several types have a bearing on the applications of physics to structural geology. Among these are experimental researches to determine laws and processes, model studies intended to duplicate field structures, and papers which attempt to analyze the forces that produce various structures or to determine what types of structure would be produced by various arrangements of forces.

The early work of Bailey Willis[1] has been particularly influential on structural interpretation of field relations, on the development of physical principles, and on model studies and their interpretation. Jeffreys[2]

---

[1] Bailey Willis, The Mechanics of Appalachian Structure, *U.S.G.S. Thirteenth Ann. Rept.*, pp. 211–282 (1891–1892); Folding or Shearing, Which?, *A.A.P.G. Bul.*, vol. 11, pp. 31–47 (1927); Bailey Willis and Robin Willis, "Geologic Structures," McGraw-Hill Book Company, Inc., New York (1934).

[2] Harold Jeffreys, "The Earth," 3d ed., Cambridge University Press, New York (1952).

gives a discussion of physical principles in his book "The Earth." Mead[1] describes some simple experiments which show the relation of fractures and folds to the forces that produce them. Anderson[2] has given an extended discussion of the dynamics of rock deformation, with particular application to faults. The same subject has also been discussed by Hafner[3] and Hubbert.[4]

Experimental work relating to the dynamics of deformation has been of two types. One type consists of studying the effect of varying physical and chemical agencies, such as pressure and the presence of water or solutions, on the strength and other physical properties of rocks. The aim is not so much to make models of the geologic structures or to duplicate the geometrical conditions as to determine laws and relations. Although a great deal remains to be done in this field, the work is yielding important data relating to the behavior of rocks at depths, and the effect of confining pressure, solutions, and time on the type of deformation. Griggs,[5] Goranson,[6] and Bridgman[7] have made investigations of this type.

Another kind of experimental investigation consists of model studies. The models are generally designed to resemble some type of structure found in the field, and the deformation of the models under stress is generally assumed to throw light on the deformation of similar structures in the field. The early model studies of Willis[8] have had a great influence on geologic thought, and were long regarded as classics in their field. Probably the most important papers on scale models in geology have

[1] Warren J. Mead, Notes on the Mechanics of Geologic Structures, *Jour. Geology*, vol. 28, pp. 505–523 (1920).

[2] E. M. Anderson, "Dynamics of Faulting and Dyke Formation with Applications to Britain," 2d ed., Oliver & Boyd, London (1951).

[3] E. Hafner, Stress Distributions and Faulting, *G.S.A. Bull.*, vol. 62, pp. 373–398 (1951).

[4] M. King Hubbert, Mechanical Basis of Certain Familiar Geologic Structures, *G.S.A. Bull.*, vol. 62, pp. 355–372 (1951).

[5] David Griggs, Deformation of Rocks under High Confining Pressures, *Jour. Geology*, vol. 44, pp. 541–577 (1936); Creep of Rocks, *Jour. Geology*, vol. 47, pp. 225–251 (1939); Experimental Flow of Rocks under Conditions Favoring Recrystallization, *G.S.A. Bull.*, vol. 51, pp. 1001–1022 (1940); Strength and Plasticity, in Handbook of Physical Constants, *G.S.A. Special Paper* 36, pp. 107–130 (1942).

[6] R. W. Goranson, Physical Effects of Extreme Pressures, *Sci. Monthly*, vol. 51, pp. 524–535 (1940); Flow in Stressed Solids, *G.S.A. Bull.*, vol. 51, pp. 1923–1934 (1940).

[7] P. W. Bridgman, Recent Work on High Pressures, *Sigma Xi Quart.*, vol. 31, pp. 1–35 (1943); Shearing Phenomena at High Pressure of Possible Importance for Geology, *Jour. Geology*, vol. 44, pp. 653–669 (1936).

[8] Bailey Willis, The Mechanics of Appalachian Structure, *U.S.G.S. Thirteenth Ann. Rept.*, pp. 211–282 (1891–1892).

been published by Hubbert.[1] The theory of scale models means that the physical properties of the materials used in the models should bear such a relation to the physical properties of the rock which form the corresponding structures in the field that similar structures will be produced during the experiments. In other words, due consideration must be given to the effects of all differences between the model and the field structure.

If the densities are the same, the strength of the material used in the experiments must be reduced in proportion to the reduction of the scale. If structures 10,000 m long are reduced to 1 m in length in the model, the strength must be reduced by a factor of 10,000. Since most of the structures duplicated by model experiments are miles in length, the materials used in the models must be exceedingly weak. The consistency of the substances used must resemble soft muds, partially melted butter, and unconsolidated powders. Hubbert points out that Nettleton, Kuenen, and Hans Cloos used materials of this nature in model experiments before the publication of his papers. However, Bailey Willis and most of the other geologists who experimented with model studies used materials which are far too strong, and their results are likely to be misleading for this reason. There is no justification for the assumption that a substance is suitable for use simply because it is convenient, without considering the effect of the difference of the scale on the physical properties needed.

DEFINITIONS

Importance of Definitions. The different physical terms commonly used by structural geologists are man-made concepts designed to clarify the discussion and description of physical processes. They have certain properties by definition. These terms are generally proposed and defined by physicists, geophysicists, engineers, or students of mechanics. When geologists use these terms, there is no reason for changing their meaning; to do so would only cause confusion with the original meanings. Clearly geologists must follow the usages established in other sciences in their application of these terms. Unfortunately, the lack of clear or consistent usage of these terms has rendered some of the publications of geologists difficult or impossible to understand. The meanings given to the terms "force," "stress," "pressure," and "strain" are especially variable or confused. There is also uncertainty as to what is meant by the arrows (presumably indicating forces or stresses) which are frequently shown on cross sections, maps, and diagrams of experiments.

[1] M. King Hubbert, Theory of Scale Models as Applied to the Study of Geologic Structures, *G.S.A. Bull.*, vol. 48, pp. 1459–1520 (1937); Strength of the Earth, *A.A.P.G. Bull.*, vol. 29, pp. 1630–1653 (1945).

Force. Force is the active agent in producing structural deformation. In physics "force" is defined as that which tends to cause acceleration, and the amount of acceleration produced in a given mass is a measure of the magnitude of the force. Unfortunately, this definition is not very helpful in structural geology, for the accelerations produced in rocks by the action of forces are generally so slight that they can usually be neglected. A force is produced by the action of one body on another, or by the action of one part of a body on another part. Thus a force may be produced by the action of a body at a distance, as in the case of gravitation, or by the action of one solid pressing against another. A force may also originate entirely within a solid mass, as when the interior of a solid is heated and creates a force by its expansion. A force acts only in one direction, and may be represented by a vector arrow, the length of which is proportional to the strength of the force. The forces acting on a body are said to be balanced if the algebraic sum of all the forces is zero—in other words, if the force acting in any direction is opposed by an equal and opposite force acting in the opposite direction. This would happen if the materials against which the force acts are so rigid and so firmly supported that no acceleration is produced in them. An unbalanced force produces acceleration.

Pressure. Pressure is stress normal to a surface; it is set up in a solid, liquid, or gas by the action of forces. Pressure is generally expressed as force per unit area. The pressure affecting gases and liquids at rest is known as hydrostatic pressure. Let it be assumed that there is a vacuum inside a cubic box immersed in a fluid and that five sides are fixed rigidly, but that the sixth side is free to move. Let it also be assumed that an outward force just sufficient to balance the hydrostatic pressure is applied to this side. This force divided by the area of the side would equal the hydrostatic pressure per unit area. The hydrostatic pressure in pounds per square inch of a fluid at rest increases downward at a rate per foot of 0.434[1] times the specific gravity. Since hydrostatic pressure acts in all directions equally, it presses outward against the walls of pores filled with fluids, and therefore opposes compaction.

The pressure on the solid constituents of a rock due to the weight of the overlying material is known as the confining pressure. The confining pressure, expressed in pounds per square inch, increases downward from the surface at a rate of 0.434 times the specific gravity of the rock for each foot. The confining pressure tends to push the walls of pores in and force the contained fluids out. It thus causes compaction. It is opposed in this action by the hydrostatic pressure. Accordingly, the amount of the compacting pressure may be determined by subtracting

---

[1] The figure 0.434 represents the weight of a column of water 1 sq in. in cross section and 1 ft high.

the hydrostatic pressure from the confining pressure. The general subject of pressures and their significance in petroleum geology has been discussed elsewhere by Russell.[1]

The standard state is defined by Anderson[2] as the condition in which the lateral pressure increases steadily with depth, so as to be everywhere the same as the confining pressure.

Stress. Although "stress" and "pressure" have somewhat similar meanings, "stress" is commonly used to describe the internal conditions in solids resulting from the application of forces. It is convenient to think of stress as being measured along three axes, each at right angles to the others, and each parallel to the principal stresses. If the stresses along all three of the axes are different, it is the difference between the greatest and the least stress which determines whether the strength of the material is exceeded. The stresses along each of the axes may be represented as two vector arrows, opposed to each other in the case of compressive stress, and directed away from each other in the case of tensional stress. The stress may be calculated in some cases by dividing the force or weight by the area which bears it or is subjected to it. Thus a weight of 50 lb resting on a column having a cross-sectional area of 10 sq in. would produce a pressure or stress of 5 lb per sq in. in the column. Forces may be resolved and their components in various directions calculated by the familiar methods; different methods must be used to treat stresses.

Strain. Strain is the deformation or yielding produced by stress. Since even the most rigid substance yields to some extent when stress is applied to it, there is always some strain when there is a stress. A solid is compressed or dilated without change in shape by variations in pressure when the pressure is equal in all directions. It is pulled out in the direction of tension, and of course compressed or shortened in the direction of the axis of greatest pressure. If the compressive stresses are all unequal, the amount of strain along the three axes will also be unequal. If the stress is not sufficient to disrupt the rock or deform it permanently, the strain disappears on removal of the stress, and there is no permanent effect of the stress. There is, however, a certain limiting stress difference which will produce permanent deformation if it is exceeded. This stress difference is known as the elastic limit. Up to the proportional elastic limit, stress and strain are proportional; this relation is known as Hooke's law.

Rigidity and Strength. The terms "rigidity" and "strength" have well-established meanings in the tests commonly used in engineering and

[1] William L. Russell, "Principles of Petroleum Geology," McGraw-Hill Book Company, Inc., New York, pp. 152–162 (1951).

[2] *Op. cit.*, p. 13.

physics. When these terms are applied to the deformation of rocks in the field, so many geological factors affect the values that it is necessary to specify the conditions of the test to give precise meaning to the two terms. Rigidity is resistance to deformation below the elastic limit. A solid is said to be the more rigid the larger the stress that is required to produce a given small strain.

In ordinary engineering tests an increasing force is applied to one face of a cube or rectangular block of rock, the opposite face being held rigidly in place. The strength of the rock is the force applied when the rock breaks divided by the area of the face.

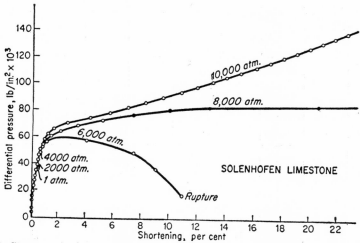

Fig. 3-1. Stress-strain diagrams of Solenhofen limestone tested in compression with confining pressures varying from 1 to 10,000 atm. Each curve represents one complete experiment on an individual specimen at the confining pressure, which is given in atmospheres. (*After Griggs, published by permission of Journal of Geology.*)

It has been found that when stress and strain are plotted against each other, as in Fig. 3-1, from a paper by Griggs,[1] there is a straight or nearly straight line near the origin, which shows that stress and strain are proportional, or nearly so. The proportional elastic limit is the stress at the end of the straight portion of this line. The ultimate strength is the stress at the highest point on the stress-strain curve. Increases in confining pressure increase the elastic limit somewhat, but not markedly. The ultimate strength, on the other hand, does increase greatly with confining pressure, as is shown by Fig. 3-1.

Griggs[2] has stated that the effects of five factors must be known in

[1] David T. Griggs, Deformation of Rocks under High Confining Pressure, *Jour. Geology*, vol. 44, p. 551 (1936).

[2] David T. Griggs, Experimental Flow of Rocks under Conditions Favoring Recrystallization, *G.S.A. Bull.*, vol. 51, pp. 2A, 1002 (1940).

order that the results of experimental tests may be applied with assurance to geological problems.   These factors are confining pressure, differential or shearing pressure, temperature, time, and the activity of solutions. Fig. 3-2, from a paper by Griggs,[1] shows how solutions affect the rate of creep of alabaster.   Creep is slow deformation at stresses below the elastic limit.   Fig. 3-2 shows that the rate of creep in wet alabaster is much faster than in dry alabaster, and moreover increases with time.   This effect is still more marked when a solution of dilute hydrochloric acid is present.   Gypsum is a good mineral to use in this type of experiment since it has the relatively high solubility in water of 1 part in 500.   This

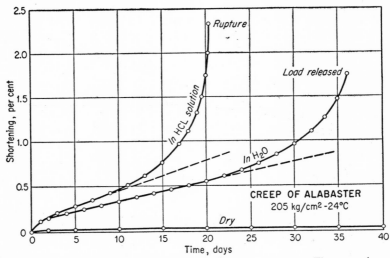

FIG. 3-2. Creep of alabaster in different chemical environments.   Three specimens, all loaded to 205 kg per sq cm, all at the same temperature, but one dry, one in distilled water, and one in dilute HCl.   (*After Griggs, published by permission of Journal of Geology.*)

means that one part by weight of gypsum dissolves in 499 parts of water. In the case of most rocks the effects of solutions would occur so slowly that they could not readily be studied experimentally.   In the case of gypsum these effects may occur within the time of the experiments.   It is therefore to be expected that ordinary rocks will show deformation of the type shown in Fig. 3-2 when stresses act for very long periods.   Under the conditions of the ordinary engineering tests on the strength of rocks, temperature differences of 200 or 300°F have little effect on the strength of most rocks.   However, increases in temperature may markedly decrease the strength when solutions or high confining pressures are present.

The term "fundamental strength" has been coined to indicate the strength under a given set of conditions.   The fundamental strength is

[1] *Ibid.*, p. 1012.

rarely known accurately in actual cases involving geologic time. However, Griggs[1] states that under field conditions rocks generally deform under differential stresses of the order of 1,000 kg per sq cm.

The foregoing discussion applies largely to consolidated rocks. Unconsolidated sediments, particularly if they contain considerable shale or clay, will deform permanently under very slight stresses. Salt, gypsum, and anhydrite in the sedimentary column are also relatively weak and plastic.

According to Kessler,[2] the compressive strength of consolidated rocks in ordinary engineering tests ranges in general from 1,000 to 3,500 kg per sq cm, the shearing strength around 100 to 300 kg per sq cm, and the tensile strength about 30 to 90 kg per sq cm. According to Griggs,[3] the crushing strength of some consolidated rocks is from 1,000 to 2,000 kg per sq cm. One kilogram per square centimeter is roughly 14 lb per sq in. or 1 atm. The shearing strength of rocks is in the neighborhood of one-tenth of the compressive strength, and the tensile strength around half of the shearing strength.

Shearing stress acts parallel to a plane, and tends to move the materials on opposite sides of the plane in opposite directions. The stresses on opposite sides of the plane are equal and opposite. The shearing stress is calculated by dividing the force causing the stress by the area over which it acts.

Types of Deformation

Recent work with precise instruments and specialized apparatus has shown that rocks deform in a number of ways. Most consolidated rocks are brittle and break rather than flow under ordinary engineering tests. Time, confining pressure, heat, and the presence of solutions all favor plastic deformation rather than fracture. However, in some materials the presence of solutions may cause fracture to occur at lower stresses than in the dry rock.

Stresses which continue for a long time may produce types of deformation which would not be suspected from ordinary engineering tests. According to Griggs,[4] the deformation below the elastic limit is of three types. There is always an immediate elastic yielding when the stress is applied. There is also a slow yielding which decreases with time and which is not permanent, since the solid gradually recovers its original shape when the stress is removed. This is called elasticoviscous flow.

[1] *Ibid.*, pp. 1005–1006.

[2] D. W. Kessler, Building Stones, "International Critical Tables," McGraw-Hill Book Company, Inc., New York, vol. 2, pp. 47–49 (1927).

[3] David T. Griggs, Strength and Plasticity, in Handbook of Physical Constants, *G.S.A. Special Paper* 36, p. 116 (1942).

[4] David T. Griggs, Creep of Rocks, *Jour. Geology*, vol. 47, pp. 225–251 (1939).

A third type of flowage under stresses below the elastic limit is called pseudoviscous flow. It is very slow but does not diminish with time. It is therefore probably very important in geologic processes which are of long duration. There is no recovery from pseudoviscous flow when the stresses are removed.

The deformation of rocks with distinct grains may involve the gliding, sliding, or rolling of the grains over one another, a process that is called intergranular deformation. If the grains are interlocking or firmly cemented to one another, as in igneous and metamorphic rocks, limestones, and dolomites, the grains must be crushed, granulated, or recrystallized in order to move over each other. In the case of many shales, clays, and poorly cemented sandstones and siltstones, the particles are free to move over one another without breaking or fracture, and these rocks may be deformed under relatively slight stresses. Since water has a lubricating effect, shales, clays, and shaly sandstones can deform slowly under much smaller stresses when they are wet than when they are dry. This action presumably involves the gliding of the grains over one another with a minimum of crushing and recrystallization. However, recrystallization may be important in the deformation of these rocks at high temperatures and pressures at great depths. This plastic deformation of shales and clays is important in the yielding of these rocks in folding, and in the production of creep, slumping, and slow landslides at the surface and at the bottom of lakes and seas.

Intragranular deformation involves crushing, internal gliding, or recrystallization of the grains of rocks. Some minerals, such as calcite or ice, are able to deform by shearing or gliding along certain planes which are determined by the crystallographic structure. There is no visible fracture when such gliding occurs. This property, together with intergranular gliding, recrystallization, and pseudoviscous flow, gives rocks a property resembling viscosity under the action of stresses of long duration. This viscosity is enormous compared to that of the familiar liquids, but even so it may be very important to geologic processes of great duration.

If deformation takes place by solution and recrystallization, it is of some importance to know in what manner the solution and recrystallization occur. The deposition of siliceous cement in the pores of a sandstone furnishes an opportunity for studying this problem, for the grains are large enough so that their crystal structure and the structure of the cementing material may be studied under the microscope in thin sections. According to the Riecke principle, the grains dissolve near their points of contact where they are under greatest stress, and the material is precipitated on the walls of the pores where the stresses are less. The result, according to the theory, is the filling up of the pores and eventual conversion of the sandstone into a quartzite. Recent work indicates that in a number of cases at least sandstones have not become cemented in this manner. There are some indications that the finer particles dissolve first, and not the portions of the larger grains under stress. However, the evidence is by no means conclusive.

ADVANTAGES OF A KNOWLEDGE OF PHYSICAL AND MECHANICAL PRINCIPLES

At this point it may be worth while to summarize the advantages to be obtained from an understanding of the physical and mechanical principles relating to structural geology. One important advantage would consist in the proper use of terms, which would enable geologists to understand each other better in these matters. Analysis of the factors in quantitative terms would be promoted, and no doubt the falseness of some ideas and theories would be detected, and they could be consigned to oblivion without publication. A true conception of the importance of model studies would be gained, and, in particular, the use of improper materials in making them would be eliminated. The numerous false assumptions regarding physical processes and their action would be exposed. In some cases it might be possible to determine the structure of areas or zones which are not accessible to observation, or at least to guess at the type of structure occurring in zones that cannot be observed. A knowledge of physical principles is of great value for testing theories and for suggesting new theories.

STRAIN ELLIPSOID AND DEFORMED SQUARE

Various conceptions or graphic devices have been used in analyzing the stresses or their relation to the resulting deformation. On a two-dimensional plane it may be useful to study ellipses resulting from the deformation of circles or parallelograms resulting from the deformation of squares. A sphere deformed by three unequal stresses becomes a strain ellipsoid. In certain fields such as studies of metamorphic rocks the strain ellipsoid has been used extensively in studying stress-strain relations, but it has been used very little in petroleum geology.

RELATIONS OF FOLDS, FAULTS, AND FRACTURES TO FORCES CAUSING DEFORMATION

An early series of experiments which has had an important influence on geologic thought was performed by Mead.[1] Figs. 3-3 to 3-5 are based on these experiments. Fig. 3-3 shows a map or plan indicating the relation of the fractures produced by tension to the tensional stress. In

[1] *Op. cit.*

Figs. 3-3 and 3-4 only the greatest stress is indicated, and it is assumed that the stresses along the other axes are too small to affect the result. Fig. 3-3 shows that the fractures resulting from tension are in general at right angles to the tensional stress.   Fig. 3-4 is a map or plan showing the folds or faults produced by horizontal compressive stress.   Both the

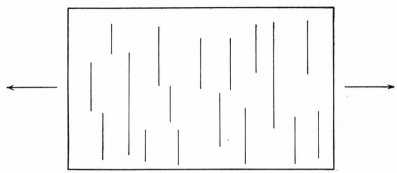

FIG. 3-3. Plan showing the relation of tension fractures to the tension causing them.

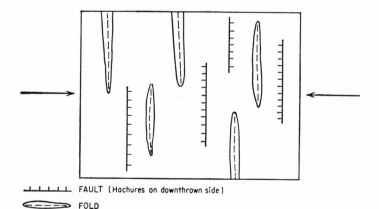

⊥⊥⊥⊥⊥⊥ FAULT (Hachures on downthrown side)
⟨⊂⟩ FOLD

FIG. 3-4. Plan showing the relation of folds and thrust faults formed by compression to the compressive force causing them.

axial planes of the folds and the reverse or thrust faults strike at right angles to the compressive stress.

Fig. 3-5 is a horizontal plan showing the folds and fractures produced by shearing.   In this figure the four arrows do not show forces or stresses. Instead, each equal and opposite pair on opposite sides of the square shows the direction of relative movement as the square was deformed. Any side of the square may be considered to be fixed in position, while the opposite side moves in the direction indicated by the arrow near it. As explained below, a great deal of caution must be used in interpreting in terms of field structure model studies such as are shown in Figs. 3-3 to 3-5.

Anderson[1] has noted that at a point in a stressed solid it is possible to select three planes at right angles to each other in such a way that there are no tangential stresses across the planes but only pressures and tensions. Hence only the compressive or tensional stresses at right angles

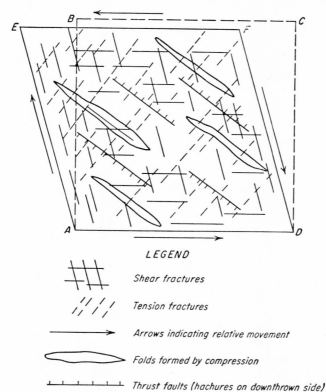

LEGEND

Shear fractures

Tension fractures

Arrows indicating relative movement

Folds formed by compression

Thrust faults (hachures on downthrown side)

FIG. 3-5. Plan showing the relation of the structures produced by shearing to the distortion of the sheared block.

to the planes need be considered. Furthermore, in the earth's crust one of these planes is generally nearly horizontal. The stresses across these planes may be represented as in Fig. 3-6. The greatest stress is 1, the intermediate 2, and the least 3. Thus in Fig. 3-6 the greatest stress is vertical, the intermediate north-south, and the least east-west.

Anderson states that faults make an angle with the axis of greatest compressive stress, which is generally less than 45°. The fault planes

[1] E. M. Anderson, "Dynamics of Faulting and Dyke Formation," 2d ed., Oliver & Boyd, Ltd., London, pp. 7–21 (1951).

are parallel to the intermediate stress axis. The dips and strikes of the fault planes under various positions of the three stresses, according to Anderson's analysis, are shown in Table 3-1.

Let it be assumed that the least compressive stress is vertical, and that the two horizontal stresses are equal. In this case the axial planes of the folds formed would be approximately vertical initially, but could have any strike. If, on the other hand, the least stress is vertical, the intermediate stress east-west, and the greatest stress north-south, the axial planes of the folds will initially be vertical with an east-west strike. The axes of the folds will be horizontal and parallel to the intermediate-stress axis. The rule may therefore be made that the axial planes of the folds formed under the influence of three unequal stresses are at right angles to the greatest-stress axis.

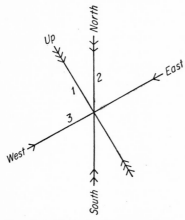

Fig. 3-6. Method of representing a three-dimensional stress system in a solid.

TABLE 3-1

Stresses			Folds				Faults					
			Axial planes of folds		Axes of folds		Thrust		Normal		Strike-slip	
Up-down	N-S	E-W	Strike	Dip	Direction	Plunge	Strike	Dip	Strike	Dip	Strike	Dip
3	2	1	N-S	90°	N-S	0°	N-S	20 to 30° E or W				
3	1	2	E-W	90°	E-W	0°	E-W	20 to 30° N or S				
2	3	1	N-S	90°	Up-down	90°					N 60 to 70° E or N 60 to 70° W	90°
2	1	3	E-W	90°	Up-down	90°					N 20 to 30° E or N 20 to 30° W	90°
1	3	2	Flat	0°	E-W	0°			E-W	60 to 70° N or S		
1	2	3	Flat	0°		0°			N-S	60 to 70° E or W		

These axial planes are also parallel to the intermediate- and least-stress axes. The axes of the folds are parallel to the intermediate-stress axis. These relations are also summarized in Table 3-1.

MODEL STUDIES AND THEIR SIGNIFICANCE

Older Types of Model Experiments. In early model studies, one of the commonest methods of producing deformation in layered material was the pressure box. This consisted of a rectangular box in which the material to be deformed was deposited. Near one end there was a piston or movable plate which could be forced into the layered material, throwing it into folds and faults. It appears that there are a number of objections to this type of experiment, in addition to the criticism that the materials used were generally far too strong. In the first place, this method of applying pressure generally has no counterpart in nature, as Mead[1] pointed out in 1920. Under natural conditions, there appears to be nothing like a piston sliding over the stationary rock masses and deforming them in front of its advance. The only possible analogies seem to be the deformation in front of advancing landslides or erosion thrusts. Furthermore, with a few rare exceptions, forces are not applied over a small area. In the pressure-box experiment the deformation is concentrated in front of the advancing piston, and the deformation dies out rapidly away from the small zone along which it is applied. This gives a false impression that in the field the deformation dies out rapidly away from some small area in which it is applied. It seems likely that in the field stresses may exist over a considerable region, and that the yielding occurs where the rocks are weakest, and not necessarily where the force originates. If a chain is placed under increasing tension, everyone knows that it will break at its weakest link, regardless of whether this is near or far from the point of application of the tension. The pressure-box experiments appear to be largely responsible for the common idea that rocks always yield to forces near the point at which they are applied.

This type of experiment is also likely to give a false impression of the dip of thrust faults and of the type of absolute movement in thrust faults. The conditions of the pressure-box experiment prevent the development of thrust faults dipping away from the advancing piston. This gives the impression that the thrust faults always dip in a direction opposite to the applied force. Under normal field conditions the deformation would be produced by a stress in two opposed directions. Furthermore, pressure-box experiments appear to have been arranged so that the piston always advances while the box remains stationary. This gives the false impression that the hanging wall of a thrust fault always moves and that

[1] *Op. cit.*, p. 521.

the foot wall is always stationary. Since we are accustomed to seeing objects move over a stationary earth, everyone has a natural tendency to believe that the hanging wall of a thrust does the moving, and the pressure-box experiment reinforces this prejudice. Geologists hold different opinions about the relative importance of movements of the foot wall and hanging wall of thrust faults; in view of this uncertainty, it is very undesirable to prejudice the minds of students in favor of one answer to the question. This difficulty could presumably be avoided by arranging the pressure box so that either the piston or the box could do the moving.

Scale Models and Dimensional Analysis. The principles of dimensional analysis of scale models have been explained by Hubbert.[1] Most of those who have made model experiments used materials that were far too strong; however, Nettleton,[2] Nettleton and Elkins,[3] and Dobrin[4] made model experiments using suitably weak materials. The structures obtained by following the principles of dimensional analysis look much more like the structures in the field than do the structures obtained when these principles are disregarded. Parker and McDowell[5] have applied Hubbert's theories to scale models of salt domes. Structures very similar to actual salt domes were obtained.

Value of Model Studies of Structural Problems. Model studies of structures and structural problems may be useful for illustrating and explaining structural processes, for proving or disproving theories, and for determining or interpreting the structure where it is unknown or uncertain. There can be no doubt about the value of experiments in explaining structural theories and processes. Experiments and model studies stimulate more interest than descriptions or pictures, and are remembered better. Even simple experiments such as folding cards or sheets of paper may be used to illustrate the relation of folds to the lateral pressures that produce them, and the manner in which the upper beds slide over the lower toward the axes of the anticlines. The difficulty in model demonstrations for students is that they may give rise to prejudices, misinterpretations, or erroneous theories.

[1] M. King Hubbert, Theory of Scale Models as Applied to the Study of Geologic Structures, *G.S.A. Bull.*, vol. 48, pp. 1459–1519; Strength of the Earth, *A.A.P.G. Bull.*, vol. 29, pp. 1630–1653 (1945).

[2] L. L. Nettleton, Recent Experimental and Geophysical Evidence of Mechanics of Salt Dome Formation, *A.A.P.G. Bull.*, vol. 27, pp. 51–63 (1943).

[3] L. L. Nettleton and Thomas A. Elkins, Geologic Models Made from Granular Materials, *Am. Geophys. Union Trans.*, vol. 28, pp. 451–466 (1947).

[4] Milton D. Dobrin, Some Quantitative Experiments on a Salt Dome Model and Their Geological Implications, *Am. Geophys. Union Trans.*, vol. 22, pp. 528–542 (1941).

[5] Travis J. Parker and A. N. McDowell, Scale Models as Guide to Interpretation of Salt-dome Faulting, *A.A.P.G. Bull.*, vol. 35, pp. 2076–2086 (1951).

The use of model studies to test structural theories requires an extensive knowledge of all the physical, geophysical, and geological factors which have a bearing on the problem. Certainly all the differences between the model and the field should be taken into account. If an explanation or theory can be demonstrated by experiments, this is naturally in its favor, but all proofs by means of model studies should be analyzed critically before being accepted. However, even if model tests do not prove a theory, they may in some cases be the means of illustrating or explaining it. For example, assume that tar has been poured into cracks in a flat plate of cement or other rigid material. If the cement is heated sufficiently, its expansion will force the tar out of the cracks to form ridges. If a geologist wished to develop a theory that this process is important in making anticlines or uplifts, his best means of explaining the theory to other geologists would be to describe the experiment.

The interpretation of model experiments is beset by so many uncertainties that particular caution must be exercised in using them to interpret unknown structures. However, even at the present time model studies might be useful in getting ideas as to how structural data should be interpreted. The scale-model study of Parker and McDowell is an example of this. In general, the value of such studies in interpreting structure is suggestive or qualitative rather than quantitative. The model studies may suggest certain explanations, for which confirming evidence must be sought in the field.

DEVELOPMENT OF QUANTITATIVE STRUCTURAL THEORIES

Theories are continually being proposed by geologists and geophysicists to explain the structures found in the field. Some of these theories are purely geologic in their nature, and some purely mathematical or geophysical, but many of them touch on both geology and geophysics. In exploring for oil, it has been found that the best results have been obtained by the combined efforts of geologists and geophysicists. It is reasonable to expect that more progress will be made by geologists and geophysicists working together to develop and test structural theories than by either group alone.

Geophysicists are wont to express their theories in the form of equations, many of which are based on geological assumptions or may be tested by observing whether the observed geological conditions agree with what is calculated. Since the value or truth of the geophysical theories may depend on the geological evidence, the progress of structural geology would be promoted if geophysicists would explain enough of the geological aspects of their theories so that geologists could appraise the geological evidence bearing on them.

It need hardly be stated that geologists should be particularly cautious about embodying their structural theories in equations. In order to express a geological theory accurately by means of an equation, either a number of physical properties and conditions must be known accurately or an equal number of assumptions must be made. One assumption is that the relation can be expressed by an equation. Frequently some of the quantitative data are not known accurately, and it is assumed that the uncertainty is not large enough to affect the value of the equation. In other cases the equation depends on the assumption that some factors do not affect the results appreciably.

ADDITIONAL REFERENCES

Balk, R.: Structural Behavior of Igneous Rocks, *G.S.A. Mem.* 5 (1937).

Barton, D. C.: Review of Experiments in Connection with Salt Domes by Escher, B. G., and Keunen, H. H., *Leidsche Geologische Mededeelingen*, Deel III, Affevering, 3, II, pp. 151–182 (1929).

Billings, M. P.: "Structural Geology," Prentice-Hall, Inc., New York (1954).

Birch, F., and Bancroft, D.: The Effect of Pressure on the Rigidity of Rocks, *Jour. Geology*, vol. 46, pp. 59–87, 113–141 (1938).

Boyd, J. E., and Ott, P. W.: "Mechanics," McGraw-Hill Book Company, Inc., New York, p. 48 (1950).

Bridgman, P. W.: Some Implications for Geophysics of High-pressure Phenomena, *G.S.A. Bull.*, vol. 62, pp. 533–535 (1951).

Campbell, J. D.: Some Aspects of Shearing Deformation, *Am. Jour. Sci.*, vol. 249, pp. 625–639 (1951).

Clark, B. L.: Folding of the California Coast Range Type Illustrated by a Series of Experiments, *Jour. Geology*, vol. 45, pp. 296–319 (1937).

Clark, S. K.: Mechanics of the Plains-type Folds of the Mid-Continent Area, *Jour. Geology*, vol. 40, pp. 46–61, 1932.

Cloos, E.: Lineation, a Critical Review and Annotated Bibliography, *G.S.A. Mem.* 18, 122 pp. (1946).

Daly, R. A.: "Strength and Structure of the Earth," Prentice-Hall, Inc., New York (1940).

DeLury, J. S.: Compressional Creep of Rubber and Rock, *Jour. Geology*, vol. 50, pp. 189–199 (1942).

Evans, J. W.: Regions of Tension, Presidential Address to Geological Society, *Geol. Soc. London Quart. Jour.*, vol. 81, p. lxxx (1925).

Fairbairn, H. W.: "Structural Petrology of Deformed Rocks," 2d ed., Addison-Wesley Press, Cambridge, Mass. (1949).

Foley, L. A., and Mead, M. J.: Discussion of Paper by T. A. Link, Some Applications of the Strain Ellipsoid, *A.A.P.G. Bull.*, vol. 14, pp. 231–244, 1930.

Gutenberg, B.: Viscosity, Strength and Internal Friction in the Interior of the Earth, in Internal Constitution of the Earth, "Physics of the Earth," McGraw-Hill Book Company, Inc., New York, vol. 7 (1939).

Harker, A. H.: "Metamorphism," Methuen & Co., Ltd., London, 2d ed. (1939).

Houwink, R.: "Elasticity, Plasticity and Structure of Matter," Cambridge University Press, New York (1937).

Hubbert, M. K.: The Direction of Stresses Producing Given Geologic Strains, *Jour. Geology*, vol. 36, pp. 75–84 (1928).

Lahee, F. H.: "Field Geology," McGraw-Hill Book Company, Inc., New York, 5th ed. (1953).

Leith, A.: Application of Mechanical Structural Principles to the Western Alps, *Jour. Geology*, vol. 39, pp. 625–640 (1931).

———: The Strain Ellipsoid, *Am. Jour. Sci.*, 5th ser., vol. 33, pp. 360–368, 1937.

———: "Structural Geology," Henry Holt and Company, Inc., New York (1923).

Link, T. A.: Experiments Relating to Salt-dome Structures, *A.A.P.G. Bull.*, vol. 14, pp. 483–508 (1930).

———: Relationship between Over and Under-thrusting as Revealed by Experiments, *A.A.P.G. Bull.*, vol. 12, pp. 825–854 (1928).

———: Some Applications of the Strain Ellipsoid, *A.A.P.G. Bull.*, vol. 13, pp. 1449–1466 (1929); Discussion, *A.A.P.G. Bull.*, vol. 14, pp. 231–244 (1930).

Lovering, T. S.: The Fracturing of Incompetent Beds, *Jour. Geology*, vol. 36, pp. 709–717 (1928).

Nádai, A.: "Plasticity: A Mechanics of the Plastic State of Matter," McGraw-Hill Book Company, Inc., New York, 1931.

Nettleton, L. L.: Fluid Mechanics of Salt Domes, *A.A.P.G. Bull.*, vol. 18, pp. 1175–1204 (1934).

Rettger, R. E.: Experiments on Soft-rock Deformation, *A.A.P.G. Bull.*, vol. 19, pp. 271–292 (1935).

Robinson, W. I.: Folds Resulting from Vertically Acting Forces, *Jour. Geology*, vol. 31, pp. 336–343 (1923).

Wallace, R. E.: Geometry of Shearing Stress and Relation to Faulting, *Jour. Geology*, vol. 59, pp. 118–130 (1951).

CHAPTER 4

FOLDS

To the petroleum geologist, folds are the most important of the various structures found in the field. The great success of the anticlinal theory constitutes a striking proof of the importance of folds. Though many oil fields occur on traps which are partly of a stratigraphic nature, even in such cases the folding is commonly responsible in part for determining the location or character of the trap. Furthermore, in most regions it is folding or warping which has the dominant effect on the general attitude of the strata.

CHARACTERISTICS AND NATURE

A fold in the geologic sense may be defined as a warping or bending of the rocks of the earth. The bending may be so gentle that it is not perceptible to the unaided eye and can be determined only by surveying instruments of considerable accuracy. At the other extreme, folding may produce dips which are vertical or overturned. Folds vary in size from microscopic wrinkles or crumplings to vast features of regional extent. Many folds are long and narrow; some are nearly round; others have no well-defined shape. The folds which produce oil and gas, though they show great variations in shape, are limited as to size. Folds at the surface which are only a few hundred feet across are generally too small to be worth drilling. There also appears to be an upper limit to the size of folds which have formed traps that have localized oil fields. In many cases the producing formations have been eroded from the higher portions of folds more than one or two hundred miles across. In some areas oil and gas fields show a tendency to be concentrated near the crests of these regional uplifts where the productive formations have not been removed by erosion. Even in such cases, however, it is usually merely the general location of the oil and gas fields which is determined by the regional anticlines. The local traps may be produced by smaller anticlines or by stratigraphic conditions. Regional folds are discussed in Chap. 12.

PARTS

Axial, Crestal, and Trough Planes. Most folds may be divided by a plane into two halves which are more or less similar to each other. This plane is called the axial plane; usually it passes through the portions of the fold which are bent most sharply. The strata in an anticline dip away from a plane at the crest of the anticline where they are highest, and toward a plane along the bottom of the syncline where they are lowest. These planes are called respectively crestal and trough planes. On cross sections at right angles to the trend of the folds, crestal planes show up as lines passing through the highest points on each bed. Similarly, trough planes show up as lines passing through the lowest points on each bed. The portion of a fold between the axial planes of an anticline and an adjacent syncline is known as the limb or flank. Axial,

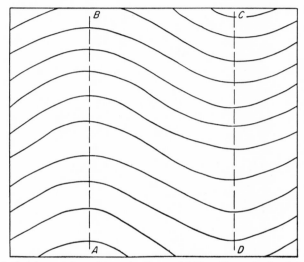

Fig. 4-1. Axial, crestal, and trough planes of folds with vertical axial planes.

crestal, and trough planes are not true geometrical planes, but may be warped or bent considerably.

Fig. 4-1 shows the axial, crestal, and trough planes of symmetrical folds. In this case the two axial planes are vertical and coincide with the crestal and trough planes. In Fig. 4-1, AB is the trace of the crestal and axial planes of the anticline on the cross section, and CD is the trace of the axial and trough planes of the syncline. Fig. 4-2 shows the axial, crestal, and trough planes of asymmetrical folds with inclined axial planes. AB is the crestal plane and CD the axial plane of the anticline, which is slightly overturned on its right-hand flank. EF is the axial plane and GH the trough plane of the adjacent syncline.

The best prospects for oil and gas production are near the crestal plane of an anticline; this plane coincides with the axial plane only where the latter is vertical. Where these planes are considerably off vertical, careful consideration must be given to locating wildcat wells so that they will test the reservoir rocks at the crests of the anticlines. This is explained on pages 93–95.

Axis and Axial Trace. The intersection of each stratum with the axial plane of a fold produces a line which is called the axis. The dips of these axes constitute an important characteristic of folds, as is explained in the next paragraph. Since there is an axis in every bed, a vast number of them must lie in each axial plane. Where the axial plane comes to the surface, these axes intersect the surface in a multitude of points

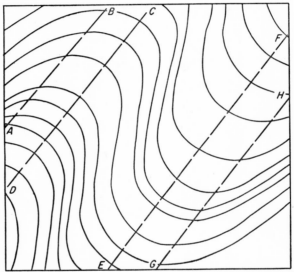

FIG. 4-2. Axial, crestal, and trough planes of folds with inclined axial planes.

along a line which is known as the axial trace. The axial trace is therefore the line marking the outcrop of the axial plane. Some writers, however, make no distinction between "axis" and "axial trace." The term "axis" therefore has a double meaning. It may indicate either the intersection of each stratum in a fold with the axial plane, or the outcrop of the axial plane. However, it is obvious that the use of the same term to indicate two different features renders its meaning less clear. In this book, therefore, the outcrop of the axial plane will be referred to as the axial trace.

Plunge. The plunge of a fold is the dip of the axis at the particular point where the plunge is determined. The description of the plunge of a fold should include the designation of the angle between the axis and a horizontal plane, and a statement of the direction of the dip. For example, it may be stated that the axis trends N. 22° E., and plunges 3° NE.

If the description refers to an axis which is shown on maps, it may be sufficient to give the angle of the plunge and the quadrant toward which the axis plunges.

Anticline and Syncline. It should not be necessary to state that the most important type of fold to petroleum geologists is the anticline. An anticline is a fold which is convex toward the younger strata. Since in the vast majority of cases the younger strata lie above, this means that anticlines are generally convex upward. A syncline is a fold which is concave toward the younger strata and generally concave upward. Where the axial planes are vertical or dip steeply, the dips of the strata are generally away from each other on opposite sides of the axial plane in the case of the anticline, and toward each other in the case of the syncline. Where the axial planes dip steeply, the strata are above the general level or "run high" near the axial plane of the anticline, and are below the general level near the axial plane of the syncline. Where the axial planes of the folds are nearly horizontal, these rules do not apply. In the great majority of cases the axial planes of the folds which are associated with oil fields dip steeply, though some oil fields occur in overturned anticlines with gently dipping axial planes. A large percentage of the oil and gas fields of the world occur on anticlines, far more than on any other type of structure. A few oil and gas fields are found in synclines merely as a matter of chance, but this occurrence is not common. Where both oil and gas occur in a folded reservoir, the oil may migrate into the synclines because of its greater specific gravity.

Geosynclines, geanticlines, basins, platforms, shelves, and flexures are discussed in detail in Chap. 12.

Plunging Anticline or Syncline. The term "plunging" is applied to folds whose axes dip at appreciable angles, and which show no closure in the area under consideration. Since the axes of folds are rarely horizontal, practically all of them might be referred to as plunging. However, the term "plunging" is generally used by petroleum geologists to mean "without closure," even though this meaning does not follow logically from the definition of the term. An anticline whose axis plunges in opposite directions away from a point would ordinarily be referred to as closed rather than as plunging.

The term "doubly plunging" is occasionally applied to anticlines or synclines. Generally it indicates that the fold referred to plunges in two opposite directions. Since there is likely to be doubt whether the term indicates a saddle or a closed area, it seems better to use a word which indicates the relations more accurately.

Dome. "Dome," as used by petroleum geologists, may have two meanings. It may indicate simply a local closure along the axis of an anticline.   Within a closed dome of this type the axis would plunge in opposite directions from the highest point on the dome.   The shape of the closed area in this type of dome may be rounded, oval, or long and narrow.   The other meaning of the word indicates a closed anticline with more or less circular outlines.

Nose.   The structural feature called a nose is a rather short, plunging anticline without closure.   Presumably an anticline of considerable length without closure would be referred to as a plunging anticline rather than as a nose.   Usually a typical nose shows a flattening of the dip or of the plunge of its axis along a part of its course.   The term "nosing" is sometimes used to indicate the development of short, poorly defined anticlines

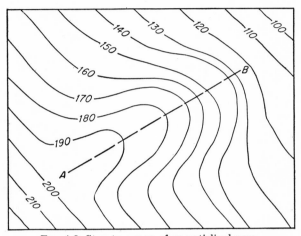

Fig. 4-3. Structure map of an anticlinal nose.

without closure.   Fig. 4-3 shows a typical anticlinal nose, which extends from *A* to *B* in the figure.

Saddle.   A saddle is a structural low along the axis of an anticline. The anticlinal axis always plunges toward the saddle from both directions.   The saddle may lie between two domes.   It may be bounded on one side by a dome and on the other by a plunging axis without closure, or it may be bounded on both sides by plunging axes without closure. Along the axis of a single anticline, there may be many saddles separated by domes or closed areas.

Monocline, Terrace.   A monocline is a belt of steep dip between two belts of gentle dip.   All these dips must be in the same direction.   A terrace is a belt of gentle dip with areas of steeper dip on both sides. Again, all the dips must be in the same direction.   Fig. 4-4 shows a monocline and a terrace.

Homocline, Regional Dip. A homocline is a structural feature characterized by dips in about the same direction and amount over a great area. Of course the amount of dip may be quite different in horizons separated by great thicknesses of strata, but the dip at the same horizon is more or less uniform. The Gulf Coast homocline is a well-known example of this type of structure. Regional dip is the average dip over a great area. It is generally recognized that the regional dip may be interrupted by local folds. A homocline of great area would ordinarily also show local

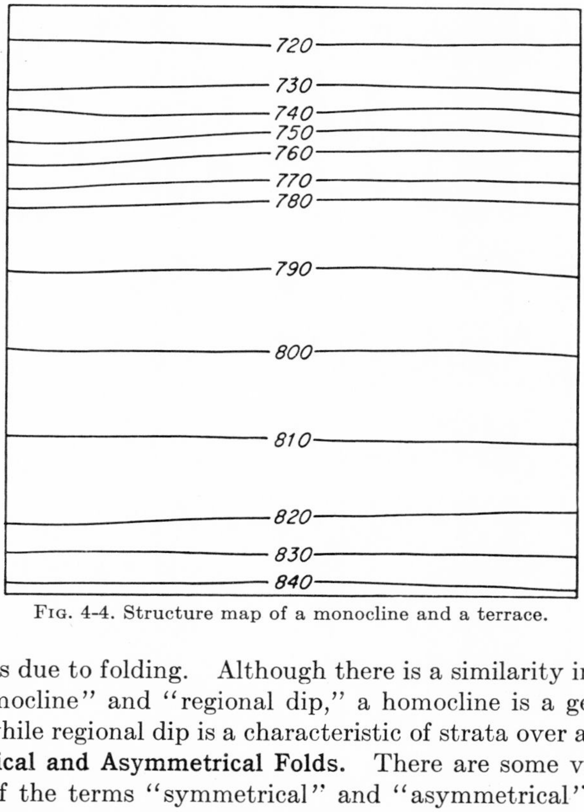

Fig. 4-4. Structure map of a monocline and a terrace.

irregularities due to folding. Although there is a similarity in the meaning of "homocline" and "regional dip," a homocline is a geologic field structure, while regional dip is a characteristic of strata over a great area.

Symmetrical and Asymmetrical Folds. There are some variations in the usage of the terms "symmetrical" and "asymmetrical" as applied to folds. According to the preferred usage, a symmetrical fold is one in which the dips on both sides of the axial plane are approximately the same in angle, and an asymmetrical fold is one in which the dips on opposite sides of the axial plane are markedly different in angle. According to this definition, folds with strongly inclined axial planes would necessarily be asymmetrical. It should be kept in mind that the dips on both sides of the axial plane are never exactly at the same angle, even in the most symmetrical folds encountered in the field.

Supratenuous Fold. In a supratenuous anticline the formations or intervals between the strata decrease in thickness in passing over the crest. Thus the structure becomes more pronounced with depth, and an anticline of slight amplitude at a shallow depth may be underlain by a much more pronounced structure at greater depth. Usually it is merely the height and closure of an anticline which increase with depth. The area covered by the fold does not ordinarily change. Supratenuous anticlines are illustrated in Figs. 4-5 and 15-1.

Fɪɢ. 4-5. Cross section of a supratenuous fold.

Disharmonic Fold. Disharmonic folds are folds which do not persist throughout the geologic column. They die out upward and downward and are replaced by other folds which show no definite relation to them. This disappearance of the fold upward and downward is not sudden. If it were, the horizon at which the fold disappeared would probably be a fault, unconformity, or igneous contact, and the folds would not be classed as disharmonic. All folds change their shapes more or less with depth, and all folds doubtless disappear at some depth. These changes are not, however, taken to indicate a disharmonic fold unless they occur relatively rapidly. Presumably the folds have to disappear and be replaced by other folds within a few hundred or a few thousand feet if the folding is to be called disharmonic. Small folds are more likely to be disharmonic than larger ones. Disharmonic folds are more likely to occur in soft and incompetent beds than in competent formations. A sketch of disharmonic folding is shown in Fig. 4-6, and Fig. 13-4 is a cross section of some existing disharmonic folds.

Orogen. The term "orogen" is used to designate an extensive system of folds. Many anticlines and synclines comprise an orogen, and they extend over an area that is generally at least a hundred miles in length, and usually several hundred. The folds are pronounced and of large amplitude; a system of small or gentle folds would not be considered an orogen, even if it covered a large area. Usually the belt of folds is

FIG. 4-6. Cross section of disharmonic folding.

relatively long and narrow, and the axes of the folds trend parallel to the longest dimensions of the system. The word "orogen" means "mountain making," and orogens are considered to be related to mountains. However, the mountains formed along with the orogens may have long since been eroded away. In many cases the mountains now found associated with orogens were not formed by direct uplift during the folding, but were produced by uplifts which took place long after folding ceased.

Overturned, Recumbent, and Isoclinal Folds. In an overturned anticline the axial plane is inclined and the strata immediately beneath it have been tilted past the vertical, so that the usual order of succession is reversed, and younger beds lie beneath older. If a vertical bore hole were drilled through an overturned anticline, the strata would be in normal sequence above the axial plane, where they would not be overturned.   Just below the axial plane this sequence would be reversed in the overturned beds, and some of the same strata encountered above the axial plane might be encountered again.   Beneath the overturned formations the beds would again be in normal sequence, with the younger strata on top.   The same beds might be encountered for a third time in this sequence.   The strata in folds with vertical axial planes are rarely overturned except locally.   However, it should be noted that fan folds may have vertical axial planes.   Small areas of overturned strata in a fold containing elsewhere upright beds do not cause a fold to be classed as overturned.   Only folds in which a considerable part of the axial plane

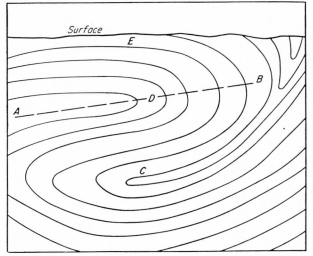

Fig. 4-7. Cross section of an overturned and recumbent anticline.

is underlain by overturned strata are considered overturned.   The axial planes of recumbent anticlines and synclines may lie nearly level. Thus the strata are overturned on the limb of the fold beneath the axial plane of a recumbent anticline, and right side up on the limb above the axial plane.   Isoclinal folds are so tightly compressed that the dips of the exposed strata on both sides of their axial planes are roughly in the same direction and at the same angle.   The belts of gently dipping beds which would normally be expected along the axial planes of folds are either absent in isoclinal folds or so inconspicuous that they might not be noticed.   Thus the false impression may be obtained that there is an enormous thickness of strata with the same dip and strike.   Generally the impression of uniform dip is obtained from exposures at the surface.   At great depths the folds may change their shapes so that they are no longer isoclinal, though this is usually a matter of conjecture. Isoclinal folds are confined to regions that have been intensely compressed and strongly deformed.

Fig. 4-7 shows an overturned and recumbent anticline. The nearly flat attitude of the axial plane, *AB*, is a characteristic of a recumbent fold. The strata are shown overturned from *D* to *C* and right side up from *D* to *E*. Fig. 4-8 shows isoclinal folds. At the surface the strata

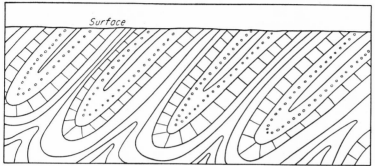

FIG. 4-8. Cross section of isoclinal folds.

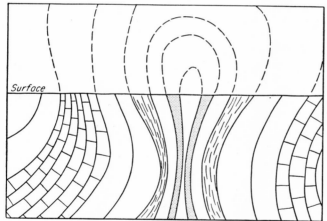

FIG. 4-9. Cross section of a fan fold. Dashed lines indicate position of formation contacts before erosion.

appear to dip to the left at a uniform steep angle, with little or no change in dip at the axial planes of the folds. The sketch shows the isoclinal folds changing to normal folds at great depths. This is of course hypothetical, as the only evidence is obtained at the surface.

Fan Folds. The strata in a fan fold are overturned on both sides of the axis and apparently dip toward it on both sides. Fig. 4-9 shows a cross section of a fan fold. The type is rare and is confined to intensely compressed regions, where the formations are drawn out as though they were plastic.   It should hardly be necessary to state that oil and gas production is not ordinarily associated with isoclinal or fan folds.

Diapir Folds.   Diapir folds are characterized by an intrusive core of sedimentary rock.   The material of the intrusive core may be any sedimentary rock which is more plastic than the surrounding formations. Salt, shale, anhydrite, gypsum, and sandy shale are common constituents. Salt differs from the other rock types which form the cores in that it is of lower specific gravity than most of the sedimentary rocks with which it is associated.   As a result it is in unstable equilibrium and tends to rise through the overlying sediments to form salt domes.   Salt domes

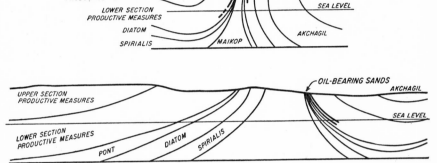

FIG. 4-10. Cross sections of two diapir folds.   (*From a paper by Goupkin, published by permission of the American Association of Petroleum Geologists.*)

are described in detail in Chap. 8 and will not be discussed further at this point.

Diapir folds having cores composed of materials other than salt occur in regions of strong folding.   In pronounced folds the plastic strata tend to thicken by flowage at the crests and troughs of anticlines and synclines. This thickening along the axial planes increases as the folding becomes more intense.   At first the flowage of plastic strata is of the concordant type, in which the plastic formations merely swell up along the axial planes but do not break through the overlying rocks to cut across them. At a later stage in the development of diapir folds the plastic material is forced across the strata and pushes upward through the overlying strata. Diapir folds of this type are called piercement.   Diapir folds have been discussed by Bohdanowicz[1] and Goubkin.[2]   Fig. 4-10, from the paper by Goubkin,[3] shows cross sections of two diapir folds in the Caucasus region.

[1] Karol Bohdanowicz, Geology and Mining of Petroleum in Poland, *A.A.P.G. Bull.*, vol. 16, pp. 1061–1091 (1932).

[2] I. M. Goubkin, Tectonics of Southeastern Caucasus and Its Relation to Productive Oil Fields, *A.A.P.G. Bull.*, vol. 18, pp. 603–671 (1934).

[3] *Ibid.*, p. 653.

The core or central mass of these anticlines has been intruded vertically upward, cutting across the younger strata. Diapir folds occur in the oil-producing regions of the Caucasus, Rumania, and Poland. Some anticlines with diapir structure produce considerable oil. The production is obtained, not from the intrusive core, but from reservoirs which are in contact with the intrusive core at depth and dip away from it.

Chevron or Zigzag Folds. Generally folded strata bend in rounded or flowing outlines, and they should be shown in this manner in cross sections, unless there is definite information to the contrary. Occasionally, however, the bending at the axial planes of the folds is very sharp, producing a chevron or zigzag pattern in cross sections or outcrop maps.

Similar and Parallel or Concentric Folds. Folds in general may be of two different types: parallel and similar. Similar folds have the

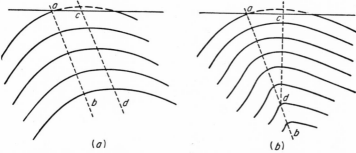

(a)   *(b)*

Fig. 4-11. Similar and parallel folds. (*From a paper by Lahee, published by permission of the American Association of Petroleum Geologists.*)

same shape at all depths. This means that the stratigraphic formations and intervals must thin out on the flanks and thicken along the axial planes. The more pronounced the folding, the greater must be this thinning and thickening. Folds in which the thickening and thinning of this type are very marked are called closed folds. This use of the term "closed" should be carefully distinguished from the meaning of the same word when used in the term "closed anticline." The latter usage is discussed on pages 86–90. Most anticlines which produce oil and gas are similar folds. Ordinarily the thinning on the flanks is not a conspicuous feature of these folds, though it must be present if the dips are steep.

In parallel or concentric folds the intervals between the beds remain the same. This type of fold changes its shape rapidly with depth. Fig. 4-11, from a paper by Lahee,[1] shows the nature of this change. The similar asymmetrical fold, (*A*, Fig. 4-11) maintains its shape with depth, but the axial and crestal planes shift toward the more gently dipping side. The parallel fold having the same size and shape at the surface

[1] Frederic H. Lahee, Discussion, *A.A.P.G. Bull.*, vol. 5, p. 329 (1921).

(*B*, Fig. 4-11) rapidly diminishes in area downward. Furthermore, the axial and crestal planes converge and meet, instead of remaining parallel as in the similar fold. Lahee points out that a surface geologist would be more likely to notice the crestal plane of the fold, with its change in dip direction, than the axial plane. Usually it is found in drilling that anticlines either become more pronounced with depth or do not change much. Apparently parallel folds are rare in oil-producing regions.

Ameboid Folds. The typical anticline formed by compression is oval or long and narrow in horizontal plan. Furthermore, the long axes of these folds are generally parallel to each other and to the general trend of the belt of folding. Another variety of fold has no prevailing trend and no definite shape. This type has been appropriately termed "ameboid." The dips of this type of fold are low, generally varying from a few feet to several hundred feet per mile. If faults are present in association with ameboid folds, they are of the normal type and of no great length, and tend to be arranged with their downthrown side toward the crest of the anticlines. Ameboid anticlines and synclines vary in width from a few hundred feet to a few miles. They may be either closed or without closure. Those which are closed tend to have rather small closures, usually less than 100 feet. They have been found in relatively undeformed areas of low regional dip, such as western South Dakota and western Kansas. They also occur in the lower Paleozoic strata of Kentucky and Tennessee. Fig. 4-12, from a paper by Born and Burwell,[1] shows some typical ameboid structures. Some small shallow production of oil has been obtained from fractures in Ordovician limestones in some of the anticlines shown in the figures.

Isolated Uplifts. In addition to anticlines clearly belonging to the well-defined fold systems, there are a number of important anticlines which are so far from other folds that they may be considered isolated. Many of them belong to recognized systems of folds but have an unusually large separation from the other folds of these systems. The folds may be either long and narrow or rounded in outline. Many of them are of great area and closure. If a sufficiently thick section of sediments is preserved, large and important oil and gas pools may occur on them. The dips of the strata in these isolated folds are usually low or moderate, being rarely over 10 or 20°. Any faults present are generally of the normal type, and their relation to the uplift suggests that they are produced by the stretching of the beds as they were arched in forming the anticline. The Black Hills uplift and the Bowdoin dome in Montana are well-known examples of this type of fold.

[1] Kendall E. Born and H. B. Burwell, Geology and Petroleum Resources of Clay County, Tennessee, *Tennessee Div. Geology Bull.* 47 (1939).

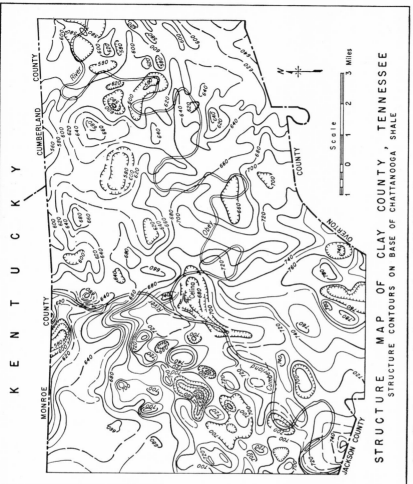

STRUCTURE MAP OF CLAY COUNTY, TENNESSEE

STRUCTURE CONTOURS ON BASE OF CHATTANOOGA SHALE

FIG. 4-12. Structure map showing typical ameboid folds. (*From a paper by Born and Burwell, Tennessee Geological Survey.*)

Recurrent Folds.   Subsurface studies of oil and gas fields have shown that many of them are located on folds which have been uplifted during a number of intervals of geologic time.   In some cases the folding took place gradually but continuously, and in others the uplift stopped for a considerable period, only to be renewed again at a later date.   It is quite common to find that the axial planes of the folds formed during various epochs are almost exactly the same.   In other cases the axial planes of the earlier and later folding may be as much as a mile apart, though still close enough to show that the fold as a whole has had repeated uplifts. Recurrent folds are recognized by the thinning of formations and intervals near their crests, by the disappearance of certain formations near their crests, and by local angular unconformities which are present only in the higher parts of the anticlines.

Recurrent folds which produce oil and gas have been described by Powers,[1] Reeves,[2] McCoy,[3] Rich,[4] and Clark.[5]   Recurrent folds are so common and so widespread that they have been described in hundreds of papers.

Minor Folds.   In addition to the larger anticlines on which oil and gas fields are located, there are many folds which are too small for oil production.   Folds only a few hundred feet across might have an important effect on production if they occurred in the producing formations. However, individual folds of this size at the surface would probably not persist down to the depths at which oil and gas production is found. Many small folds are apparently produced by the same forces which produced the larger ones.   These are discussed in more detail in Chap. 14.

Although too small for oil production, minor folds and crumplings are important to the petroleum geologist.   Unless they are recognized and their nature understood, they are likely to be confused with other structural features.   Where poorly exposed, steep dips due to minor folds are likely to be mistaken for steep dips on the flanks of larger folds.   All local dips due to minor folding are worthless for working out the structure of the major anticlines which produce oil and gas.   Steep dips due

[1] Sidney Powers, Structural Geology of the Mid-Continent Region, a Field for Research, *G.S.A. Bull.*, vol. 36, pp. 379–392 (1925).

[2] John R. Reeves, El Dorado Oil Field, Butler County, Kansas, "Structure of Typical American Oil Fields," American Association of Petroleum Geologists, Tulsa, vol. 2, pp. 160–167 (1929).

[3] Alex W. McCoy, An Interpretation of Local Structural Development in Mid-Continent Area Associated with Deposits of Petroleum, "Problems of Petroleum Geology," American Association of Petroleum Geologists, Tulsa, pp. 581–627 (1934).

[4] John L. Rich, Circular Structural Depressions in Central Kansas, *G.S.A. Bull.*, vol. 41, pp. 315–320 (1930).

[5] Stuart K. Clark, Mechanics of the Plain Type Folds of the Mid-Continent Area, *Jour. Geology*, vol. 40, pp. 46–61 (1932).

to minor folds, if found in cores, may be misinterpreted as due to faulting or to angular unconformities.

Mechanical Adjustments

Slippage and Stretching. As sedimentary formations are folded, various mechanical adjustments must take place between upper and lower beds and between different portions of the fold. These adjustments consist in part in slippage between beds, flowage of beds, and fracturing and faulting owing to stretching at the anticlinal axes. The only way in which a fold can have the same shape throughout a great vertical extent of strata is by flowage or by slippage of one bed over another. If this slippage did not take place, the strata near the crest and near the surface would be pulled apart by the stretching, with the result that faulting

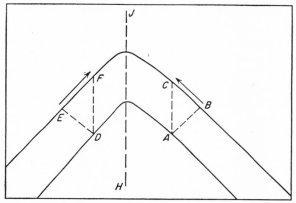

Fig. 4-13. Diagram illustrating reason for slippage of beds in folding.

would take place and blocks would drop down near the anticlinal crest. The common occurrence of such grabens near the anticlinal axes shows that this stretching does occur in many instances. On the other hand, the fact that many pronounced anticlines are not faulted shows that adjustments must be made by slippage or flowage.

Adjustments by flowage consist in a thickening of the formations near the anticlinal and synclinal axes and a thinning in the intervening flanks. The thinning and thickening occur chiefly in the more incompetent or plastic formations. If some formations are strong and competent and others weak and plastic, all the thinning and thickening may occur in the latter.

Where the adjustments are made by slippage between beds, the upper strata move toward the anticlinal axis, relative to the lower strata. This movement is entirely of one bed compared with another; actually, points in both beds tend to stay the same relative distances from the axial plane. These conditions are brought out in Fig. 4-13. *HJ* is the axial plane of the anticline. Before folding, point B was directly over A, and E was directly over D. Hence when the beds were lying flat before folding, a line from A at right angles to the bedding would pass through B and a similar line from D would pass through E. After folding, a line at right angles to the bedding from A would still pass through B and a similar line from D would pass through E, but the original points at B and E can no longer be at positions B and E after folding. If they were, the line along the bed $EFCB$ would be so lengthened by the bending that the bed would be broken up by faulting. Accordingly, the original points B and E have slipped over the underlying bed to positions C and F, the same distance from the axial plane as the points which were originally directly beneath them when the strata were flat. The result is that the upper beds slip toward the anticlinal axis, relative to the lower. This movement is toward the anticlinal axis all the way from the synclinal axis. The movement becomes zero at the anticlinal and synclinal axes.

The frequent occurrence of grabens near the crests of anticlines, and of normal faults dipping toward the anticlines, shows that in many cases the slippage is not sufficient to eliminate stretching near the anticlinal axis. Normal faulting of this type seems to be more common where thick, incompetent strata are folded.

Drag Folds. In any sedimentary sequence containing relatively rigid and plastic beds or formations, the rocks which are more rigid, stronger, and less easily deformed are known as competent. The incompetent beds are relatively soft, plastic, and easily bent. If a fold consists of competent and incompetent strata, the slippage due to movement of the competent beds is likely to produce drag folds in the incompetent strata between them. The general relations are shown in Fig. 4-14. Fig. 4-14 also shows the relations of the drag folds to the major folds that produce them. These drag folds are produced in the incompetent strata as the competent formations slide over one another. The friction causes the axial planes of these drag folds to be oriented as shown in Fig. 4-14. The acute angles which the axial planes of the drag folds make with the strata point in the direction of the relative movement of the beds during slippage.

The principle that the younger bed moves upward toward the anticline, relative to the lower bed, may be used to determine the top and bottom of vertical strata in which drag folds are observed. The bed which moves relatively upward must be younger and at the top. This is illustrated in Fig. 4-15. An exposure consists of vertical strata, containing two competent beds A and B, with incompetent beds showing drag folds between them. The direction of the acute angles of the drag folds show that bed B moved upward, relative to bed A. Bed B is therefore the younger, and the top is at the right of the exposure. The lines

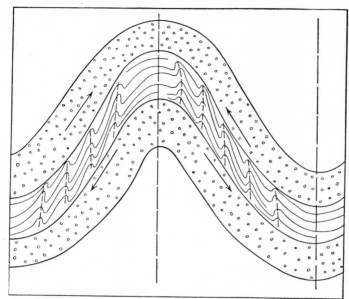

Fig. 4-14. Cross section showing relation of drag folds to major folds.

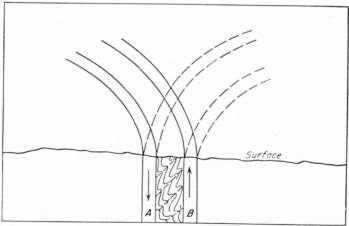

Fig. 4-15. Cross section showing how drag folds may be used to determine top and bottom of vertical strata.

extending above the surface indicate the former position of beds *A* and *B* before they were eroded. The solid lines show the correct interpretation, that the anticline was to the left. The interpretation shown by the dashed lines is incorrect because it would have involved relative movements of *A* and *B* just the opposite of those observed. Although drag folds may be used in this manner in working out the structure, the method is not infallible.   Furthermore, well-defined drag folds are commonly associated with intensely deformed sediments, and are not common in oil fields.   This problem has been discussed in detail by Shrock.[1]

Competent and Incompetent Rocks.   Incompetent rocks flow or fold with relative ease.   They tend to be comparatively soft or plastic. Competent beds are relatively more rigid and offer more resistance to bending or flowing.   Characteristics which make a rock competent are hardness, rigidity, massive rather than thin-bedded nature, resistance to fracturing, and ease of healing fractures by cementation.   Shales, clays, gypsum, anhydrite, and salt are generally incompetent.   Massive limestones, dolomites, and quartzites are competent.   Sandstones, if massive and well cemented, may also be competent.   Whether a rock is regarded as competent or incompetent is determined more by comparison with adjacent rocks than by its absolute hardness or plasticity.

Competent rocks conform to the larger folds of the region.   Incompetent strata are affected by minor crumplings and drag folds.   These small folds may cause mistakes in working out the structure unless their nature is realized.   In areas of intense deformation even the most competent beds may be crumpled and sharply bent, but oil is rarely found in association with such structures.

Absence of Large Voids.   It is a matter of observation that large voids are rarely formed during the development of geologic structures. One might suppose that large spaces would be produced by fault blocks not fitting together, or beneath anticlines where the upper beds are folded more sharply than those below.   Voids are occasionally seen beneath the crests of small, sharp anticlines formed within a few feet of the surface, but structures formed more than a few hundred feet below the surface generally develop without large open spaces.

Calculating Depth of Folding.   A method of calculating the depth of folding has been described by Chamberlin.[2]   The principle of this method is illustrated in Fig. 4-16.   Let it be assumed that before folding the cross section of the block of sediments constituted the rectangle *ACDG*, and that this rectangle has been deformed by lateral pressure into the rectangle *ABFE*.   If it is assumed that there is no change in volume, these two rectangles have the same area.   If *GD* is a stratum at the top of the original rectangle before folding, it is represented after folding by the curved line from *E* to *F*.   The average elevation of this folded line is equal to the elevation of the straight line *EF*, and if the curved line were straightened out its length would equal the line *GD*.   Since the two

[1] Robert R. Shrock, "Sequence in Layered Rocks," McGraw-Hill Book Company, Inc., New York (1948).

[2] R. T. Chamberlin, The Appalachian Folds of Central Pennsylvania, *Jour. Geology*, vol. 18, pp. 228–251 (1910).

rectangles *GEFH* and *BHDC* have the same area, if *GH*, *HF*, and *HD* are known, *FB*, the assumed depth of folding, can be calculated. *HD* is the shortening due to folding. *GD*, the length of the section before folding, is determined by straightening out the curved line from *E* to *F* and adding to it the heaves of the thrust faults, if any. *EF* is the present map distance between the two ends of the cross section. *GD* − *EF* = *HD*, the shortening. The height of uplift, *HF*, is the difference between the

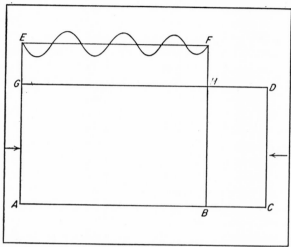

FIG. 4-16. Cross section to illustrate principle of method for calculating depth of folding.

average elevation of the key bed where it is undeformed, and its average elevation where it is deformed. Because *EF* × *FH* = *HD* × *DC*,

$$DC = \frac{EF \times HF}{HD}$$

Since all these lengths can be determined except *DC*, it is possible to determine the depth of folding, if all the assumptions are correct.

This solution is evidently based on the assumption that conditions in the field are similar to those in the pressure-box experiment described on pages 61–62. The important points to be remembered about this method are the assumptions on which it is based and the evidence for and against them. One fundamental assumption is that there is a definite base at which folding stops. This is true only where folding is bounded downward by a thrust fault or decollement. Another assumption is that the uplift of the average position of the key horizon in the deformed area is due to folding. This is frequently not the case where the deformed area is very large. In such cases the general elevation may be determined by isostasy. It is also in many cases very difficult to determine with reasonable accuracy the difference in average elevation of the key horizon before and after folding. Furthermore, the final elevation may be determined by faulting or by broad upwarps that have nothing to do with folding. This method would be very useful to petroleum geologists if it could determine how far down a given anticline would persist. It is sometimes very difficult or impossible to find out in advance of drilling whether or not a promising surface anticline continues down to the horizons where production is expected. Unfortunately, it does not appear that this method of calculating depth of folding is generally useful in such cases. The conditions under which it can be used accurately seem to be limited to decollements. The discussion of this method is given in detail to show how a structural theory should be criticized, and how it is affected by the various assumptions on which it is based.

Characteristics of Folds Important to Petroleum Geologists

The common occurrence of oil and gas fields on anticlines gives these folds a greater importance than any other type. Among the properties of anticlines which are useful for indicating their nature are length, breadth, height, shape, symmetry, and angle of dip. There are in addition several characteristics of anticlines which have a special bearing on their value as potential producing structures. The most important of these characteristics are closure and closed area.

Closure. The closure is the total amount of dip away from the crest of an anticline in the direction in which the dip is least. If the structure-contour interval were infinitely small, it could also be defined as the difference in elevation between the highest structure contour on the anticline and the lowest structure which completely surrounds it. The anticline would have no closure if there were no areas on it completely surrounded by some of these structure contours.

Of course synclines may have closure also, but because oil and gas production is rarely found in them there is comparatively little interest in the closure of synclines. The rules for determining the closure of anticlines apply in reverse to determining the closure of synclines. If an impervious layer is assumed to have exactly the same configuration as the key horizon on which the structure contours are drawn, and if water is poured into depressions in this impervious layer until the water overflows, then the depth of the water in these structural depressions is equal to their closure.

Figs. 4-17 and 4-18 show how the closure of an anticline may be estimated from a structure map. The anticline extends from A to B with a closed area in the vicinity of X and a saddle at Y. The closure is clearly the difference in elevation along the axis AB from the crest of the anticline near X to the bottom of the saddle at Y. The structure-contour

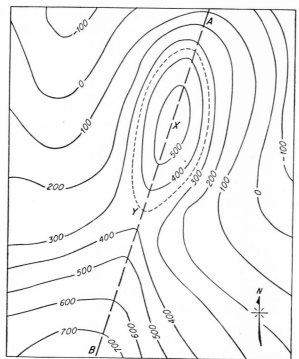

Fig. 4-17. Structure map showing how closure of an anticline is estimated.

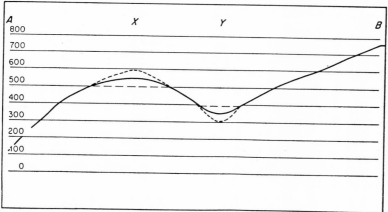

Fig. 4-18. Cross section showing how closure of an anticline is estimated.

map indicates that the key bed rises to between 500 and 600 ft elevation near X and descends to between 300 and 400 ft elevation near Y, but the map does not show the exact position of the key bed between the structure contours. The reason for this uncertainty is shown in Fig. 4-18. At the crest near point X the highest possible position of the key bed is just below 600 ft elevation, as shown by the dotted line, and the lowest possible position just above 500 ft as shown by the dashed line. Similarly in the saddle at Y the highest possible position is just below 400 ft elevation, shown by the dashed line, and the lowest just above 300 ft, shown by the dotted line. Hence the minimum possible value of the closure is 100 ft, and the maximum possible 300 ft. The most reasonable or likely value would seem to be halfway between the two extremes, which would give a closure of 200 ft. The position of the key bed which would give a closure of 200 ft is shown by the solid line in Fig. 4-18.

The principle that the closure is halfway between the maximum and minimum values gives the rule that the closure is equal to the number of structure contours completely enclosing the closed area times the structure-contour interval. The fact that the uncertainty is always twice the structure-contour interval should not be forgotten. It is evident that the ratio of the uncertainty or range in possible values to the closure decreases as more structure contours encircle the closed area. If only one structure contour surrounds the closed area, the uncertainty is twice as large as the estimated closure.

There are some exceptions to the rule given in the last paragraph. It is sometimes possible to make a better estimate of the elevation of the key bed at the top of the structure and at the point of closure than by assuming that these elevations are halfway between the elevations of the nearest structure contours. The point of closure is the point at which the closure is determined. It is where the key horizon reaches its lowest point along the axis in the saddle which establishes the closure. This point of closure is at Y in Figs. 4-17 and 4-18 and at C in Fig. 4-19. The configuration of the structure contours suggests that in Fig. 4-19 the elevation of the key horizon at the top of the closed area would be about 720 ft, not 750, and at the point of closure about 490 ft, and not 450. Thus the closure in this case would be estimated as 230 ft, and not 300 ft, as it would be according to the rule.

Cross-folding and Multiple Axes in Relation to Closure. It is quite common for two or more folds to intersect, producing what is known as cross-folding. Cross-folding is of considerable importance in petroleum geology, because of the fact that domes or closures are likely to be produced where two anticlines intersect. Each fold has an axis, and it may be advisable for special reasons to show all the axes on a structure map. The anticlinal axes are illustrated in Fig. 4-20. The anticlinal axis

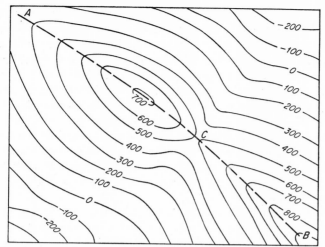

Fig. 4-19. Structure map showing how estimation of closure is affected by configuration of structure contours at point of closure.

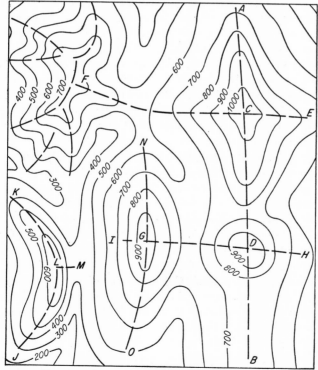

Fig. 4-20. Structure map showing anticlinal axes.

AB is clearly cut by the minor anticlinal axis FE, producing a closure or dome with its crest at C. The anticlinal axes ON and AB may be considered to be intersected by the minor anticline IH, producing domes at G and D. It is evident that whether cross folds are considered to be present or not depends somewhat on the point of view and on what it is desired to emphasize. Geologists looking at the structure map of the anticline ON might not think of it as the result of cross-folding unless there were some special reason to bring out this aspect. At F there is an irregular or ameboid structure with several anticlinal axes radiating from it. It should be noted that the point of closure may not be on the major axis of the anticline. The point of closure of the anticline JK is at M, on the insignificant anticlinal axis LM. There is always a saddle at the point of closure.

Closed Area. The closed area is the area covered by the portion of the anticline which is closed. If the structure-contour interval were infinitely small, the area surrounded by the lowest structure contour would be the closed area. In a structure map with ordinary structure-contour intervals, there would be some uncertainty about the exact position of the boundary of the closed area. Thus in Fig. 4-17 it is assumed that at the point of critical closure, Y, the key bed is at an elevation halfway between the next structure contour below and above, or 350 ft. The closed area would therefore be bounded by a structure contour at an elevation of 350 ft, which is shown by the dashed line, and which would presumably cross the anticlinal axis at a point midway between the points where the two 400-ft structure contours cross it, and would pass around the closed area midway between the 300- and 400-ft structure contours. The significance of closure and closed area is discussed further in Chap. 17.

Reversal. Reversal is dip opposite to the regional dip. Except along faults, a reversal always implies an anticline, the position of the anticlinal axis being in the direction of the regional dip from the reversal. All closed anticlines have a reversal at least as great as the closure, but an anticline without closure may have a large reversal. The surface geologist, in making a reconnaissance for structures suitable for testing, searches particularly for reversals, because in some cases they are the most conspicuous indications of the presence of a closed structure. In general, the larger the reversal, the more promising the anticline. An anticline with 20 ft of closure and 200 ft of reversal would in general be more promising than an anticline with 20 ft of closure and 20 ft of reversal.

Two steps are necessary to determine the reversal of anticlines. The first is to determine the direction of the regional dip. Until this is done, it is generally impossible to estimate the reversal. After the direction of the regional dip is determined, each anticline in the area under consideration is examined to determine where it has the greatest amount of dip in the opposite direction. The anticline *AC* in Fig. 4-21 shows the greatest dip opposite to the regional dip from *A* to *B*. This dip amounts to 700 ft, while the closure of this anticline is 400 ft. The closure and reversal of the anticline at *K* are both 300 ft. The anticline extending from *F* to *G* has no closure, but shows 400 ft of reverse dip from *H* to *I*.

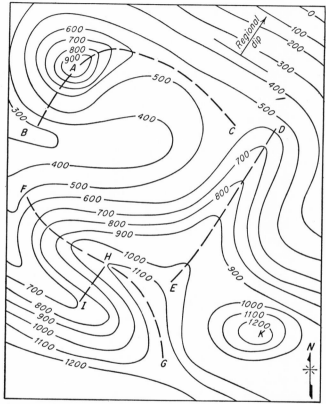

Fig. 4-21. Structure map illustrating how reversal is calculated.

The direction of the regional dip is simply the general or average dip. It cannot be determined accurately unless the structure map covers a large enough area to distinguish the general dip from the dips produced by the individual folds.

Character of Anticline after Subtracting Regional Dip. It occasionally becomes advisable to find out what the structure of a given area would be like if the regional dip were removed. The way to remove the regional dip from a structure map is as follows: First the regional dip and strike are determined.   The regional strike is the direction in which the strata are, on the average, level, when the whole area is taken under consideration.   The direction of the regional dip must be at right angles to this.   The amount of regional dip is computed by taking the average elevation of an area far down the dip and far up the dip, and dividing the difference between these two by the component of the distance between them which is at right angles to the regional strike.   Lines are then drawn on the map parallel to the regional strike with sufficient distance between them for the regional dip to amount to one structure-contour interval.   Thus if the structure-contour interval is 100 ft and the regional dip is 200 ft per mile, the lines will be half a mile apart. One of these lines is given a number equal to the average elevation of the key horizon along the line, and the other lines are lower in the direction of the regional dip and higher in the opposite direction.   The numbers of each line are higher or lower than the next by one structure-contour interval.   By means of these lines, the correction to be subtracted or added to any point to eliminate the effect of regional dip can be estimated.   The whole map is then divided into squares of a suitable width.   The elevation of the key horizon at the corner of each square and the correction number are estimated, and the correction number is subtracted from the elevation.   The remainder is then contoured.   The result is a structure-contour map with the regional dip eliminated.

This method is illustrated in Fig. 4-22.   The solid lines are structure contours, indicating a regional dip to the north at a rate of 100 ft per mile.   An anticline with around 50 to 100 ft of closure is shown.   The dotted lines are contours on the amount of correction.   By means of these lines and the structure contours, it is possible to estimate at any point on the map both the elevation of the key bed and the amount of correction needed to eliminate the regional dip.   In order to get enough corrected values to draw structure contours, squares 1 mile in width were drawn on the map.   The elevation of the key horizon and the amount of correction are estimated at the corner of each square; the correction is subtracted from the elevation of the key horizon and the remainder plotted at the corner of each square.   When these values are contoured, the heavy dashed lines of Fig. 4-22 are obtained.   These lines show the structure with the regional dip eliminated.   Evidently eliminating the regional dip increases the closure of the anticline from 50 to 100 ft to about 200 ft and moves the crest of the anticline about 2 or $2\frac{1}{2}$ miles north.   If the regional dip originated after the folding, the heavy dashed lines show the anticline as it was before the formation of the regional dip.

There are several situations in which it is desirable to know how an anticline would look with the regional dip eliminated.   It may be known from regional studies that the regional dip and the folds on it were formed at entirely different times.   For example, the anticlines might have developed in the Pennsylvanian, while the tilting that caused the regional dip may have occurred in the Pliocene.   Under these conditions, a map of the structure with regional dip eliminated is needed to show where the oil and gas would have accumulated from the Pennsylvanian to the Pliocene.   If the crest of the anticline was in a different position in pre-Pliocene time, the oil might have been sealed in the former crest by

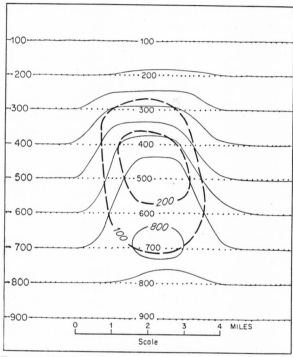

Fig. 4-22. Map illustrating method of removing regional dip.

reactions with the connate water.   The walls of the pores may have absorbed substances from the oil while it was in its earlier position. This may give the reservoir different properties where it contained oil in pre-Pliocene time from those found where it contained oil only after the Pliocene tilting.

Determining Dips of Axial and Crestal Planes.   A geologist who makes a location on a structure for a test below horizons previously drilled should always consider the possible effects of a shifting of the axial and crestal planes with depth.   The effects of shifting axes are more likely to be serious in steep folds than in those which are gently dipping. In broad, flat-topped folds axial shifting does not produce as much effect as in folds with sharper crests. If the anticlines are symmetrical, then the axial and crestal planes are vertical. There are, in general, three types of folds in which the crests demonstrate a horizontal shift with depth. One type consists in folds which have undergone two or more periods of deformation. The strata at the depth at which production is expected may have been folded before the deposition of the beds used to map the known structure. If there is no relation at all between the axes of the earlier and the later folding, it would be misleading to say that the axes of the folds were shifted with depth; it would be more precise to say that the axes were different at depth. If, however, the axial planes of the earlier and the later folding correspond fairly closely, but not exactly (as commonly happens), the effect will be that the axial planes of the anticlines appear to be shifted in the deeper strata. The structure of the shallower formations does not indicate the direction or amount of this shifting of the axial plane. However, some idea of how the axial plane is likely to be affected by depth in such cases may be obtained by studies of the results of drilling similar folds in the region.

Asymmetrical anticlines appear to be of two types. In one type the axial plane dips toward the gentler side; in the other the axial plane dips toward the steeper side. The first type is evidently produced by compression, and is much more common than the latter. It is therefore advisable to assume that the axial plane dips toward the gentler side of an anticline unless there is definite evidence to the contrary. To find the dip of the axial plane in this type of fold, bisect the angle formed by the average dip of the strata on both flanks. In some folds the axial plane is of irregular configuration, and no rule can predict its location in depth under such conditions.

The other type of asymmetrical fold is apparently produced by the combination of a fault or monocline with regional dip or with one limb of a fold. In this case the steeper side either overlies a fault or consists of a fold of monoclinal nature. The dip on the other flank is usually gentle, frequently only a few degrees and in many cases less than 1°. In some cases the monoclinal nature of the fold on one side may be recognized by its steepness and straightness. The results of drilling have shown that certain of these monoclines pass downward into faults. However, many monoclines are known which do not pass downward into faults within the sedimentary section. Large monoclines of great length are especially common in the Rocky Mountain region west of the Front Range. If it is known that the steep flank of an anticline is produced by a normal fault at depth or by a monocline, the axial plane probably but not certainly dips steeply toward the steep side.

According to Lloyd,[1] the axial planes of the anticlines in the Cat Creek field, Montana, and the Grass Creek and Lance Creek fields, Wyoming, are shifted toward the steeper side with depth. Lafferty[2] states that the axes of some of the northeast-southwest–trending anticlines in West Virginia are several miles farther northwest in the Devonian limestone than in the surface or shallow strata. Sherrill[3] mentions that the gentler folds of the Appalachian region are on the average 1.3 times as steep on the southeast side as on the northwest side, and probably increase in size and migrate toward the northwest with depth.

Change in Size of Folds with Depth. The question of the continuity of a fold with depth is perhaps even more important than the dip of its axial plane. Many folds get neither much larger nor much smaller with depth. A number of folds grow steeper and more pronounced with depth. A few grow smaller with depth and eventually die out. It is often difficult or impossible to determine in advance of drilling to which of these classes a fold belongs. A few general observations may, however, be of some assistance. Where the regional convergence is known, its effect on the closure of folds with depth may be predicted in advance of drilling. This problem has been discussed by Levorsen.[4] In southeastern Oklahoma the interval between the middle Pennsylvanian and the Ordovician increases toward the southeast at a rate of about 250 ft per mile. This has a very pronounced effect on the closure to be expected on surface anticlines in the deeper formations. Figs. 4-23 and 4-24, from Levorsen's paper,[5] illustrate this. Fig. 4-23 shows structure maps at three different levels of the fold on which the Garrison field, Oklahoma, is located. There is no closure on the uppermost horizon, while on the lowest there is 200 ft of closure. Fig. 4-24 shows how the same fold will appear as a closed dome or as a terrace owing to the effect of convergence. The manner in which the effect of convergence or regional thinning may be allowed for in changing the horizons on which the structure contours are drawn has been described on earlier pages. Not all the increase in size of folds with depth in regions of convergence is necessarily due to the convergence. Much of it may be in some cases ascribed to the effect of repeated folding with the same structural axes during the time interval

[1] E. Russell Lloyd, Discussion of a Paper by Bailey Willis Entitled "Folding or Shearing, Which?" *A.A.P.G. Bull.*, vol. 11, p. 46 (1927).

[2] Robert L. Lafferty, The Oriskany in West Virginia, *A.A.P.G. Bull.*, vol. 22, p. 187 (1938).

[3] R. E. Sherrill, Some Problems of Appalachian Structure, *A.A.P.G. Bull.*, vol. 25, p. 417 (1941).

[4] A. I. Levorsen, Convergence Studies in the Mid-Continent Region, *A.A.P.G. Bull.*, vol. 11, pp. 657–682 (1927).

[5] *Ibid.*, pp. 668, 671.

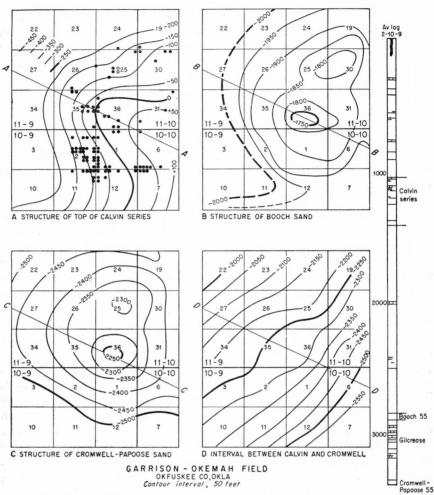

FIG. 4-23. Structure of Garrison field, Okfuskee county, Okla., at various horizons. The geologic column at the right shows the relative positions of the horizons contoured. *D* is the difference between *A* and *C*, and may be considered to be a structure-contour map at the time of the deposition of the top of the Calvin series. (*After Levorsen, published by permission of American Association of Petroleum Geologists.*)

between the deposition of the strata at depth and that of the surface strata.

A fold is supratenuous if the folding continued during the deposition of the sediments which are folded. If folding took place during the time gaps in sedimentation represented by unconformities, there will be an angular unconformity and an increase in closure at the unconformity. In many cases there is no way of determining from surface observations whether the fold is supratenuous at depth or not. Measurements made of the exposed formations may, it is true, show whether folding was going on when they were deposited, but the important point is how much folding took place between the time when the prospective producing formations were deposited and the time when the surface strata were laid down. In many regions, however, it is already known that surface or shallow folds increase greatly in closure with depth because of folding that is repeated along the same axes. For example, in north central and northeastern parts of Oklahoma and adjacent portions of Kansas small anticlines in the Pennsylvanian strata are very frequently underlain by very large anticlines in Ordovician formations. In some regions it has been noted that all anticlines change in a certain manner with depth. In others, the nature of the changes with depth is related to the shape,

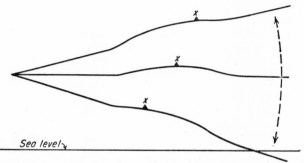

Fig. 4-24. Cross section showing how convergence may cause change in closure and horizontal shift of the crest of an anticline. (*After Levorsen, published by permission of the American Association of Petroleum Geologists.*)

size, or orientation of the shallow anticlines. Thus the results of drilling on anticlines in a region may be used to predict the character at depth of the untested anticlines in the same region.

It is known that some anticlines do die out with depth. Usually the information as to such anticlines is meager, because they are very likely to be dry. If there are no wildcat wells in the vicinity, the geologists in charge of the operation may not even know whether the test well ran low or high on the deeper formations. In an area in which there has been considerable wildcatting, it is usually known whether the test ran low or high. However, even when it is known that the test ran low, there may be doubt as to whether this was because the anticlinal axis shifted with depth or because the fold died out completely. Usually it is not possible to plot a detailed section to show how the fold dies out with depth unless production happens to be found at a lower horizon.

It is not definitely known why some anticlines persist with depth while others die out, and there seems to be no sure means of determining which ones will die out. In general, the larger the area covered by a fold and the larger its closure, the more likely it is to persist with depth. Salt domes and other folds due to movement of a salt layer cannot persist below the layer from which the salt is derived. This problem is discussed again in Chap. 13. Folds due to compaction, which increase in size with depth, are described in Chap. 9.

ADDITIONAL REFERENCES

Babenroth, D. L., and Strahler, A. N.: Geomorphology and Structure of the East Kaibab Monocline, Arizona and Utah, *G.S.A. Bull.*, vol. 56, pp. 107–150 (1945).

Bailey, E. B.: West Highland Tectonics, *Geol. Soc. London Quart. Jour.*, vol. 90, pp. 462–525 (1934).

Bailey, T. L.: Late Pleistocene Coast Range Orogenesis in Southern California, *G.S.A. Bull.*, vol. 54, pp. 1549–1568 (1943).

Bain, G. W.: Flowage Folding, *Am. Jour. Sci.*, 5th ser., vol. 22, pp. 503–530 (1931).

Baker, A. A.: Geologic Structure of Eastern Utah, *A.A.P.G. Bull.*, vol. 19, pp. 1472–1507 (1935).

Baker, C. L.: Nature of the Later Deformation in Certain Ranges of the Great Basin, *Jour. Geology*, vol. 21, pp. 273–278 (1913).

Ballard, N.: Stratigraphy and Structural History of East-central United States, *A.A.P.G. Bull.*, vol. 22, pp. 1519–1555 (1938).

Bartram, J. G.: Summary of Rocky Mountain Geology, *A.A.P.G. Bull.*, vol. 23, pp. 1131–1152 (1939).

——— and Hupp, J. E.: Subsurface Structure of Some Unsymmetrical Anticlines in Rocky Mountains, *A.A.P.G. Bull.*, vol. 13, pp. 1275–1286 (1929).

Bradley, W. H.: Geomorphology of the North Flank of the Uinta Mountains, Utah, *U.S.G.S. Prof. Paper* 185(i) (1936).

Brown, R. W.: Experiments Relating to Factors Causing the Localization of Folds, *A.A.P.C. Bull.*, vol. 12, pp. 617–623 (1928).

———: Origin of the Folds of Osage County, Oklahoma, *A.A.P.G. Bull.*, vol. 12, pp. 501–513 (1928).

Bucher, W. H.: "Deformation of the Earth's Crust," Princeton University Press, Princeton, N.J. (1936).

———: Geologic Structure and Orogenic History of Venezuela, *G.S.A. Mem.* 49, pp. 1–113 (1952).

———, Thom, W. T., and Chamberlin, R. T.: Geologic Problems of the Beartooth Bighorn Region, *G.S.A. Bull.*, vol. 45, pp. 167–188 (1934).

Campbell, J. D.: Some Aspects of Rock Folding by Shearing Deformation, *Am. Jour. Sci.*, vol. 249, pp. 625–639 (1951).

Chamberlin, R. T.: Basement Control in Rocky Mountain Deformation, *Am. Jour. Sci.*, vol. 243-A, pp. 98–116 (1945).

———: Diastrophic Behavior around the Bighorn Basin, *Jour. Geology*, vol. 48, pp. 673–716 (1940).

Clapp, F. G.: Geology of Eastern Iran, *G.S.A. Bull.*, vol. 51, pp. 1–102 (1940).

Clark, B. L.: Folding of the California Coast Range Type Illustrated by a Series of Experiments, *Jour. Geology*, vol. 45, pp. 296–319 (1937).

———: Tectonics of the Coast Ranges of Middle California, *G.S.A. Bull.*, vol. 41, pp. 728–828 (1930).

Clark, L. M.: Geology of Rocky Mountain Front Ranges near Bow River, Alberta, *A.A.P.G. Bull.*, vol. 33, pp. 614–633 (1949).

Collet, L. W.: "The Structure of the Alps," Edward Arnold & Co., London, 2d ed. (1935).

Collingwood, D. M.: Graphic Method of Determining Surface Projection of the Axis and Crest Traces at Any Depth of an Asymmetrical Anticline, *A.A.P.G. Bull.*, vol. 5, pp. 159–162 (1921).

Colloquium on Plastic Flow and Deformation within the Earth, *Am. Geophys. Union Trans.*, vol. 32, pp. 497–543 (1951).

Cotton, C. A.: A Review of Tectonic Relief in Australia, *Jour. Geology*, vol. 57, pp. 280–296 (1949).

Cox, G. H., and Dake, C. L.: Geologic Criteria for Determining the Structural Position of Beds, *Missouri Univ. School of Mines and Metallurgy Bull.*, vol. 2, no. 4, pp. 7–59 (1916).

Darton, N. H.: Some Structural Features of the Northern Anthracite Coal Basin, Pennsylvania, *U.S.G.S. Prof. Paper* 193(d) (1940).

Decker, C. E.: "Studies in Minor Folds," University of Chicago Press, Chicago (1920).

DeJuana, C. G.: Elements of Diastrophic History of Northeastern Venezuela, *G.S.A. Bull.*, vol. 58, pp. 689–702 (1947).

Demorest, M.: Critical Structural Features of the Bighorn Mountains, Wyoming, *G.S.A. Bull.*, vol. 52, pp. 161–176 (1941).

Dobbin, C. E.: Exceptional Oil Fields in Rocky Mountain Region of the United States, *A.A.P.G. Bull.*, vol. 31, pp. 797–823 (1947).

————: Structural Conditions of Oil and Gas Accumulation in Rocky Mountain Region, United States, *A.A.P.G. Bull.*, vol. 27, pp. 417–478 (1943).

Eardley, A. J.: Geology of the North-central Wasatch Mountains, Utah, *G.S.A. Bull.*, vol. 55, pp. 819–894 (1944).

————: Paleozoic Cordilleran Geosyncline and Related Orogeny, *Jour. Geology*, vol. 55, pp. 309–342 (1947).

————: "Structural Geology of North America," Harper & Brothers, New York (1951).

————: Structure of the Wasatch–Great Basin Region, *G.S.A. Bull.*, vol. 50, pp. 1277–1310 (1939).

Fath, A. E.: The Origin of the Faults, Anticlines and Buried "Granite Ridge" of the Northern Part of the Mid-Continent Oil and Gas Field, *U.S.G.S. Prof. Paper* 128(c) (1920).

Gallup, W. B.: Geology of Turner Valley Oil and Gas Field, Alberta, Canada, *A.A.P.G. Bull.*, vol. 35, pp. 797–821 (1951).

Gibson, H. S.: Oil Production in Southwestern Iran, *World Oil*, vol. 128, no. 1, pp. 271–280; vol. 128, no. 2, pp. 217–226 (1948).

Goodman, A. J.: Tectonics of East Side of Cordillera in Western Canada, *A.A.P.G. Bull.*, vol. 35, pp. 783–796 (1951).

Gregory, J. W., ed.: "Structure of Asia," Methuen & Co., Ltd., London (1929).

Griggs, D. T.: The Creep of Rocks, *Jour. Geology*, vol. 47, pp. 225–251 (1939).

Hake, B. F., Willis, R., and Addison, C. C.: Folded Thrust Faults in the Foothills of Alberta, *G.S.A. Bull.*, vol. 53, pp. 291–334 (1942).

Harrison, J. V., and Falcon, N. L.: Collapse Structures, *Geol. Mag.*, vol. 71, pp. 529–539 (1934).

———— and ————: Gravity Collapse Structures and Mountain Ranges as Exemplified in Southwestern Iran, *Geol. Soc. London Quart. Jour.*, vol. 92, pp. 91–102 (1936).

Honess, C. W.: Geology of the Southern Ouachita Mountains of Oklahoma, *Oklahoma Geol. Survey Bull.* 32, part 1 278 pp. (1923).

Ickes, E. L.: Similar Parallel and Neutral Types of Folding, *Econ. Geology*, vol. 23, pp. 575–591 (1923).

Jacobsen, L.: Structural Relations on East Flank of Anadarko Basin, Cleveland and McClain Counties, Oklahoma, *A.A.P.G. Bull.*, vol. 33, pp. 695–719 (1949).

Keith, A.: Outlines of Appalachian Structure, *G.S.A. Bull.*, vol. 34, pp. 309–380 (1925).

King, P. B.: Geology of the Marathon Region, Texas, *U.S.G.S. Prof. Paper* 187, 148 pp. (1938).

———: Tectonic Framework of Southeastern United States, *A.A.P.G. Bull.*, vol. 34, pp. 635–671 (1950).

———: "Tectonics of Middle North America," Princeton University Press, Princeton, N.J. (1951).

———: Tectonics of Northern Mexico, *Proc. Eighth Am. Sci. Cong.*, vol. 4, pp. 395–398 (1942).

Lahee, F. H.: "Field Geology," McGraw-Hill Book Company, Inc., New York, 5th ed. (1952).

Landes, K. K., and Ockerman, J. W.: Origin of Domes in Lincoln and Mitchell Counties, Kansas, *G.S.A. Bull.*, vol. 44, pp. 529–540 (1933).

Lees, G. M.: Foreland Folding, *Geol. Soc. London Quart. Jour.*, vol. 108, pp. 1–34 (1952).

——— and Richardson, F. D. S.: The Geology of the Oil-field Belt of Southwest Iran and Iraq, *Geol. Mag.*, vol. 77, pp. 227–252 (1940).

Link, T. A.: Interpretations of Foothills Structures, Alberta, Canada, *A.A.P.G. Bull.*, vol. 33, pp. 1475–1501 (1949).

Longwell, C. R.: Structure of Northern Muddy Mountain Area, Nevada, *G.S.A. Bull.*, vol. 60, pp. 923–968 (1949).

McCoy, A. W., and others: Types of Oil and Gas Traps in Rocky Mountain Region, *A.A.P.G. Bull.*, vol. 35, pp. 1000–1037 (1951).

Miser, H. D.: Structure of Ouachita Mountains of Oklahoma and Arkansas, *Oklahoma Geol. Survey Bull.* 50 (1929).

Nelson, V. E., and Church, V.: Critical Structures of the Gros Ventre and Northern Hogack Ranges, Wyoming, *Jour. Geology*, vol. 51, pp. 143–166 (1943).

Powers, S.: Structural Geology of Northeastern Oklahoma, *Jour. Geology*, vol. 39, pp. 117–132 (1931).

Price, P. H.: The Appalachian Structural Front, *Jour. Geology*, vol. 39, pp. 24–44 (1931).

"Problems of Petroleum Geology," American Association of Petroleum Geologists, Tulsa (1934).

Reed, R. D.: "Geology of California," American Association of Petroleum Geologists, Tulsa (1933).

——— and Hollister, J. S.: Structural Evolution of Southern California, *A.A.P.G. Bull.*, vol. 20, pp. 1533–1721 (1936).

Rettger, R. E.: Experiments on Soft-rock Deformation, *A.A.P.G. Bull.*, vol. 19, pp. 271–292 (1935).

Rodgers, J.: Evolution of Thought on Middle and Southern Appalachians, *A.A.P.G. Bull.*, vol. 33, pp. 1643–1654 (1949).

———: Mechanics of Appalachian Folding as Illustrated by Sequatchie Anticline, Tennessee and Alabama, *A.A.P.G. Bull.*, vol. 34, pp. 672–681 (1950).

Selk, E. L.: Types of Oil and Gas Traps in Southern Oklahoma, *A.A.P.G. Bull.*, vol. 35, pp. 582–606 (1951).

Sellards, E. H., Baker, C. L., and others: Geology of Texas: II, Structural and Economic Geology, *Univ. Texas Bur. Econ. Geology Bull.* 3401 (1934).

Sheets, M. M.: Diastrophism during Historic Time in Gulf Coastal Plain, *A.A.P.G. Bull.*, vol. 31, pp. 201–226 (1947).

Stark, J. T., and others: Geology and Origin of South Park, Colorado, *G.S.A. Mem.* 33, pp. 1–188 (1949).

Steers, J. A.: The Unstable Earth, E. P. Dutton & Co., Inc., New York (1932).

"Structure of Typical American Oil Fields," American Association of Petroleum Geologists, Tulsa, vols. 1 and 2 (1929); vol. 3 (1945).

Suess, E.: "The Face of the Earth," Oxford University Press, New York, 5 vols. (1904–1924).

Taliaferro, N. L.: Geologic History and Structure of the Central Coast Ranges of California, *California Dept. Nat. Resources, Div. Mines Bull.* 118, pp. 119–162 (1943).

Tanton, T. L.: Determination of Age Relationships in Folded Strata, *Geol. Mag.*, vol. 67, pp. 73–76 (1930).

Thomas, E. P.: Mississippi Structures and Their Relation to Oil Accumulation, *A.A.P.G. Bull.*, vol. 34, pp. 1502–1516 (1950).

Thomas, H. D.: Geologic History and Geologic Structure of Wyoming, *Wyoming Geol. Survey Bull.* 42 (1949).

Tomlinson, C. W.: Odd Geologic Structures of Southern Oklahoma, *A.A.P.G. Bull.*, vol. 36, pp. 1820–1840 (1952).

Townsend, R. C.: Deformation of Fort Union Formation near Lignite, North Dakota, *A.A.P.G. Bull.*, vol. 34, pp. 1552–1564 (1950).

Umbgrove, J. H. F.: "The Pulse of the Earth," M. Nijhoff, The Hague, 2d ed. (1947).

Weaver, C. E.: Geology of the Coast Ranges Immediately North of the San Francisco Bay Region, *G.S.A. Mem.* 35, pp. 1–242 (1949).

Webb, J. B.: Geological History of Plains in Western Canada, *A.A.P.G. Bull.*, vol. 35, pp. 2291–2315 (1951).

Willis, B.: Folding or Shearing, Which? *A.A.P.G. Bull.*, vol. 11, pp. 31–47 (1927).

——— and Willis, R.: Geologic Structures, McGraw-Hill Book Company, Inc., New York, 3d ed. (1934).

CHAPTER 5

FAULTS

The importance of faults in petroleum geology is second only to that of folds. It is true that there are many oil fields and many large areas in oil-producing regions where faults are entirely absent. On the other hand, many of the traps which cause oil or gas accumulation are caused by faults. In other cases faults modify the traps produced by folds or by stratigraphic causes. Furthermore, unless faults are recognized and their effects allowed for, errors are likely to be made in interpretations of the structure and stratigraphy.

Studies of fault planes and associated phenomena are likely to be a neglected phase in the education of a petroleum geologist. During field courses geologists are trained in mapping formations, measuring stratigraphic sections, and collecting fossils. But in the vicinity of most summer field camps there are generally not enough exposures of fault planes of various types to give geologists the needed practice in interpreting the structural conditions associated with faults. For this reason, the subject is treated with some detail in this chapter.

NATURE

A fault is defined as a fracture along which there has been appreciable motion parallel to the break. A joint differs from a fault in the absence of motion parallel to the fracture. There is an enormous range in the lengths of faults and in their displacements. Many faults are so small that they can be seen only under the microscope. Other faults are over 100 miles long, and their displacements amount to many miles.

All faults are due to shearing, and gravity plays a part in the motion of all faults, though it is not the only cause. As everyone knows, there is a relation between faults and earthquakes. Many earthquakes are accompanied by visible faulting at the surface, and it is likely that in many cases in which no surface faulting accompanies the earthquake, there is a fault at depth. However, many earthquakes originate some distance below the surface, and in some cases even the most violent shocks are not accompanied by any faulting at the surface.

According to Reid,[1] both faulting and earthquakes may be explained by the elastic-rebound theory. Because hard, rigid rocks, when bent without breaking, exert a strong force tending to restore them to their original shape, potential energy accumulates in the rocks which are bent. If the movement of the blocks is sufficiently great, the forces accumulate until they exceed the breaking strength of the rock and the resistance due to friction. Almost immediately after the break, the rocks on both sides snap back to their original shapes with great violence. This sets up vibrations in the rocks of the earth which produce the earthquake.

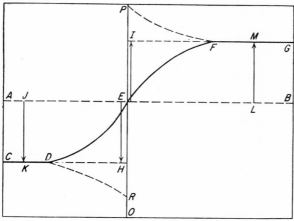

Fig. 5-1. A horizontal plan or vertical cross section illustrating the elastic-rebound theory and also one theory for the origin of reverse drag.

The mechanism of the production of earthquakes according to this theory is shown in Fig. 5-1. This figure may represent either a ground plan or a vertical cross section. It is assumed that two blocks of the earth's surface move past each other in opposite directions. The two blocks are separated by the line OP, along which the fault will occur. Until the elastic limit is reached, the effect of the movement of the two blocks is to cause an increasing amount of bending at their junction. Before any motion takes place a straight dike or stratum is represented by the dashed line AB. The block on the right moves very slowly in the distance and direction indicated by the arrow LM, and the block on the left moves the same distance JK in the opposite direction. At first the shearing strength of the rocks is not exceeded, with the result that they are bent into the curve FED. The sharpness of this curve is, of course, greatly exaggerated. Finally the motion is so great that the

[1] Harry Fielding Reid, Mechanics of Earthquakes, Elastic Rebound Theory, Regional Strain, in Seismology, "Physics of the Earth," National Research Council of the National Academy of Sciences, Washington, D.C., vol. 6, pp. 96, 100 (1933).

strength of the rock is exceeded, and a break occurs along the line of the fault *OP*.   If the elastic force tending to restore the rocks to their original shape on both sides of the fault exceeds the frictional resistance, the rocks on both sides will move suddenly from position *E* toward positions *I* and *H*.   If the movement is enough to restore the original shape exactly, the movement will be from *E* to *H* and *I*, and the lines *CDH* and *GFI* will be straight.   The dotted lines *RD* and *PF* illustrate a possible explanation of reverse drag, as discussed on pages 121–124.

This type of faulting apparently occurs both in the basement rocks at considerable depths and at the surface.   It is possible that many faults in soft sediments occur without producing elastic rebound or earthquakes. It is known that in relatively plastic rocks such as shales and clays faults without elastic rebound do occur.   Koch[1] has described a fault in sediments in California in which the movement is $1\frac{1}{2}$ in. per year, with no earthquakes.   Kirkham and Johnson[2] have described faulting in Idaho involving vertical movements of 7.35 ft per year and horizontal movement of 3.5 ft per year, with no known earthquakes resulting.   The movements involved in large-scale slumping also occur gradually without the production of anything resembling elastic rebound.   It seems likely that many faults involving thick deposits of clastics occur without elastic rebound, but the relative proportions of faults of the two types occurring in sedimentary rocks is not known.

Whether elastic rebound takes place or not, there is no doubt that the formation of large faults is a long process.   Displacements of thousands of feet may take millions of years.   The total displacement may be the sum of numerous small, sudden displacements each amounting to only a few feet.   As the uplifted side rose, erosion had time to cut into it, and in many cases the sediments derived from the rising scarp were deposited on the subsiding side.   Not only were some faults active over a period of millions of years, but faults which have been quiescent for millions of years may begin to move again.   In this respect faults are like folds. The time relations of faults are discussed further on pages 352–355.

FAULT PLANE

Character.   The surface separating the two displaced blocks is called the fault or fault plane.   The term "fault plane" is used when its geometrical aspect is emphasized.   Actually the fault surface may be far from a plane.   When first formed it may have had various irregularities

---

[1] Thomas W. Koch, Analysis and Effects of Current Movement on an Active Fault in Buena Vista Hills Oil Field, Kern County, California, *A.A.P.G. Bull.*, vol. 17, pp. 694–712 (1933).

[2] V. R. D. Kirkham and M. Johnson, Active Faults near Whitebird, Idaho, *Jour. Geology*, vol. 37, pp. 700–711 (1929).

and bends, and a fault plane, even if originally nearly a geometrical plane, may be bent, broken, or otherwise distorted by later folding and faulting. Furthermore, the fault may split apart and come together again, or it may consist of several parallel breaks. Along the fault there may be fractured, crushed, and brecciated rock or finely ground material. The thickness of this fractured zone along the fault may vary from a fraction of an inch to several hundred feet. However, in spite of all these irregularities and variations, it is generally satisfactory for practical purposes to consider the fault as lying in a plane.

Dip, Strike, and Hade. All faults have dip and strike. The terms as applied to faults have the same meaning and are measured in the same way as in the case of sedimentary strata. Hade is the angle between the fault plane and a vertical plane. It is a term derived from mining and is not much used by petroleum geologists. When used as a verb, "hade" means "dip." Thus the statement that a fault hades east means that it dips east. Since this usage of the term is likely to be misunderstood by petroleum geologists, it seems best to avoid it.

In faults which are not vertical, one block adjoining the fault plane is over it, and the other is below it. The upper block is known as the hanging wall, the lower as the foot wall.

MOTION IN FAULTING

Slip, Heave, Throw, and Shift. Accurate description of the motion along a fault plane is essential, for this determines both the type of the

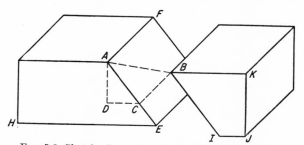

FIG. 5-2. Sketch of a rectangular block cut by a fault.

fault and its importance. Fig. 5-2 is a sketch of a rectangular block cut by the fault *FAE*. The portion of the block on the right has moved downward and away from the observer, compared with the block on the left. Points *A* and *B* were originally in contact. The distance *AB* is the total amount of movement along the fault plane. It is called the net slip. If a pebble is cut in two by a fault, the distance between the two halves of the pebble after faulting is the net slip. The net slip may be split up into three components, in relation to the strike of the fault

plane.   The component parallel to the strike of the fault plane is called
the strike slip.   It is *CB* in Fig. 5-2.   The vertical component is *AD*,
and is called the throw.   The horizontal component, at right angles to
the strike of the fault plane, is *DC*.   It is called the heave.

The description of these motions is likely to be complicated by the
presence of drag.   Drag is the bending of the strata along the fault plane
in the direction of the motion.   It is discussed further on pages 120–122.
Fig. 5-3 shows a vertical cross section at right angles to the strike of the
fault plane *AC*.   The fault displaces the stratum *HIDEKJ*, which is

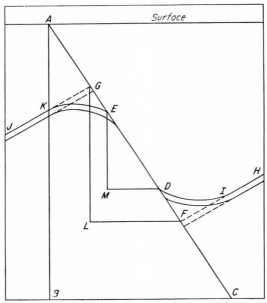

Fɪɢ. 5-3. Cross section to illustrate the effect of including the drag in estimates of displacement along a fault.

bent by the drag near the fault plane.   If the drag is not included in
the displacement, the throw is *ME* and the heave *MD*.   If the drag is
included, the throw is *LG* and the heave *LF*.

Some faults have no drag.   In estimating the displacement along such
faults, therefore, it does not matter whether or not drag is included.
Moreover, in most very large faults the drag is only a small percentage
of the total displacement.   In some faults, however, the drag is so large
that it is very desirable to indicate definitely whether or not the drag is
included in the estimates of the amount of the displacement.

The word "shift" has been suggested as a term meaning the fault displacement including drag.   This word is, however, rarely used in publications on petroleum geology.   Geologists who describe oil-field struc-

tures and structures in petroliferous regions generally do not state whether or not their estimates of displacement include drag. It is therefore necessary to ascertain how these estimates were made in order to find out whether or not drag was included. In the United States most measurements of displacements along faults near oil fields are now made from subsurface data. There are three ways to make these measurements. One method is to determine how much higher or lower the formations are than they would be if there were no fault. An estimate made in this manner would include drag. Another method is to determine the change in intervals between two horizons encountered in wells. An interval would be greater or less than normal if a borehole passed through a reverse or normal fault within the interval. This type of estimate might include all the drag if made in some places, or only part of the drag if made in other locations along the fault. The third method is to measure the thickness of the strata which are missing or repeated at faults. This gives the actual displacement or slip along the fault plane and does not include drag.

In mining operations in a fault plane it is frequently possible to determine the amount of drag accurately. In oil and gas fields the information about faults is derived from bores less than a foot in diameter which may be anywhere from 600 ft to more than a mile apart. Under these conditions it is often impossible to determine how much of the displacement is actual slippage along the fault plane and how much is drag. Furthermore, the amount of drag may vary greatly from one bed to another. Some faults consist of several nearly parallel breaks, and this makes the determination of the amount of drag especially difficult. It appears that the total vertical component of the displacement, including drag, is more easily measured and more constant than the drag. The use of the term "throw" to include drag is now firmly established in the literature of petroleum geology, and any attempts to alter this term to "shift" would doubtless be futile.

In view of this situation, the meaning given in this book to the terms describing motion along faults will be as follows. "Throw" indicates the total vertical component of the displacement, including the drag. "Heave" means the horizontal component of the total displacement including drag. The terms "net slip," "dip slip," and "strike slip" refer to the actual slippage along the fault plane and do not include drag. In most cases the amount of drag is such a small percentage of the total displacement that it is not of great importance to decide whether drag is included or not. On the other hand, it is of considerable importance to have clear and consistent definitions for the meanings of the terms.

According to the preferred usage, LG is the throw of the fault shown in Fig. 5-3, and LF the heave. If it were necessary to refer to EM and MD, they could be referred to as the vertical and horizontal components of the dip slip.

Stratigraphic Throw. The stratigraphic throw of a fault is the component of the displacement which is at right angles to the strata. It may also be defined as the thickness, measured at right angles to the strata, between the point at which a bed intersects a fault and the same bed on the opposite side of the fault. If necessary, the line parallel to the stratum on one side of the fault should be extended until a perpendicular can be drawn to the same stratum on the other side.

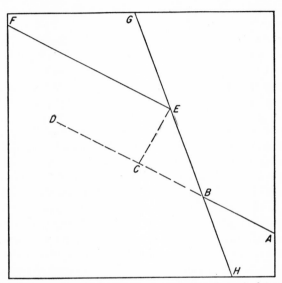

Fig. 5-4. Cross section to show how stratigraphic throw is determined.

The way in which this measurement is made is shown in Fig. 5-4. This is a cross section at right angles to the strike of the strata. The fault *GH* displaces the bed *FEBA*. The line *BD* is drawn extending the line *BA* far enough so that the line *CE* can be drawn perpendicular to *EF* and *AB*. *CE* is the stratigraphic throw of the fault.

CLASSIFICATION

Bases of Classification. Faults may be classified in many ways. In fact, almost any quality or attribute of faults may be used to classify them. In general, the useful classifications of faults have been based on geometrical relations of faults to one another, relations of faults to strike and dip of strata, attitude of net slip in relation to attitude of fault plane, relation of faults to geologic structures, absolute movements, and origin. All these methods of classification except the last two are based on geometrical relations which can be observed in the field. Consequently the classification is readily made, and geologists agree reasonably well on how each fault is to be classed. It is generally not possible to classify faults according to absolute motion or origin by means of observations made in the field alone. How a geologist would place a fault in these two classifications depends on what theories he holds as to the origin and formation of faults and as to deformation in general. Different geologists with the same observational data to go by would doubtless classify the same fault in various ways. In many cases it would doubtless be necessary to know what theories a geologist held and possibly what college he attended in order to interpret his classifications. It is true that if faults could be accurately classified according to origin, much more information about them would be given by such a classification than by the simpler geometrical classification. Nevertheless, so much confusion and misunderstanding would doubtless occur if faults were classed according to origin that under ordinary conditions the geometrical classification should be used. Classifications by absolute motion and by origin should generally be reserved for more theoretical discussions.

Table 5-1 indicates the various methods of classifying faults.

Classification According to Origin. Where the origin of faults is known it is certainly worth while to classify them according to their mode of origin. Thus they may be classed as volcanic, meteoric, due to various superficial causes, or produced by tension or compression. However, as previously mentioned, caution must be used if this type of classification is to be useful. Certainly some classifications of faults according to origin have been misleading or meaningless. As Longwell[1] says, it is especially inadvisable to mix geometrical and genetic terms in the same classification of faults, as is commonly done. According to Longwell,[2] it is not good usage to apply the term "shear" to certain faults, as in the term "shear thrust." This would imply that only certain faults are due to shear, whereas all faults are caused by shear. Longwell[3] also mentions that the term "gravity fault," as applied to a normal fault, is of unwarranted genetic implication and should be rejected. The relation of faults to the forces which produce them has been discussed on pages 58–61.

Factors Complicating the Classification. A factor which complicates the classification of faults is that the geologist is commonly dependent on the identification of the sedimentary strata on both sides of a fault in determining the direction of the movement. If the strata are flat, the apparent relative vertical movements of the hanging and foot walls are

---

[1] Chester R. Longwell, Classification of Faults, Discussion, *A.A.P.G. Bull.*, vol. 27, pp. 1633–1642 (1943).

[2] *Ibid.*, p. 1633.

[3] *Ibid.*, p. 1639.

TABLE 5-1. METHODS

Basis of classification	Strike of fault relative to strike and dip of strata	Pitch of net slip	Geometrical relation of faults to each other	Relative movement of hanging and foot walls	Relation to structures
Fault type	Strike Dip Diagonal Bedding	Strike-slip Dip-slip Diagonal- slip	Radial Parallel Peripheral Antithetic Step Distributive En echelon	Normal Reverse Thrust	Transverse Longitudinal Stretch-thrust Break-thrust

actual relative movements. In other words, in an area of flat strata, if the displacement of a bed seems to indicate that the hanging wall has gone down, it has actually gone down, relative to the foot wall. Where the strata dip at high angles, however, the case is quite different. Under such conditions, apparent normal and reverse faults can be produced by horizontal movements of the strata with no vertical components at all.

Some geologists have proposed changing the classification of faults because of this difficulty. However, as Bateman[1] points out, this difficulty does not occur if the presence of the strata is disregarded and the movement of two points on opposite sides of the fault is considered.

In some cases there is no doubt that a fault which appears normal or reverse really is as it appears to be. In other cases a fault may appear to be normal or reverse, but there is a possibility that the apparent displacement is produced by horizontal movements of dipping strata. Under these conditions, the fault could be called apparent normal, or apparent reverse. Some seemingly normal or reverse faults have clearly been produced entirely by strike-slip movements of dipping strata. These faults could be called false normal or false reverse.

TYPES

Strike, Dip, Diagonal, and Bedding Faults. The classification of faults according to the relation of the dip and strike of the fault plane to the dip and strike of the strata cut by the fault yields four fault types: strike, dip, diagonal, and bedding faults. The strike of a strike fault is the same as the strike of the associated strata, but the dip is different. The strike of dip faults is parallel to the dip of the strata. The strike of diagonal faults is parallel neither to the dip nor to the strike of the strata. In the case of bedding faults both the dip and the strike of the fault are the

[1] Allan M. Bateman, "Economic Mineral Deposits," John Wiley & Sons., Inc., New York, p. 336 (1950).

Type of motion	Relation to ground surface	Relation of net slip to trace of beds on fault plane	Absolute movement of hanging and foot walls	Origin
Translational Rotational Scissors Hinge	Erosion-thrust	Trace-slip	Underthrust Overthrust	Gravity Tensional Extensional Compressional Landslides Slumping Volcanic

same as the dip and strike of the associated strata, with the result that the fault plane lies within a single bed or stratum. Bedding thrusts are apparently more common than normal faults of this type. Faults of this type will not show up on areal maps and will not displace formation contacts or strata. They are therefore very difficult to detect. In some cases the slickensides, brecciation, and other features associated with fault planes constitute the only evidence of bedding faults. Doubtless many bedding faults go unrecognized because of the difficulty of detecting them.

Strike-slip, Dip-slip, and Diagonal-slip Faults. Another method for classifying faults is based on the relation of the direction of the net slip to the strike of the fault. The angle between these two directions is measured in the plane of the fault, and it is called the pitch of the net slip. The pitch of a line should not be confused with its plunge. The plunge of a line is the angle between the line and a horizontal plane. The pitch of the net slip, on the other hand, is the angle measured in the plane of the fault between the direction of the net slip and a horizontal line in the same plane, which is the strike of the fault plane. These two angles are equal only when the fault plane is vertical.

If faults are characterized by the relation of the net slip to the strike of the fault, there are three possible types: strike-slip, dip-slip, and diagonal-slip faults. In strike-slip faults the movement along the fault is parallel to the strike of the fault plane. The net slip is therefore equivalent to the strike slip. This type of motion would produce slickensides parallel to the strike of the fault plane. The movement of dip-slip faults is parallel to the dip of the fault plane. Hence dip slip equals net slip. In diagonal-slip faults the direction of the movement is at an angle with both the dip and the strike of the fault plane. The pitch of the net slip of strike-slip faults is 0°, of dip-slip faults 90°, and of diagonal-slip faults between 0° and 90°.

Trace-slip Faults. Faults may also be classified according to the relation of the direction of the net slip to the trace of the bedding in the fault plane. In most faults the line formed by the intersection of the strata with the plane of the fault does not happen to be parallel to the direction of the net slip. In trace-slip faults, however, the direction of the net slip is parallel to the trace of the bedding on the fault plane. Trace-slip faults are like bedding faults in that they produce no apparent displacement of the beds at the fault plane. The only evidence of a trace-slip fault may be the various structural features characteristic of fault planes, such as slickensides, fracturing, and brecciation.

Comparison of Types of Net Slip Movement. The different types of motion discussed above are shown in Fig. 5-5. The face of the block,

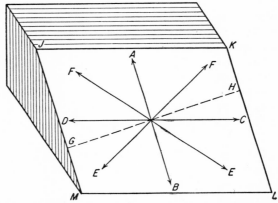

Fig. 5-5. Block showing a fault plane with the hanging wall removed.

MJKL, is also a fault plane. It slopes toward the observer. The arrows and the descriptions of movement given in this paragraph refer to the movements of the opposite side, which has been removed. The block shown in the figure is assumed to remain stationary. Faults with motion parallel to the line *DC* are strike-slip faults. Those with motion parallel to the line *AB* are dip-slip faults. The movement of diagonal-slip faults may be parallel to a line in any direction but *AB* and *DC*. Movement parallel to the line *EF* would constitute a diagonal-slip fault, but obviously the movement could be in many other directions. Let *GH* be the trace of a bed on the fault plane, that is, the line formed by the intersection of the fault plane and a bed. Then faults with a net slip parallel to *GH* are trace-slip faults. Normal faults are represented by arrows and direction of motion which trend downward, i.e., below the horizontal line *DC*. Reverse faults are indicated by arrows directed upward. The arrow *A* represents a reverse fault, and the arrow *B* a normal fault.

Radial, Parallel, Peripheral, En Echelon, Step, Distributive, and Antithetic Faults. Faults may also be classified according to their geometrical relations to each other. Radial faults radiate from a common point. Parallel faults are parallel to each other, and peripheral faults are parallel to the tangents of concentric circles. En echelon faults were named from the military formation; they are parallel, and one commences near where another ends. Faults of these types may be shown on a map or horizontal plan. They are illustrated in Fig. 5-6.

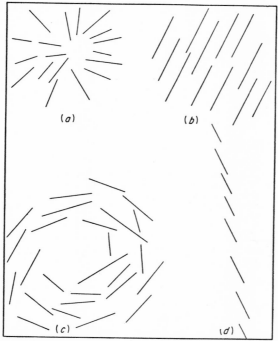

Fig. 5-6. Map showing the following types of faults: radial (*a*), parallel (*b*), peripheral (*c*), and en echelon (*d*).

The geometrical relations of other types of faults show up in cross sections. Step and distributive faults consist of a number of parallel breaks, each with a throw in the same direction. Antithetic faults are found in association with a major normal fault. In many cases the major fault is accompanied by some smaller faults parallel to it. On the downthrown side of the large normal fault there are in some cases smaller, normal faults striking parallel to the main fault and dipping toward it. These are the antithetic faults. Antithetic faults are shown in Fig. 5-7 and step faults in Fig. 5-8.

Normal, Reverse, and Thrust Faults. The most important basis for the classification of faults is the relative up-and-down movements of the hanging and foot walls. If the hanging wall has gone down relative to the foot wall, the fault is normal. If the hanging wall has moved upward relative to the foot wall, the fault is reverse. It should be understood

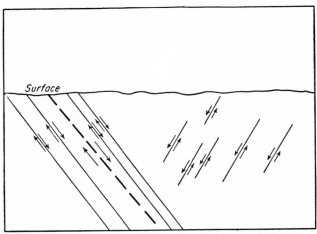

FIG. 5-7. Cross section showing antithetic faults. The heavy dashed line is the major normal fault. The lighter lines sloping to the right are the subsidiary faults parallel to it. The antithetic faults are in the block which is downthrown by the major normal fault and dip toward it.

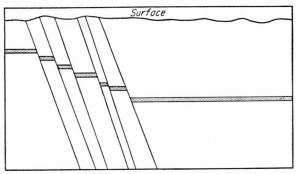

FIG. 5-8. Cross section showing step faults.

that these are relative movements of one block compared to the other. They have no meaning with reference to sea level or to the center of the earth. While a block was dropping 100 ft with reference to sea level, the whole area might have been uplifted 1,000 ft with reference to sea level, with the result that the downthrown block ended up 900 ft higher than before the faulting started.

The term "thrust fault" has been used with several different meanings. It does not seem advisable to limit the term to a fault of any definite amount of displacement. To do so would mean that one would not know whether it was a thrust fault or not until the movement had been measured. On the other hand, the dip of a fault is easily measured. As used in this book, "thrust fault" means a reverse fault with an average dip of less than 30°. Normal, reverse, and thrust faults are shown in Fig. 5-9.

Translational, Rotational, Scissors, and Hinge Faults. Movement along faults may be considered to be either translational or rotational. If the motion is translational, there is very little rotation of one side of the fault relative to the other during faulting. As a result, lines which were parallel before faulting are almost parallel afterward. If the lines

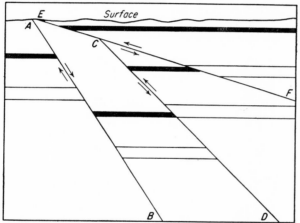

FIG. 5-9. Cross section showing normal fault, *AB*, reverse fault, *CD*, and thrust fault, *EF*.

on opposite sides of the fault which were parallel before faulting are no longer parallel afterward, the motion is considered rotational. However, if this definition were interpreted strictly, there would be no translational faults, for the throw of a fault changes gradually along its course, and this means that the lines which were originally parallel are no longer parallel after faulting. Under actual conditions a fault is considered translational unless the change in throw is very rapid, or unless the throw changes in direction. As some faults are followed, the throw gradually decreases to zero and then increases, but in the opposite direction. These faults are called scissors or hinge. A line across the fault at the point of zero throw is known as the hinge line. It is considered that one or both blocks have rotated about the hinge line as an axis. True scissors or hinge faults are uncommon in the vicinity of most oil fields. A geologist might work in oil fields for many years without running across one.   Furthermore, if there are many faults in an area, it would be expected that two faults with throws in opposite directions would occasionally line up with each other just as a matter of chance. On the other hand, there are certain regions in which hinge faults are fairly common.

Longitudinal and Transverse Faults.   A fault crossing a structural feature such as an anticline is transverse.   A longitudinal fault is parallel to the associated structural feature.   Longitudinal and transverse faults are shown in Fig. 5-10.

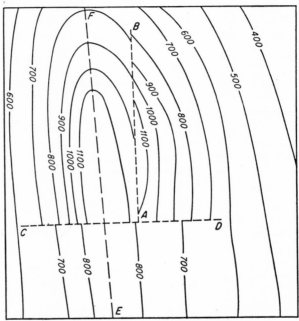

FIG. 5-10. Structure map showing a longitudinal fault, *AB*, and a transverse fault, *CD*.

Erosion Thrusts.   The forward or upper ends of large thrust faults commonly emerge from underground, and the hanging wall is driven over the surface.   This portion of a thrust is called an erosion thrust.   As in the case of other thrust faults, the term "erosion thrust" does not imply that the hanging wall moved and the foot wall stood still.   The term would still be used if the hanging wall stood still and the foot wall were driven under it, although in that case it would also be termed an under-thrust.   As the hanging wall advances over the ground (relatively speaking), sediments eroded from the scarp are commonly deposited in front of it.   These sediments may later be overridden by the hanging wall.   If such overridden sediments are found beneath a fault plane, they constitute proof that the fault is an erosion thrust.   It is probable that many thrust faults of great size at the time of their formation emerged from the surface as erosion thrusts. However, in most cases this portion of the thrust has been destroyed by erosion.

Underthrust and Overthrust. The geometrical classifications of faults given above do not indicate which side is stationary, or whether both share in the movement. However, the term "underthrust" implies a low-angle fault with a stationary hanging wall and a moving foot wall. Many geologists use "overthrust" to mean a low-angle reverse fault, and do not intend to imply that the hanging wall did the moving. On the other hand, it is apparent from the context of a number of papers in which "overthrust" is used that the authors supposed that the movement was in the hanging wall. The term "overthrust" is so likely to imply that the hanging wall alone moved that it seems better to restrict the term to faults in which the hanging wall is supposed to have moved, and use the word "thrust" when it is not desired to indicate that one side or the other did the moving.

Structural Features Associated with Fault Planes

Importance. Every petroleum geologist should be thoroughly familiar with the structural features associated with fault planes. These structural features may be the only evidences of the existence of a fault, and often they are also the only indications of the direction of motion. Moreover, a thorough knowledge of these structural features is frequently needed in order to make correct interpretations of complicated conditions. It need hardly be said that a familiarity with the characteristics of exposed faults is a great help in recognizing faults in the subsurface, where only meager clues may be available.

Slickensides. Slickensides are probably the commonest and most important of the various structural features associated with large faults. If the outcrop of a large fault is well exposed, slickensides may generally be found, though in some cases they appear in the subsidiary fractures and not in the main break. Slickensides form most readily in argillaceous or in slaty rocks; they may fail to form in sand that is coarse. Slickensides consist of grooved and smoothed or polished surfaces. The grooves or scratches are small, generally only a fraction of an inch in width. Usually they are parallel unless the movements along the fault have been in two or more different directions, or unless a block has been rotated during the faulting. Slickensides do not always indicate faulting of any magnitude; well-developed slickensides may be found along faults with displacements of only a few inches. This is a point to remember in interpreting slickensided cores. Slickensides are generally parallel to the last movement of the fault which formed them. If the movement along the fault has been in different directions at different times, slickensides varying in direction may also be preserved.   In the oil-producing regions of the United States east of California, the slickensides generally run up and down the fault planes.

Gouge, Mylonite.   Gouge is the finely ground material between the walls of faults.   Generally it resembles clay, but it is likely to have fragments of the wall rocks embedded in it.   Gouge commonly has a massive structure, though it may also show streaks or bands parallel to the fault plane.   It may be either hard or soft, depending on the amount of cementation.   Sandy gouge is commonly cemented by lime or silica.   Gouge frequently shows slickensides.   Mylonite is a very fine-grained, hard, siliceous material which may show streaks or banding.   It may appear like chert.   It is found chiefly along faults in rocks that are strongly altered or very deeply buried.   It should therefore not be common in the vicinity of oil fields.

Breccia.   Breccia is a rock composed largely of angular fragments. Although breccia is common along fault planes, the possibility that an occurrence of breccia is of sedimentary or volcanic origin should be considered before deciding that it is of tectonic origin.   Tectonic breccias have certain characteristics which aid in recognizing them.   If they occur in fault planes, the rock fragments may be of the same types found in the wall rocks along the sides of the fault.   The fragments may also consist of vein materials such as quartz and calcite, or of wall rocks which have been silicified or otherwise altered.   If the fault traverses rocks of only one type, the fragments of the wall rock in the breccia are of that type alone.   Some fragments of tectonic breccias fit together.   Generally evidences of shattering or crushing are present, and the fragments may be slickensided.   Tectonic breccias follow zones of faulting, shearing, or structural deformation.   The breccia may pass gradually, with no well-defined break, through shattered rock into undeformed wall rock. In some cases rocks over a broad zone may be brecciated, while in others the width of the breccia is only a few feet or a few inches.   The fragments in the breccia may be cut by veins of quartz or calcite, and these veins themselves may be faulted, indicating more than one movement of the fault.   The material which fills the spaces between the rock fragments of a tectonic breccia generally consists either of more finely ground rocks like those of the larger fragments, or of vein material deposited from solution.   Calcite, dolomite, quartz, and gypsum are some of the common minerals which cement breccia fragments.   Breccias are relatively common along normal and strike-slip faults, and rare along thrust faults.   Breccias are entirely missing along many faults.   The various types of breccia have been described by Norton.[1]

[1] W. H. Norton, A Classification of Breccias, *Jour. Geology*, vol. 25, pp. 160–194 (1917).

Mullion Structure. The term "mullion structure" is applied to large grooves, several feet across and several inches deep, which have been found along faults. They differ from the small grooves and scratches of slickensides in being much larger. Mullion structures are such large features that they are found only on exposures of fault surfaces which cover a considerable area. Extensive exposures of fault surfaces are not common along most faults in the softer sedimentary rocks. Accordingly, exposures of mullion structures are rare in these sediments, though relatively more common in the harder rocks.

Cementation, Silicification, and Mineralization. It is very common to find that the strata along faults have been cemented by silica or carbonates, and cementation of the breccia or gouge is even more common. In faults cutting soft sediments this cementation is very irregular in its occurrence, even along the same fault. Any porous and permeable rock along the course of the fault may be cemented, but the effects are especially noticeable in sandstone. Some of the Tertiary sandstones of the Gulf Coast region are cemented by opal. The siliceous cementing matter along faults seems to be quartz generally, but there is a lack of information as to this point. In some cases the resistance of the strata to erosion is so increased by the cementation that small ridges are formed. In small faults the cementation may extend only a few feet or a few tens of feet from the fault plane, but along great faults it may affect the strata for hundreds or even thousands of feet from the fault. It should be emphasized, however, that along small faults in soft formations there may be little or no sign of cementation. It is quite common to find that near faults and in the gouge and breccia small fractures have been cemented by quartz or silica in the sandstones and by carbonates in the limestones and dolomites. These fractures filled with quartz or carbonates are sometimes one of the best means of tracing faults.

Where the cementation near faults is extensive, it is likely to render any reservoir rocks too impervious to produce oil and gas. However, it is only in the case of large faults that this cementation needs to be taken into account in locating wells.

The large quartz veins which occur along faults in certain regions appear to have an unfavorable bearing on the oil and gas prospects of the areas in which they occur. The cementation of small fractures along faults is not an unfavorable indication, but any strong development of quartz veins or silicification is. If the deposition of ore minerals along faults occurs extensively, it also has an unfavorable bearing on the oil and gas prospects.

Veins and mineral deposits along faults have been produced by solutions traveling along the fault plane. However, it is not certain that the cementation along faults in slightly altered sediments originates in the same manner. Some of these faults do not reach to great depths, occur in areas where no igneous intrusions are known, and in some cases seem to offer no permeable path for solutions to travel along. Where faults cut soft, unconsolidated clays and shales, the fault plane is frequently so choked by an impervious gouge that it is difficult to imagine the passage of solutions. It is possible that the heat or pressure generated by the faulting has caused cementation in such cases.

Joints and Fractures along Faults. Joints and fractures are exceedingly common along faults. The harder the rock, the more likely it is to show fracturing. Joints and fractures are discussed in more detail in Chap. 6. Much of the published literature regarding the fractures associated with faults deals with faults in igneous or metamorphic rocks or in strongly altered sediments. Some of the papers deal with rare features which are generally not seen in faults in the softer sediments. In the relatively unaltered sedimentary strata which occur in the regions of oil fields, faults are commonly accompanied by fractures or smaller faults which are in general roughly parallel to the fault planes. These joints and fractures decrease in frequency away from the fault planes. In harder rocks such as consolidated sandstones, limestones, and dolomites, there may be a network of fractures of no particular trend near the faults. Such fractures may in some cases be used to identify and trace faults. These fractures are commonly cemented by quartz or carbonates. Some fractures that have been cemented in this manner may be cut by other fractures, indicating more than one period of movement. As described in the next chapter, the fractures along faults serve as reservoirs of oil in some fields. The writer has found in a number of cases that the most prominent joint system tends to strike parallel to the strike of the faults in the vicinity, but more observations are needed to set up a rule.

Horses and Slices. Blocks and masses of the country rock are commonly broken off by the faulting and either embedded in the gouge or breccia or surrounded by branches of the main fault. Large blocks of rock in the fault plane are known as horses if they are in the normal fault, and as slices if they are associated with reverse faults. Where the stratigraphic position of these blocks can be determined, it is generally found that they lie between the equivalent strata on both sides of the fault plane. A horse and a slice are shown in Fig. 5-11.

Drag. The relation of drag to the measurements of throw and shift has been discussed on pages 106–107. Drag is clearly produced by the friction of the opposite side of the fault. The bending on one side is always in the direction of movement of the other side. The great value of drag to the geologist is that it indicates the direction of motion of the opposite side. In nearly every case the drag also indicates the direction of displacement of the fault. There may, however, be a few cases in which the direction of the movement along the fault plane has reversed. Under such conditions the drag would indicate the direction of latest movement. If the displacement in the direction of the drag was less than the earlier displacement in the opposite direction, the drag may not be in the direction of the total displacement. It is believed, how-

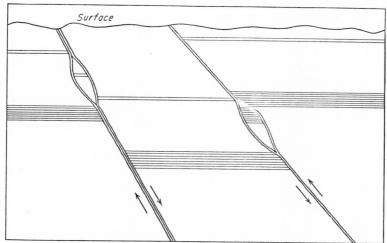

Fig. 5-11. Cross section showing a horse and a slice.

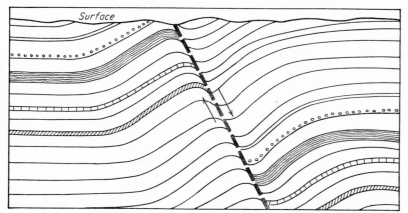

Fig. 5-12. Cross section showing normal and reverse drag along a fault.

ever, that faults of this nature are extremely uncommon in oil-producing regions. Drag is illustrated in Figs. 5-3 and 5-12.

Drag is better developed in soft, plastic formations than in those which are hard and rigid. However, under the right conditions almost any kind of rock may be affected by drag. Usually drag may be found in extensive exposures of faults in sediments. Nevertheless, in some cases there is no sign of drag, and the direction of the movement must be determined by other means. In most faults the amount of displacement due to drag is small compared to the actual slippage along the fault plane, but some faults change gradually upward into monoclines, and others change to monoclines along the strike. The percentage of the displacement due to drag increases along these faults until just before the fault changes to a monocline, where the drag is nearly 100 per cent of the total displacement.

Reverse Drag. *Nature.* Reverse drag is the bending of the strata along faults in a direction opposite to the normal drag. Reverse drag is especially common along normal faults in regions of slight deformation and gentle dip. It is well developed, for example, in the San Juan Basin, in the Gulf Coast, and in the Cretaceous deposits of the western Great Plains, particularly South Dakota. It has not been clearly recognized along reverse or thrust faults or in faults associated with tightly compressed folds.

Reverse drag is a much larger structural feature than normal drag. Along faults where the normal drag extends from a few feet to a few tens of feet from the fault plane, reverse drag may extend hundreds or thousands of feet from the fault. It is often extensive enough to produce anticlines on which oil and gas production is found. On the Gulf Coast there are a number of large strike faults with the downthrown side down the dip. The reverse drag dipping into these faults produces anticlines on which a number of oil fields are located. Reverse drag has been discussed by Strahler,[1] Sears,[2] Quarles,[3] and Russell.[4]

Reverse drag is commonly developed on the downthrown sides of faults, where it causes the strata to dip into the fault plane. It also occurs on the upthrown sides, though occurrences on this side are rarer. Where reverse drag is found along a fault, it may be developed only at intervals along the fault trace. Furthermore, where there are many normal faults in a region, only certain ones may show reverse drag. The amount of dip produced by reverse drag is roughly proportional to the size of the faults along which it occurs. This dip may amount to several hundred feet along some of the extensive faults. Reverse drag is illustrated in Figs. 5-1, 5-12, and 17-2.

Origin. The cause of reverse drag has not been definitely established, although several explanations have been suggested. It seems certain,

---

[1] Arthur N. Strahler, Geomorphology and Structure of the West Kaibab Fault Zone and Kaibab Plateau, *G.S.A. Bull.*, vol. 59, pp. 513–540 (1948).

[2] Julian D. Sears, Geology and Coal Resources of the Gallup-Zuni Basin, *U.S.G.S. Bull.* 767, p. 23, figs. XIIB, XIII (1925).

[3] Miller W. Quarles, Salt-ridge Hypothesis on Origin of Texas Gulf Coast Type of Faulting, *A.A.P.G. Bull.*, vol. 37, pp. 489–508 (1953).

[4] William L. Russell, "The Possibilities of Oil in Western Ziebach County," *South Dakota Geol. and Nat. Hist. Survey Circ.* 20, pp. 18–20 (1925).

however, that reversal of movement is not the general cause, though it may possibly explain a few cases. According to this theory, the normal faults along which reverse drag occurs were at first reverse faults, and the reverse drag was originally the normal drag along these reverse faults. An objection to this suggestion is that very large reverse faults would have been required, for the reverse drag in places extends for thousands of feet from the accompanying fault. In every case this movement which caused the reverse faults must have been changed to the type of motion which produced normal faults. Moreover, this latter motion must have always exceeded the original motion which caused the reverse faults, since the faults always end up as normal. Reverse drag is typically developed in regions where reverse faults are either absent or exceedingly rare. Furthermore, signs of the extensive compressive forces which would have accompanied the reverse faulting are generally absent. On the Gulf Coast, where reverse drag is common, reverse faults are rarely if ever found, and other signs of extensive compression are also lacking.

Another theory is that the reverse drag is produced by elastic rebound. When the actual break along a fault occurs, elastic rebound tends to restore the blocks on each side of the break to the original spatial arrangement which they had before the bending at the fault started. Thus elastic rebound would tend to make the stratum on each side of the fault snap back from its bent position to form the straight lines CH and GI of Fig. 5-1. If momentum or other forces could carry points I and H past their original position to points R and P, reverse drag would be produced along DR and FP. There are, however, two objections to this theory. In the first place, it is not known that elastic rebound does overcompensate or carry the strata past their original configurations. Furthermore, elastic rebound is presumably most effective in hard, rigid rocks in which great amounts of energy can be stored as strain. Reverse drag is best developed in sediments, and in many cases these sediments are relatively soft, plastic, and unconsolidated. It is very doubtful whether elastic rebound occurs along faults in these sediments. Many of these faults are developed entirely in the sediments and do not penetrate the basement.

Reverse drag on the downthrown sides of normal faults may be produced by slumping into the potential void produced by the pulling apart of the two blocks. Extension of the surface might produce both a normal fault and a settling into the space which tends to be formed by the separation of the blocks. Since the sedimentary rocks are not strong enough to hold up their own weight, it is certain that they would settle instead of maintaining a large open space. This theory may explain reverse drag occurring on the downthrown sides of normal faults. It cannot, however, explain reverse drag on the upthrown sides.   Quarles[1] has explained reverse drag on the Gulf Coast as being produced by mechanical adjustments of strata over deep ridges of salt.   Reverse drag is, however, well developed in regions where there is no salt, and it is certain that all the occurrences cannot be explained by any theory which involves the presence of salt.

It may be possible in some cases to explain reverse drag as the result of various mechanical adjustments in folding.   For example, if a sharp monocline is formed in flat-lying sediments, the extension or stretching of the strata would be likely to produce normal faults striking parallel to the monocline.   If the dip of the normal faults is opposite to the dip of the strata in the monocline, features like reverse drag will be produced as these faults cross the monocline.

NOMENCLATURE OF FEATURES RELATED TO THRUST FAULTS

Foreland and Hinterland.   A special set of terms has been developed to describe the various geologic structures, conditions, and features associated with thrust faults.   The stable region toward which the relative

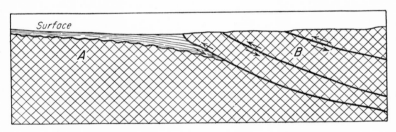

Fig. 5-13. Cross section showing autochthon and allochthon.

movement of the hanging walls of great thrusts is directed is known as the foreland.   It is in the vicinity of A, Fig. 5-13.   The rocks of this area, which are still in place where they were formed, are known as the autochthon.   The region from which the hanging walls of the thrusts moved (relatively) is the hinterland.   In Fig. 5-13 it would be in the vicinity of B.   The rocks of this area are called the allochthon; they have been moved by thrusting from the place where they were formed.

Klippe and Fenster.   The terms "klippe" and "fenster" are illustrated in Fig. 5-14.   The heavy dashed line VW is a thrust fault, which has moved older strata on top of younger beds.   The lettered formations grow progressively younger from A to F.   The beds overlying the thrust faults are generally older than the strata immediately beneath it.   In the vicinity of X there is a small, isolated area of older rocks above the

[1] *Op. cit.*

plane of the thrust fault, separated by the thrust fault from the younger rocks immediately beneath it. This constitutes a klippe. The fenster, at Y, is an isolated area of younger rocks beneath a thrust fault, separated by the thrust fault from the older rocks above the thrust which surround it. "Fenster" is the German word meaning "window," and

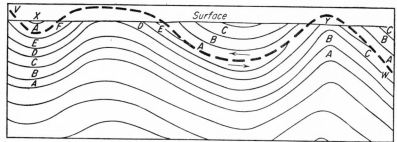

FIG. 5-14. Cross section showing klippe and fenster.

it is often also called "window." In this description of "klippe" and "fenster" it is assumed that the strata on the upthrown side of the thrust are older than those beneath it. This is generally but not always the case. Where the thrust cuts sediments which are strongly folded or which have a complex structure, the strata above the thrust may chance to be younger than those beneath it.

Outlier and Inlier. "Outlier" and "inlier" have no connection with faulting, but they had best be described here in order to distinguish them

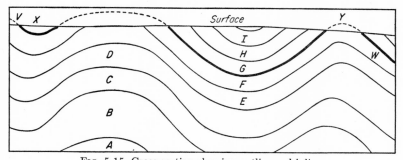

FIG. 5-15. Cross section showing outlier and inlier.

from "klippe" and "fenster." In Fig. 5-15, X is the outlier and Y the inlier. The heavy line VW is a horizon which marks the boundary between two formations. The lettered beds grow progressively younger from A to I, and it should be noted that there is no reversal in the sequence, as there is at the thrust fault in Fig. 5-14. In Fig. 5-15 there is no faulting, but merely a succession of beds which have been folded.

The outlier may be defined as a small, isolated area of younger strata surrounded by older.   The inlier may be defined as a small, isolated area of older beds surrounded by younger.   If the surface is flat, the outliers are in synclines and the inliers in anticlines.   However, outliers and inliers may be produced by topography in areas of uniform dip, as is illustrated by Figs. 2-5 and 2-6.

Structures Associated with Faults

A number of structural features are best discussed in connection with faults, either because they are produced by faults or because they are associated with them.   Some of these structures are important in petroleum geology because they produce or modify the traps in which oil and gas occur.   Others are worth considering because they are of common occurrence or because of their bearing on regional relations.

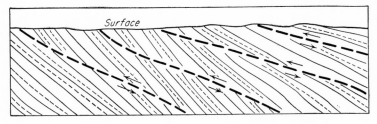

Fig. 5-16. Cross section showing imbricate structure.

Imbricate or Shingle Structure.   Imbricate or shingle structure involves a number of repetitions of the outcrops of the same formations as a result of a series of roughly parallel thrust faults.   The thrust faults dip in the same general direction as the strata, but not necessarily at the same angle.   The dip is moderate to steep but not vertical.   Imbricate structure is shown in Fig. 5-16.

Horsts and Grabens.   A graben is a structurally depressed portion of the earth's crust, bounded on both sides by faults.   The faults must be downthrown toward the graben on both sides.   Many large grabens are also topographic valleys or lowlands; however, the term has no topographic significance.   Many grabens are known only from subsurface data and do not come to the surface at all.   Grabens tend to have their greatest length in a direction parallel to the two faults bounding them.   It is not necessary that the two ends be also bounded by faults, and there is no limit to the number of faults which may bound a graben.   Grabens range in size from structures only a few feet in width to regional features tens of miles across and over a hundred miles in length.   The faults which bound grabens are generally normal, but they may also be reverse.

If the faults which bound grabens reach the surface, the grabens generally occupy valleys in the first stage of their existence. However, after the scarps of the bounding faults have been eroded away, whether the graben occupies a topographic high or a topographic low depends on the resistance of the rocks to erosion. Large grabens exposed at the surface are more likely to occupy valleys than ridges, because of the initial depression which causes them and because the younger rocks within them are on the average less resistant than the older rocks which surround them.

A horst is a block of the earth's crust which is structurally elevated and is bounded on both sides by faults. The bounding faults are both

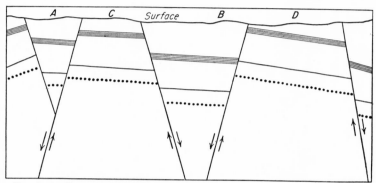

Fig. 5-17. Cross section showing horsts, *C* and *D*, and grabens, *A* and *B*.

downthrown away from the horst. Although horsts may have no relation to the topography, they tend to occupy ridges. Horsts tend to be about the same size as grabens. Horsts and grabens are illustrated in Fig. 5-17.

Fault Blocks, Block Mountains, and Basin and Range Structure. Where horsts and grabens are developed on a large scale they are generally referred to as fault blocks. If mountains are produced by the faulting, these mountains may be called block mountains. If the fault blocks produce long ranges separated by intervening valleys, the result is known as basin and range or basin range structure. Fault blocks, block mountains, and basin and range structure may be produced by faults which have the downthrown side in the same direction. In such cases no true grabens or horsts would be formed. These structures have been called half-grabens.

Basin and range faults are typically developed in a region of Nevada and adjacent parts of Utah, Idaho, California, and Arizona which was referred to in old reports as the "Great Basin." It is now frequently

called the Basin and Range province.   In typical basin and range structure, the valleys or basins are filled with sediments derived from the
ranges.   These sediments were deposited in the valleys over a long period
of time as the adjacent ranges were uplifted by faulting.

The basin and range problem has been discussed by Davis,[1] Gilbert,[2]
Longwell,[3] Nolan,[4] Taber,[5] and Waters.[6]   The history of the Basin and
Range region appears to be complex, with folding and thrust faults
developing during the Mesozoic and early Cenozoic, and normal faults
in the latter part of the Cenozoic.   The mountain ranges and sediment-
filled valleys which form the chief elements of the topography at present

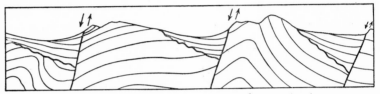

Fig. 5-18. Cross section showing basin and range structure.

appear to have been developed chiefly by normal faulting.   Basin and
range structure is shown in Fig. 5-18.

Rift Valleys.   Rift valleys are grabens of great length which have been
covered by sediments.   The sediments were deposited as the graben sank,
and are generally not found on the upthrown areas on either side.   Rift
valleys are generally over 100 miles long and over 10 miles across.   In
some cases the faults which bound them were in existence during the
Mesozoic, but were rejuvenated during the Pleistocene.   The region surrounding the rift valleys is in many places highest at the crest of the
bounding scarps, and slopes gently away from the rift valleys in both
directions.   The best-known rift valleys are the Jordan Valley, parts of
the Rhine Valley, the Red Sea, and the great topographic depressions
near the headwaters of the Nile in east-central Africa.   They have been

[1] W. M. Davis, The Peacock Range, Arizona, *G.S.A. Bull.*, vol. 41, pp. 293–313
(1930).

[2] G. K. Gilbert, Studies of Basin Range Structure, *U.S.G.S. Prof. Paper* 153 (1928).

[3] Chester R. Longwell, Structural Studies in Southern Nevada and Western
Arizona, *G.S.A. Bull.*, vol. 37, pp. 551–584 (1926); The Muddy Mountain Overthrust
in Southeastern Nevada, *Jour. Geology*, vol. 30, pp. 63–72 (1922).

[4] T. B. Nolan, The Basin and Range Province in Utah, Nevada and California,
U.S.G.S. Prof. Paper 197(d) (1943).

[5] Stephen Taber, Evidence on Basin Range Structure, *Science*, n. s., vol. 62, pp.
436–437 (1925).

[6] A. C. Waters, The Nature and Origin of the Horst and Graben Structure of
Southern Oregon, *Jour. Geology*, vol. 37, pp. 204–238 (1929).

described by Dixey,[1] Escher,[2] Hills,[3] Wellings and Willis,[4] and Willis.[5] There are three theories for the formation of rift valleys. One is that they are ramps, another that they are produced by strike-slip faults, and the third that they are bounded by normal faults and produced by stretching or extension of the earth's crust. Fig. 5-19 illustrates the

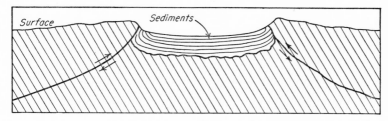

FIG. 5-19. Cross section illustrating the ramp theory for the origin of rift valleys.

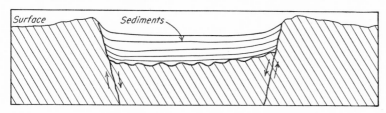

FIG. 5-20. Cross section showing a rift valley interpreted as a large graben.

ramp theory for the origin of rift valleys. It is supposed that two thrust faults bound the rift valleys, and that the whole feature is the result of compression. It might be difficult, according to this theory, to explain why two thrust faults with displacement in opposite directions should be parallel for such long distances. Two lines of evidence suggest the possibility that rift valleys could be produced by strike-slip faults. Wallace[6] states that along part of the San Andreas strike-slip fault in California there are long, narrow blocks of Pliocene strata dropped into the older

[1] Frank Dixey, Erosion and Tectonics of the East African Rift System, *Geol. Soc. London Quart. Jour.*, vol. 102, pp. 339–388 (1946).

[2] B. G. Escher, Relations between the Mechanism of the Formation of Fault Troughs and Volcanic Activity, *G.S.A. Bull.*, vol. 63, pp. 749–756 (1952).

[3] G. F. S. Hills, The Rift Valleys of Africa, *Am. Jour. Sci.*, vol. 246, pp. 171–181 (1948).

[4] F. E. Wellings and Bailey Willis, Wellings' Observations of Dead Sea Structure, with a discussion by Bailey Willis, *G.S.A. Bull.*, vol. 49, pp. 659–668 (1938).

[5] The Dead Sea Problem, Rift Valley or Ramp Valley, *G.S.A. Bull.*, vol. 39, pp. 409–552 (1928); East African Plateaus and Rift Valleys, *Carnegie Inst. Washington Pub.* 470 (1936).

[6] Robert E. Wallace, Structure of a Portion of the San Andreas Rift in Southern California, *G.S.A. Bull.*, vol. 60, pp. 781–806 (1949).

crystalline rocks.   This is obviously something like a rift valley.   Moreover, Wellings and Willis[1] state that in the Dead Sea rift valley several features suggest the presence of a great strike-slip fault.   These features are the presence of anticlines outside the valley which trend obliquely to it, the presence of at least one anticline in the trough, and the indications that the block on the west has been shifted to the south.   Although other explanations should be kept in mind, the evidence at present suggests that rift valleys are large grabens bordered by normal faults.   This concept is illustrated in Fig. 5-20.   The occurrence of rift valleys near the central portions of broad, low arches of great extent suggests that possibly the stretching near the axes of these arches produced the normal faulting.

RECOGNITION IN THE FIELD

The discussion of methods by which faults are recognized will be given under six headings, only one of which includes subsurface methods. However, what is needed for the detection and mapping of faults by any of these methods is primarily a general understanding of faults and fault problems.   The discussion of surface methods of finding faults will therefore help in finding them underground.

Alignments.   The outcrops of steeply dipping fault planes are usually fairly straight or bend in broad, gentle curves.   Accordingly, any surface features associated with these faults will tend to occur in more or less straight lines.   The features which constitute the alignment may not all be of the same nature.   On the contrary, a number of different types of features may combine to form an alignment along the outcrop of the fault plane.   Among these features may be mentioned abnormal dips, displacements in any linear feature crossing the fault, fractures, veins or abnormally cemented rocks, changes in soil or vegetation, springs, and various topographic and geologic features associated with faults.   However, before accepting these occurrences as alignments indicating faulting, two other possibilities should be considered.   One is that the features in question have a random distribution and that their alignment is merely a matter of chance.   The other is that some geological cause other than faulting may account for the alignment.   Among such possible causes may be mentioned dikes, escarpments, monoclines, outcrops of formations having special characteristics, igneous contacts, angular unconformities, moraines, eskers, and the edges of flood plains.

Offsets or Displacements.   Aside from actual outcrops of the fault planes, the best evidence of faulting is generally found in displacements of any linear feature, such as valleys, ridges, escarpments, outcrops of formations, dikes, contacts, and other faults.   If the displaced features

[1] *Op. cit.*

can be recognized on both sides of the break where the displacement occurs, the evidence for faulting is particularly convincing.

Relations That Can Be Explained Only by Faulting. In some cases the best evidence for the existence of a fault is the difficulty or impossibility of explaining the observed conditions by any other means. This is of course a matter of judgment, and experience in structural interpretation should make a geologist's interpretations much more reliable. Many beginning geologists have a tendency to put faults on their maps without sufficient evidence, or at least without considering carefully all the other possible interpretations. As an example of conditions which indicate faulting, the following case may be cited: The normal stratigraphic interval between beds A and B is 200 ft. An outcrop of A is found only 50 ft horizontally from an outcrop of B. If the conditions are such that unconformities, stratigraphic thinning of the intervening formations, or squeezing of the formations by structural deformation may be ruled out, faulting must be the explanation.

TOPOGRAPHIC EXPRESSION

Faults which reach the surface may or may not have a topographic expression. A fault will be expressed in the topography if the original relative elevations or depressions have not yet been worn down, if the rocks exposed on one side of the fault are more resistant to erosion than those on the other, or if the faulting alters the resistance to erosion of the rocks along its course. The most important distinction to be made in regard to the topography produced by faulting is whether it is caused by the direct uplift and depression of the two sides, or whether it is produced solely by the difference in the resistance of the various rocks to erosion. The first type has been called fault or tectonic, and the second fault-line or erosional.

Valleys and Ridges along Faults. In regions of soft, unconsolidated strata the faulting generally does not alter the resistance of the rocks to erosion. Occasionally the rocks along the fault may be cemented so that they form ridges, but in general the fault plane is neither lower nor higher than the surrounding area, except as the formations exposed differ in resistance to erosion. In areas of hard and resistant formations, such as metamorphic and igneous rocks, highly altered sediments, chert, limestone, and dolomite, the shattering or fracturing along faults may reduce the resistance of these hard rocks to erosion. The vein material along the fault planes may be more easily eroded than the surrounding rocks. In such cases the outcrops of the fault planes are marked by valleys, depressions, notches, swales, and clefts in cliffs. Under these conditions the fault planes may be soil covered and not exposed. If the cemented zones, gouge, breccia, or mylonite along a fault are more resistant to erosion than the surrounding rocks, the fault may show up as a ridge.   Faults may produce a change in the angles of slopes and may alter the grade of streams near where they cross the faults.

Distinction between Scarps and Escarpments.   An escarpment is a slope which is steeper than normal and extends for a considerable distance.   Many escarpments are produced by the outcrop of formations or beds which are more resistant to erosion than the rocks above and below them.   If these rocks dip steeply they produce hogbacks, but if they dip gently they produce cuestas, which have a gentle dip slope in the direction of the dip and a relatively steep escarpment on the up-dip side.   Such escarpments look a good deal like fault scarps, and it is important to distinguish between the two.   Scarps along faults are slopes which are relatively steep and which extend along the faults for appreciable distances.   The outcrop of a fault is at or near the base of the scarp, and the trend of the scarp is parallel to the strike of the fault rather than to the strike of the strata.   The crest of the scarp is generally not at the same stratigraphic horizon, unless the fault happens to be a strike fault.   An escarpment, on the other hand, is parallel to the strike of the strata rather than to the strike of any faults present.   The crest of the escarpment tends to occur at the same stratigraphic horizon.   If the dip is gentle or moderate, the steep slope is updip and the gentle slope in the direction of the dip.   The crest of the escarpment is composed of rock which is relatively resistant to erosion compared to the formations stratigraphically above and below.   Scarps along faults tend to be higher where they are composed of resistant rocks, but the crest of these scarps does not ordinarily follow the outcrop of the most resistant strata.

Scarps.   *Tectonic or Fault Scarps.*   Tectonic or fault scarps are due to the actual elevations or depressions caused by faulting.   Therefore the scarp always slopes toward the downthrown side of the fault.   In large faults, the total displacement generally consists of a large number of sudden movements extending over hundreds of thousands or millions of years.   Hence the scarps of great faults are always considerably modified by erosion.   They do not slope as steeply as the dip of the fault plane, and they are cut into by valleys or canyons and intervening ridges and spurs.   In some cases the spurs end near the fault in triangular facets.   The outcrops of the fault plane itself lie at the foot of the scarp. These outcrops are very likely to be covered by talus or alluvium derived from the slope.

Erosional or Fault-line Scarps.   Erosional or fault-line scarps are produced entirely by the processes of erosion.   They occur because rocks exposed on one side of the fault have a greater resistance to erosion than those on the other.   Since under these conditions the surface is lowered faster on the side where the weaker rock crops out, a scarp will be formed which lies toward the resistant rock from the fault, and slopes toward the weaker rock. Erosional scarps are of two types, resequent and obsequent. In resequent scarps, the elevated area is on the side of the fault which originally went up. Obsequent scarps are on the side which originally went down.

Criteria for Distinguishing Tectonic and Erosional Scarps. Where fault scarps are present, it is important to determine whether they are tectonic or erosional. The older the fault, the more likely it is that the scarps associated with it are erosional. The problem of determining the age of faults is discussed in Chap. 15. Most tectonic scarps are associated with faults which were active in late Cenozoic, or Recent, time. Scarps associated with faults which have not been active since pre-Cenozoic time are probably all erosional. In the United States the age of the faulting affecting a region is generally fairly well known, and this knowledge alone may solve the problem. However, many old faults are revived by relatively recent deformation, and this possibility must be considered in deciding as to the nature of the scarps.

A scarp is tectonic if the rocks cropping out near its crest or in elevated areas along the fault are less resistant to erosion than the strata exposed at lower levels. Erosional scarps occur where the rocks differ in their resistance to erosion on opposite sides of the fault, and the scarps or high areas are always underlain by the rocks that are more resistant to erosion than those under the lowlands. Scarps along active faults are generally at least in part tectonic; however, active faults are very rare in most regions.

Scarplets or Piedmont Scarps. Sudden movements of the fault plane produce small scarps, known as scarplets or piedmont scarps, near the outcrops of faults. The height of these scarplets may vary from less than a foot up to about 20 ft. They may occur in the bedrock or in the alluvium and talus near the foot of the main scarp. Those in bedrock are in the fault plane and always slope toward the downthrown side. Those in alluvium are near the outcrop of the fault plane but not necessarily in it. Because of the slumping of alluvium down the slope during the faulting, grabens and depressions may develop, and the scarp in alluvium does not always slope toward the downthrown side of the main fault.

EXPRESSION ON AREAL MAPS

There are two reasons why a student of petroleum geology should study the expression of faults on areal maps. In the first place, a geologist may have to make and interpret areal maps in regions containing faulting. He should therefore be prepared for what may be an important part of his job. Furthermore, areal maps are an excellent means of

getting the student acquainted with problems relating to faulting.   Every
student should know whether the relations shown on areal maps indicate
faulting and if so, which side went up or down, and how much throw is
indicated.   He should also be able to draw areal maps showing faults
with definite amounts of throw.   Problems of this nature are given in
the Laboratory Supplement.

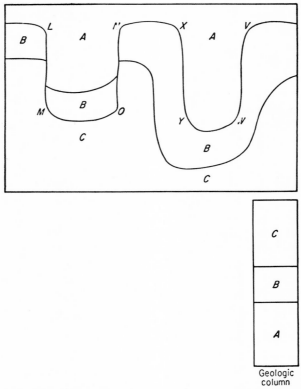

Fig. 5-21. The expression on an areal geologic map of a graben and a possible syncline.

Faulting is shown on areal maps by offsets of the boundaries of the
formations.   If any formation is cut out locally along the line of offset,
a fault is indicated with much more definiteness.   An abrupt bend in
the lines bounding the formations may have other explanations than
faulting.   It may be due to the effect of topography or to folding.   If a
younger formation occupies an area surrounded by an outcrop of an older
formation in a region of no topographic relief, the explanation may be
either that there is a graben or that there is a syncline.

This principle is illustrated in Fig. 5-21.   Along the lines *LM* and *NO*
the two contacts of formation *B* are offset.   That the sudden bends in

the outcrops are due to faulting and not to folding is indicated by the manner in which bed B is entirely cut out between L and M and between N and O. Hence the area between LM and NO is a graben and not a syncline. Along the lines XY and VW there are two other sharp bends in the lower contact of formation B. There is, however, nothing that definitely indicates faulting, and the area between XY and VW could be interpreted as a syncline, though it might also be a graben.

It is only when the surface is nearly flat or when the area covered is very large and the dips are steep that the effect of topography on areal maps may be disregarded. Making areal maps of dipping formations in areas of considerable relief is likely to be very time-consuming. The effect of topography on the outcrops of faults can be used to determine the dips of the fault planes. It should be kept in mind that faults show up on areal maps only where they intersect the outcrop of a formation boundary which is shown on the areal map. A large fault could occur without appearing on the areal map if its outcrop happened to lie wholly within a thick formation.

Expression on Airplane Photographs

It is well known that one of the best methods for finding faults which reach the surface consists in studying airplane maps and photographs made from airplanes. In many cases faults can be detected on these maps when they cannot be found by an observer on the ground. Alignments, changes in vegetation and color of soils, offsets in topographic features or formations, dips due to drag, and in some cases the jointing or fracturing near faults, may all be detected in the airplane photographs under the proper conditions. It is of course in arid regions that faults and other structural features are best expressed. The greater the cover of vegetation, the greater the difficulty of recognizing the smaller details of the structure and stratigraphy. However, even in dense vegetation, faults may frequently be recognized by their topographic effects or by the changes they cause in vegetation. Nevertheless, it should not be supposed that the advent of airplane photographs means that it is unnecessary to examine the exposures on the ground in searching for faults. In some cases the critical exposures needed to prove the existence of the fault may be so small or so covered by vegetation that they cannot be detected on the airplane maps.

Expression on Structure-contour and Isopach Maps

Under ordinary conditions the available information about the structure of an area is expressed by means of structure-contour maps. It is therefore of particular importance to know how faults are expressed on these maps. The first point to be decided is whether or not a blank strip, devoid of structure contours, is to be shown along the fault.   The key horizon is always absent in a belt along normal faults, and is duplicated in a belt along reverse faults.   Usually it is not customary to show two sets of structure contours in the same area, one on the upthrown side and one on the downthrown side, along reverse faults.   The two sets of structure contours may be shown, however, if doing so will present useful information not otherwise given.

The blank space along normal faults is absent if the fault is vertical. On small-scale maps this space is usually so narrow that it is omitted. It may also be omitted if it is not known whether the fault is normal or reverse.   It seems best to show this belt in which the key horizon is missing along normal faults if it is as much as 0.1 in. wide on the scale of the map.   The width of this belt depends on the throw of the fault and on its dip.   If the dip of a particular fault plane is not known, it may be advisable to assume that its dip is the same as the average dip of the other fault planes of the area.   In order to determine the dip of the fault plane accurately, its depth must be known in three wells.   However, if the strike of a fault plane is known, its dip may be determined from two wells, provided that they do not intersect the fault plane at the same elevation.

The zone along the fault in which the key horizon is missing may be shown in three ways.   It may be left entirely blank, it may be shown by shading, or structure contours may be drawn on the fault plane.   If structure contours are drawn on the fault plane in the belt where the key horizon is missing, they are likely to be mistaken for structure contours on the key horizon.   The upthrown side of the fault should be clearly labeled.

RECOGNITION OF SUBSURFACE FAULTS

Strata Higher or Lower than Expected.   In the United States most faults in oil-producing regions are now found by subsurface studies or by geophysics.   There are in general three indications of subsurface faults: the occurrence of formations at higher or lower levels than expected, abnormal intervals, and the omission or repetition of beds.   If the throw of a fault is so large that it causes a distinct difference in the general level of the key horizons on opposite sides, it is likely to be found first by recognizing that the strata are higher or lower than normal.   The known dip is projected from the nearest wells.   If the actual elevation of the formations is much lower or higher than would be expected from projecting the dip, some abnormality in the structure is indicated.   This abnormality may be due to faulting or to folding.   If additional wells show that the change in elevation is concentrated along a narrow zone, a fault or a monocline is indicated.   The decision as to whether to call the feature a fault or a monocline should depend on the steepness of dip and on the structural habits of the region.

It should be noted that wildcat wells scattered at random over an area are much more likely to find the first indications of faulting of great throw in the abnormal elevation of the strata than in abnormal intervals or in repeated or missing strata. Only wells which pass through the fault plane find these latter conditions. On the other hand, any well in the affected area will find the formations higher or lower than normal. The area in which the elevations are affected by the faulting is generally much larger than the area underlain by the fault plane. However, only faults of large throw can be found by this method. Moreover, the indications obtained in this manner are only suggestive of faults. The possibility must be considered that the unexpected elevations of the key horizons are due to local folds or to a change in regional dip.

Faults which were forming during the deposition of a certain interval of strata will show up on isopach maps of this interval. The thickness shown will change abruptly at the fault plane, becoming greater on the downthrown side. Faults which were not forming during the deposition of the intervals contoured will not show up on the isopach maps, unless the measurements are taken at points where the fault plane is within the interval. Generally it is advisable, in making isopach maps, to avoid using intervals which are abnormal because a well passes through the fault plane, as the erratic changes produced by the faults would only cause confusion if contoured along with intervals not affected by faults.

Abnormal Intervals. Fig. 5-22 shows how the intervals are affected in wells which pass through fault planes. The fault GH cuts two key beds, $ABCD$ and EF. Well JK finds the normal interval OP between these two beds. Well LM, however, cuts the fault plane between the intersections of the fault plane with the two beds. As a result it finds the interval between them QR, which is much smaller than normal. Similarly, wells which pass through reverse faults may find the intervals abnormally increased. In flat-lying strata, the change in interval is equal to the throw of the fault.

If subsurface correlations indicate a change in intervals, it should not be assumed without further investigation that a fault is present. On the contrary, all the other possible explanations should be considered. These include the effects of unconformities and folding during deposition. The loss of interval due to an angular unconformity occurs entirely at the unconformity. However, unless very detailed correlations are available, it may not be known that the loss of interval is concentrated in this manner. On the contrary, it may be known that the loss of interval occurs within a fairly thick zone, but it may not be possible to determine how it is distributed within this zone. Angular unconformities generally cover a considerable area and are approximately parallel to the strata above the unconformity.   These characteristics may serve to distinguish between abnormally small intervals produced by angular unconformities and those produced by normal faults.   The latter occur in belts which are long and narrow in horizontal plane, and which generally rise rapidly in the section in the direction from which the fault plane dips.

Omission and Repetition of Strata.   Where the strata may be correlated in detail, the thickness of strata repeated or omitted may be determined.   In areas where overturned folds may be ruled out, repetition of

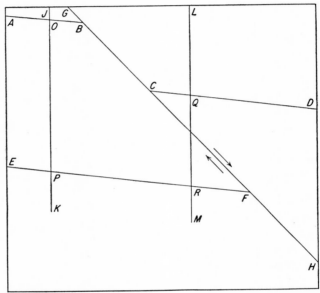

Fig. 5-22. Cross section showing how the penetration of a fault plane affects the intervals found in drilling.

strata indicates a reverse fault.   Where the effects of unconformities are known to be absent, the omission of strata within short distances indicates normal faulting.   If the effects of drag are disregarded, in flat-lying strata the thickness of omitted or repeated strata is equal to the throw of the fault.   Very accurate correlations of stratigraphic details are needed to measure the amount of omission or repetition of strata.   In many regions this detailed correlation is made possible by electrical and radio-activity logs.

The manner in which faults cause repetition and omission of beds is illustrated in Fig. 5-23.   A series of beds is numbered from 1 to 15. Well *CD* passes through the whole series and finds normal succession with no omissions or repetitions. Well *AB* passes through the normal fault plane *EF* and finds beds 5 to 14, inclusive, missing. Well *JK* passes through the reverse fault *GH* and finds beds 8 to 12, inclusive, repeated.

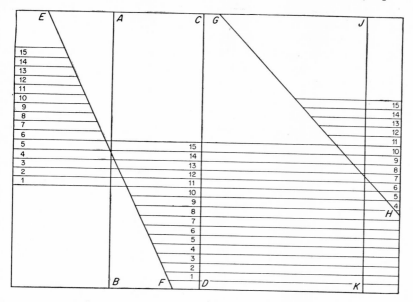

FIG. 5-23. Cross section showing the omission and repetition of beds in wells which pass through fault planes.

DETERMINING MOVEMENTS ALONG FAULTS

Ascertaining the Direction of the Movement. The most important step in determining the direction and amount of the movement along faults is to correlate the strata across the fault. Once this has been done, the displacement at right angles to the stratification can be readily determined. Over extensive regions the strata lie nearly flat, and it is known from various lines of evidence that the displacement along the faults consisted chiefly of dip slip. Under such conditions the direction and amount of the displacement may be readily determined by comparing the elevation of the strata on opposite sides. Where the beds on opposite sides of the fault cannot be correlated, the drag may indicate the direction of the displacement, or at any rate the direction of the latest movement. Slickensides are also very useful for determining the direction of the displacement. They run parallel to the movement that produced them. If the movement was in different directions at different times, the slickensides are generally parallel to the latest movement, though if the displacement occurred along different surfaces the earlier slickensides may be preserved also. In areas of flat-lying strata and simple structure, it appears that the direction of the displacement along small to medium-sized faults is generally in approximately the same direction throughout the time over which the fault is active. In such cases the slickensides show what fraction of the displacement is strike slip and what fraction is dip slip. Slickensides show that the displacement was parallel to the striations; they do not by themselves indicate in which of the two possible directions the rocks moved. In some cases this may be determined by rubbing the hand over the slickensided surface. This surface feels smoother when the hand moves in the same direction as the missing or opposite side. Projections of harder material and steplike features in the slickensided surfaces may also help to show the direction of the displacement. The projections may have ridges trailing out behind them, and the steplike features are arranged so that the opposite side moves away from the steep face of the step, and not against it.

Measurements of Throw and Strike Slip. In flat-lying strata the throw of a fault is equal to the difference in the elevation of the same stratum on opposite sides of the fault. The throw of a fault is equal to the dip slip multiplied by the sine of the angle of dip of the fault plane, and the heave is equal to the dip slip multiplied by the cosine of the angle of dip of the fault plane. The strike slip is usually very much more difficult to measure. If slickensides are visible in outcrops, they may be used to identify strike-slip faults, provided that the direction of the movement along the fault did not change during its development. In some cases the amount of strike slip may be determined by noting the displacement of steeply dipping beds, anticlinal and synclinal axes, or vertical dikes. Unfortunately these features are generally not present where they are needed to determine the strike slip.

As already mentioned, several lines of evidence suggest that in the great areas of flat-lying strata east of the Rocky Mountains in the vicinity of the oil fields of the United States, the displacement along the faults has been chiefly dip slip, with strike slip relatively unimportant. The chief evidence consists in the observation that the slickensides generally run up and down the fault plane, rather than parallel to its strike. Furthermore, in such regions anticlinal and synclinal axes and vertical faults are not displaced. The absence of structural disturbance in the associated strata also suggests the occurrence of normal faults rather than strike-slip displacements. In many cases the dips of the beds are so gentle that enormous horizontal movements would be required to produce small apparent vertical displacements of the beds.

It should be clearly understood that the generalizations about the scarcity of strike-slip faults apply only to the relatively undisturbed regions of flat-lying strata. Strike-slip faults are important in California, the Ardmore Basin, the British Isles, and the Jura Mountains. Probably they occur in many other regions of complex structure.

CLOSURE AND CLOSED AREA OF FAULTED STRUCTURES

In view of the fact that closure is the most important single characteristic indicating the value of structures as prospective traps for oil and gas, and since the closure of faulted structures is frequently largely determined by faults, careful consideration should be given to the relation between faults and closure. It is important to know how the presence of faults on closed anticlines affects their closure, how to determine closure against faults, and under what circumstances faults may be considered to close a structure. It does not appear that there is any well-established procedure for solving these problems. Since this is the case, a geologist in giving the closure of faulted structures should state what method he used for calculating the closure.

In this chapter only the characteristics of closure which can be determined from structure maps are considered. The bearing of the stratigraphy and lithology on the characteristics of faulted traps is discussed in Chap. 17.

Closure against Faults. *Principles Involved.* The intersection of two or more faults or of faults and anticlinal noses commonly produces structures in which the dip of the strata forms a closure in all directions except where the faults form the boundaries. How the closure would be estimated in such cases depends on what assumptions are made about the imperviousness of the fault planes.

Even if fault planes are sealed to the movement of oil and gas up them to the surface, it does not follow that they make a seal to movement across the fault planes. The first involves a vertical movement of hundreds or thousands of feet, while the second merely involves moving across the fault zone, which may be only a few inches or a few feet in thickness. There are three possible assumptions: that the fault does not make a seal at all, that it makes on the upthrown side a seal which is as high as its throw, and that it makes a complete seal regardless of its throw. According to the first assumption there would be no closure against a fault, according to the second the closure could not be greater than the throw, and according to the third the closure would depend entirely on the structure on the downdip side of the fault.

Closure of Anticlines Bounded by Faults on Updip Side. Let it be assumed that a plunging anticline without closure is cut by a fault which is roughly parallel to the regional strike. In this case, there would be no closure if it were not for the fault. The situation is somewhat different according to whether the downthrown side of the fault is in the updip or downdip direction. Fig. 5-24 shows the fault *GH* cutting the plunging anticline *EF* at *A*.   The downthrown side is up the dip, and the throw of the fault is 100 ft.   If it is assumed that the closure of the faulted

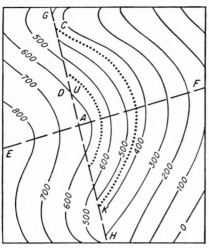

structure on the downdip side of the fault centering at *A* can be no greater than the throw of the fault, the closure is 100 ft, and the boundary of the closed area is shown by the dotted line halfway between the 600- and 700-ft structure contours.   The boundary to the left is the fault.   The key bed on the anticline is supposed to rise to a height of 750 ft at *A*.   If, on the other hand, the fault is assumed to form a complete seal, regardless of its throw, the closure is the least dip away from *A* on the upthrown side of the fault.   This least dip is 300 ft from *A* to *C*.   Hence the boundary of the closed area is 300 ft below the crest of the anticline

Fig. 5-24. Structure map to show how closure of anticlines on upthrown sides of faults is estimated.

and is shown by the dotted line halfway between the 400- and 500-ft structure contours.

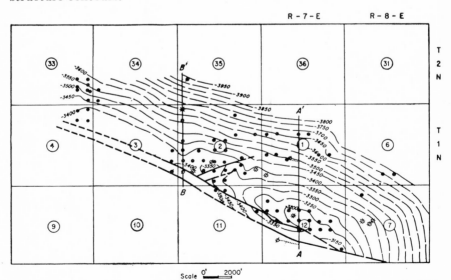

Fig. 5-25. Structure map of Jessie Pool, Okla.   Structure contours are drawn on the Viola limestone.   (*After Boyd, published by permission of the American Association of Petroleum Geologists.*)

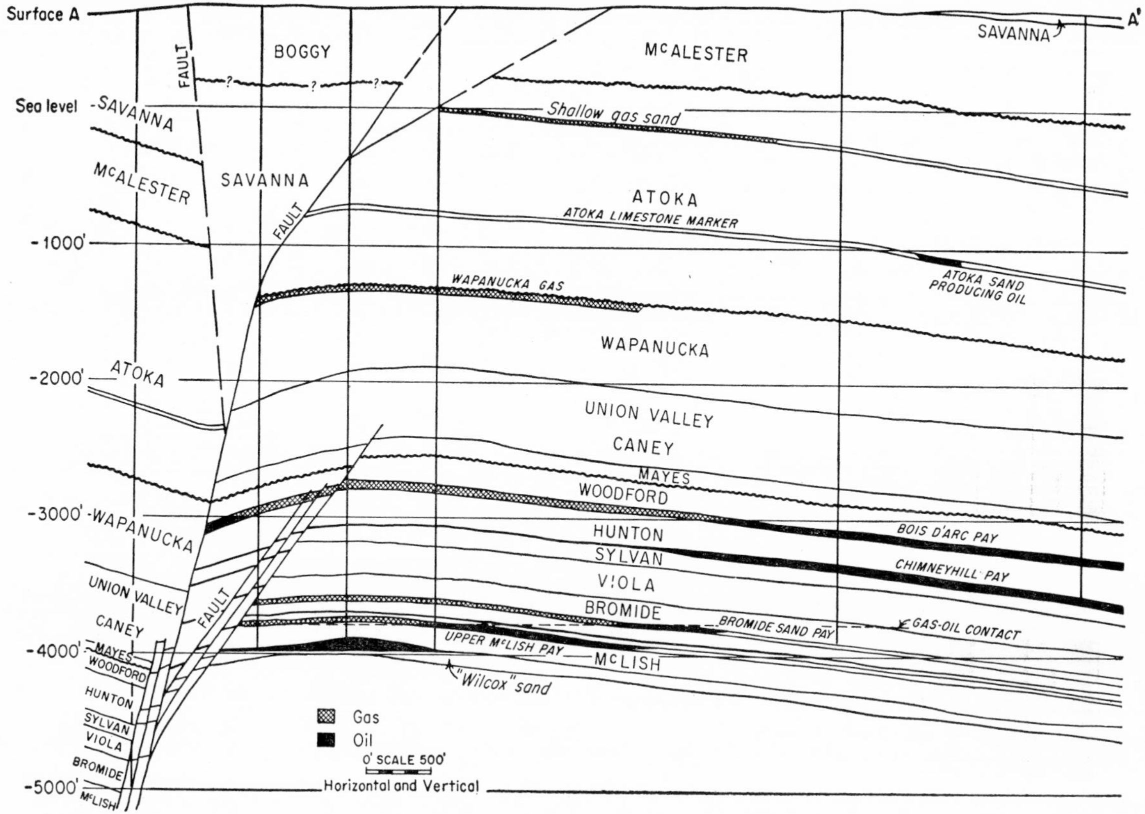

Fig. 5-26. Cross section through points A-A' of Fig. 5-25. (After Boyd, published by permission of the American Association of Petroleum Geologists.)

143

The Jessie field, Oklahoma, is a good example of this type of structure. It has been described by Boyd.[1]   Figs. 5-25 and 5-26, from Boyd's paper, show a structure map and a cross section through this field.   The structure map shows a closure of 300 ft on the upthrown side of the fault. The cross section shows that the fault is distributive or compound, with small faults which dip less steeply branching off the main fault.   The total throw of the faults seems to be about 1,400 ft.   The cross section shows that the closure against the fault is evidently responsible for the accumulation of oil or gas in seven different reservoirs.

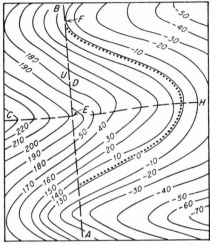

Fig. 5-27. Structure map to show how closure of anticlines on the downthrown sides of faults is estimated.

If the downthrown side of the fault is in the downdip direction, the closure may be calculated on the assumption that it is equal to the least dip away from the crest of the anticline on the downdip side. This condition is illustrated in Fig. 5-27.   The fault AB, with a throw of 130 ft and a downthrow in the downdip direction, cuts the anticline CH at E. Assuming that the elevation at E is 70 ft, the least dip from E is 70 ft from A to F.

The boundary of the closed area is the fault and the dotted line following the 0 structure contour.

Closures Produced by Intersecting Faults.   Faults intersect each other to form all sorts of patterns, and the question arises as to whether closures can be formed by the intersection of two or more faults.   Petroleum geologists might disagree as to whether or not closures can be formed in this manner.   However, if it is assumed that faults seal the reservoir rocks, then they may form closures, and the size of the closures and closed areas may be calculated according to the assumptions.   Fig. 5-28 shows how the closure is calculated under the two assumptions for this type of structure.   On the right side of Fig. 5-28 an uplifted block is shown between the two faults GA and NA.   The throw of the two faults at A is about 900 ft, for the key horizon rises to about 2,100 feet between the faults and is at an elevation of 1,200 feet at this point just outside the faults.   According to the assumption that the closure along a fault is no greater than the throw of the fault, the closure would be 900 ft and the boundary of the closed area would be the dotted line PR, 900 ft down

[1] W. Baxter Boyd, Jessie Pool, Pontotoc and Coal Counties, Oklahoma, *A.A.P.G. Bull.*, vol. 22, pp. 1560–1578 (1938).

the dip from the crest of the uplift. On the assumption that faults form a complete seal regardless of the amount of throw, the closure would be 1,800 feet and the closed area the triangle *AGN*.

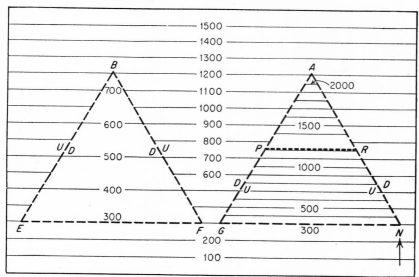

FIG. 5-28. Structure map to show how amount of closure formed by intersecting faults is determined.

On the left side of Fig. 2-28 a triangular area is shown dropped down between the faults *EB* and *FB*. If the faults are assumed to form a seal, the closure is 450 ft and the closed area the triangle *ABF*.

REVERSALS DUE TO FAULTING

Faults having their downthrown sides in a direction up the regional dip are occasionally said to form reversals of the regional dip. Although this usage may be considered inaccurate by many geologists, it is worth while to know what the term means when applied to faults. The displacement of a fault should not be called reversal unless the fault is roughly parallel to the regional strike and the downthrown side is in a direction opposite to the regional dip. Under these conditions the reversal is equal to the throw of the fault. However, it is worth noting that faults at right angles to the regional strike could not have reversals.

RELATION OF FAULTS TO FOLDS

General Relations. Many faults have no definite relation to folds, and many folds, even some that are quite pronounced, are not faulted. On the other hand, great numbers of faults are closely related to the folds on which they occur. Furthermore, some thrust faults have been folded. The folding in these cases occurred later than the formation of the thrust fault, though possibly it was due to the continuance of the same compressive forces which produced the thrust fault.

In some cases, the formation of an overturned fold is the first stage in the development of a thrust fault. As the fold becomes more and more overturned it may develop a break thrust, which cuts across the bedding at a considerable angle. Fig. 5-29 shows a break thrust. The continuance of the folding may stretch the beds so that a fault nearly parallel to the strata is formed. This type of fault, known as a stretch thrust, is shown in Fig. 5-30.

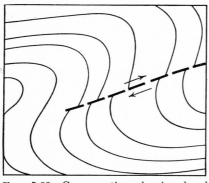

Fig. 5-29. Cross section showing break thrust.

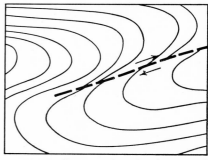

Fig. 5-30. Cross section showing stretch thrust.

Normal faults may be produced by stretching over anticlines, as already mentioned. The prevailing dip of these faults is toward the anticlinal axes. They may be longitudinal or peripheral. Transverse normal faults may be produced by elongation of the anticlinal axes as compression takes place at right angles to the axes. The complex normal faulting over salt domes is discussed in Chap. 8.

The Origin of En Echelon Folds and Faults. *Mechanical Principles.* According to the evidence of experiments and to considerations of the mechanics involved, faults and folds with en echelon arrangement may be produced by strike-slip movements in the basement rocks. Fig. 5-31 shows the relation of the en echelon folds and faults to the strike-slip fault in the basement that produces them. *GH* is the strike-slip fault below the sediments. The two sides moved relatively as shown by the arrows. As a result of this movement the original square *ABCE* is deformed by shearing into the parallelogram *AFDB*. Since the diagonal *AD* of the parallelogram is shorter than the diagonal *AC* of the square, there will be compression near the fault along lines parallel to *AD*. The result should be a series of folds with axes parallel to the dotted lines in the figure. Since the diagonal *BF* is longer than the diagonal of the original square *BE*, stretching or tension should develop along lines parallel to *BF*. The result should be normal faults parallel to the dashed lines in the figure.

Field Evidence. If this situation occurs in the field, one would expect a series of en echelon folds or faults arranged over strike-slip faults in the basement. The only evidence is the structure of the sediments. Many long lines of en echelon folds or faults have been mapped, but these differ from the arrangement shown in Fig. 5-31 in two respects. The faults and the axes of the folds are more nearly parallel to the general trend of the fault zone, and either folds or faults are present, but generally not both. It has not been definitely proved that any of these en echelon folds or faults have been generated by strike-slip faults in the basement. Nevertheless, the process should be kept in mind as a possible explanation of the conditions.

The En Echelon Faults of Oklahoma. Two well-known en echelon structures may be mentioned as possible results of the process described above. The en echelon faults of northeastern Oklahoma have long interested the geologists who worked in that area. These faults have been described by Foley,[1] Kramer,[2] McCoy,[3] Melton,[4] Clark,[5] and Sherrill.[6] The en

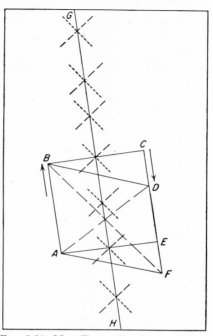

Fig. 5-31. Map illustrating theory of production of folds and of fractures due to tension along strike-slip faults in basement. Arrows show direction of relative movement, which deforms original square *ABCE* into parallelogram *ABDF.* The axial planes of the folds due to compression strike parallel to the dotted lines, and the fractures due to stretching strike parallel to the dashed lines.

echelon faults occur in belts which strike north-northeast. The individual faults strike more nearly northeast than do the belts. Some

[1] Lyndon L. Foley, Origin of Faults in Creek and Osage Counties, Oklahoma, *A.A.P.G. Bull.,* vol. 10, pp. 293–303 (1926).

[2] William Kramer, En Echelon Faults in Oklahoma, *A.A.P.G. Bull.,* vol. 18, pp. 243–250 (1934).

[3] Alex W. McCoy, An Interpretation of Local Structural Development in Mid-Continent Areas Associated with Deposits of Petroleum, "Problems of Petroleum Geology," American Association of Petroleum Geologists, Tulsa, pp. 581–627 (1934).

[4] Frank A. Melton, Age of the Ouachita Orogeny and Its Tectonic Effects, *A.A.P.G. Bull.,* vol. 14, pp. 57–72 (1930).

[5] Frank R. Clark, En Echelon Fault Belts, Discussion, *A.A.P.G. Bull.,* vol. 14, p. 330 (1930).

[6] R. E. Sherrill, Origin of the En Echelon Faults in North-central Oklahoma, *A.A.P.G. Bull.,* vol. 13, pp. 31–37 (1929).

geologists have supposed that the belts lie over strike-slip faults in the basement. Other geologists, however, point out that the belts are exactly parallel to the regional strike, and conclude that the faults merely appear to occur in belts because they can be mapped only where certain key horizons crop out. According to this interpretation, the faults are not en echelon, but merely have a parallel strike.

Newport–Beverly Hills Trend. Another series of en echelon structures which have been variously interpreted extends from Newport to Beverly Hills, on the west side of the Los Angeles Basin, California. This feature is variously known as the Newport–Beverly Hills, or Newport-Inglewood, fault, fold, uplift, trend, or belt. There are a number of anticlines, each with an oil field on it, along this belt. Each anticline trends slightly at an angle to the line through the series of anticlines. The trend has been described by Hoots and Herald,[1] Reed and Hollister,[2] and Eaton.[3] It has been explained as an anticline due to compression and as a series of en echelon anticlines produced by movement along a strike-slip fault in the basement. One objection to the last theory is that there are no evidences of a strike-slip fault where the older rocks are exposed in the mountains to the north and south.

A possible explanation of en echelon faults and folds is that they are produced over longer faults and folds at depth by slight differences in the orientation of the stresses between the level of the deeper, long folds and faults and the level of shallower en echelon folds and faults. If the direction of the stresses differed slightly at the two levels, the long faults and folds would presumably split up into en echelon structures nearer the surface. Anderson[4] has given a similar explanation for the formation of en echelon dikes.

Relation of Faults and Folds to Basement Structure

There is no doubt that the large, gently folded uplifts and depressions which affect the gently dipping strata of the stable regions of the earth displace the basement rocks. In the intensely deformed strata of orogens there are many overturned folds and thrust faults which do not bring up the basement rocks. This suggests that the thrust faults and folds exposed at the surface do not extend down to the basement. If this is

---

[1] Harold W. Hoots and Stanley C. Herald, Natural Gas Resources of California, "Geology of Natural Gas," American Association of Petroleum Geologists, Tulsa, pp. 113–220 (1935).

[2] R. D. Reed and J. S. Hollister, Structural Evolution of Southern California, *A.A.P.G. Bull.*, vol. 20, pp. 1529–1692 (1936).

[3] J. Edmund Eaton, Long Beach California Earthquake of March 10, 1933, *A.A.P.G. Bull.*, vol. 17, p. 733, fig. 1 (1933).

[4] E. M. Anderson, "Dynamics of Faulting and Dyke Formation, with Application to Britain," Oliver & Boyd, Ltd., London, pp. 55–56 (1951).

the case, the basement may be affected by thrust faults and folds of a similar type which do not reach to the surface, or it may have a different type of structure. Between the basement and the exposures at the surface there may be decollement, that is, a thrust fault of low dip and great extent which separates the zones of different structure. Evidently there are two explanations of the structure of highly deformed areas, one that the structures extend downward to the basement and one that they are without roots and terminate downward above the basement. In drilling in these regions, it is clearly important to learn whether there is such a lower limit to the downward extent of the surface structures, and if so, at what depth it occurs. These two theories should be kept in mind in studying the areas to which they apply; at present it seems that more evidence is needed to understand fully the structure of orogens.

RELATIONS OF OIL AND GAS FIELDS TO FAULTS

The relations of oil and gas fields to faults are extremely variable. In some great producing regions there are no faults at all. In some cases the faults, though present, had nothing to do with the formation of the trap in which the oil or gas accumulated. In other cases the faults make the trap, and there could be no pools if the faults were not present. The faults associated with oil and gas fields may be normal, high-angle reverse, or thrust. Their displacements range from less than a foot to thousands of feet.

In a number of well-known oil fields and oil-producing districts the occurrence of faults is especially noteworthy. In Alberta, Canada, several oil and gas fields, of which Turner Valley is the best known, have been developed in association with thrust planes in the foothills of the Rocky Mountains. Along the Luling-Mexia-Talco fault zone in Texas there are many oil fields in which the trap responsible for the oil accumulation owes its existence to the faults. These fields occur on the upthrown and downdip sides of the faults. Many salt-dome oil fields are intensely faulted, as is described in Chap. 8. Oil production is found in a group of fault blocks in the Comodoro-Rivadavia field in Argentina, described by Fossa-Mancini,[1] and in the oil fields of northwest Peru, described by Iddings and Olsson.[2]

ADDITIONAL REFERENCES

Anderson, J. L.: Petroleum Geology of Colombia, South America, *A.A.P.G. Bull.*, vol. 29, pp. 1065–1142 (1945).

[1] Enrico Fossa-Mancini, Faults in the Comodoro-Rivadavia Oil Field, Argentina, *A.A.P.G. Bull.*, vol. 16, pp. 556–575 (1932).
[2] Arthur Iddings and A. A. Olsson, The Geology of Northwest Peru, *A.A.P.G. Bull.*, vol. 12, pp. 1–39 (1928).

Bailey, E. B.: "Tectonic Essays, Mainly Alpine," Oxford University Press, New York (1935).

———: West Highland Tectonics, *Geol. Soc. London Quart. Jour.*, vol. 90, pp. 462–525 (1934).

Bailey, T. L.: Late Pleistocene Coast Range Orogenesis in Southern California, *G.S.A. Bull.*, vol. 54, pp. 1549–1568 (1943).

Bain, G. W.: African Rift Valleys: American Triassic Troughs, *G.S.A. Bull.*, vol. 52, p. 1889 (1941).

Baker, A. A.: Geologic Structure of Southeastern Utah, *A.A.P.G. Bull.*, vol. 19, pp. 1472–1507 (1935).

Baker, C. L.: Nature of the Later Deformations in Certain Ranges of the Great Basin, *Jour. Geology*, vol. 21, pp. 273–278 (1913).

Baldry, R. A.: Slip-planes and Breccia Zones in the Tertiary Rocks of Peru, *Geol. Soc. London Quart. Jour.*, vol. 94, pp. 347–358 (1938).

Barton, D. C.: Surface Fracture System of South Texas, *A.A.P.G. Bull.*, vol. 17, pp. 1194–1212 (1933).

Bartram, J. G.: Summary of Rocky Mountain Geology, *A.A.P.G. Bull.*, vol. 23, pp. 1131–1152 (1939).

Beckwith, R. H.: Trace-slip Faults, *A.A.P.G. Bull.*, vol. 25, pp. 2181–2193 (1941).

Benioff, H.: Earthquakes and Rock Creep, *Seismol. Soc. America Bull.*, vol. 41, pp. 31–62 (1951).

———: Seismic Evidence for the Fault Origin of Oceanic Deeps, *G.S.A. Bull.*, vol. 60, pp. 1837–1856 (1949).

Billings, M. P.: Physiographic Relations of the Lewis Overthrust in Northern Montana, *Am. Jour. Sci.*, 5th ser., vol. 35, pp. 260–272 (1938).

———: Thrusting Younger Rocks over Older, *Am. Jour. Sci.*, 5th ser., vol. 25, pp. 140–165 (1933).

Blackwelder, E.: The Recognition of Fault Scarps, *Jour. Geology*, vol. 36, pp. 289–311 (1928).

Bryan F.: Evidence of Recent Movements along Faults of Balcones System in Central Texas, *A.A.P.G. Bull.*, vol. 20, pp. 1357–1371 (1936).

Bucher, W. H.: "Deformation of the Earth's Crust," Princeton University Press, Princeton, N.J. (1936).

———: Geologic Structure and Organic History of Venezuela, *G.S.A. Mem.* 49, pp. 1–113 (1952).

———, Thom, W. T., and Chamberlin, R. T.: Geologic Problems of the Beartooth Bighorn Region, *G.S.A. Bull.*, vol. 45, pp. 167–188 (1934).

Burbank, W. S., and Goddard, E. N.: Thrusting in Huerfana Park, Colorado, and Related Problems of Orogeny in the Sangre de Cristo Mountains, *G.S.A. Bull.*, vol. 48, pp. 931–976 (1937).

Butts, C.: Fensters in the Cumberland Overthrust Block in Southwestern Virginia, *Virginia Geol. Survey Bull.* 28 (1927).

Challinor, J.: The "Throw" of a Fault, *Geol. Mag.*, vol. 70, pp. 385–393 (1933).

Chamberlin, R. T.: Diastrophic Behavior around the Bighorn Basin, *Jour. Geology*, vol. 48, pp. 673–716 (1940).

——— and Miller, W. Z.: Low-angle Faulting, *Jour. Geology*, vol. 26, pp. 1–44 (1918).

Clark, B. L.: Tectonics of the Coast Ranges of Middle California, *G.S.A. Bull.*, vol. 41, pp. 727–828 (1930).

Clark, L. M.: Geology of Rocky Mountain Front Ranges near Bow River, Alberta, *A.A.P.G. Bull.*, vol. 33, pp. 614–633 (1949).

Clark, R. H., and McIntyre, D. B.: The Use of the Terms Pitch and Plunge, *Am. Jour. Sci.*, vol. 249, pp. 591–599 (1951).

Clark, S. K.: Classification of Faults, *A.A.P.G. Bull.*, vol. 27, pp. 1245–1265 (1943).

—— and Royds, J. S.: Structural Trends and Fault Systems in Eastern Interior Basin, *A.A.P.G. Bull.*, vol. 32, pp. 1728–1749 (1948).

Collet, L. W.: The Structure of the Alps, Edward Arnold & Co., London, 2d ed. (1935).

Cotton, C. A.: A Review of Tectonic Relief in Australia, *Jour. Geology*, vol. 57, pp. 280–296 (1949).

——: Tectonic Scarps and Fault Valleys, *G.S.A. Bull.*, vol. 61, pp. 717–757 (1950).

Crowell, J. C.: Probable Large Lateral Displacement on San Gabriel Fault, Southern California, *A.A.P.G. Bull.*, vol. 36, pp. 2026–2035 (1952).

Daly, R. A.: "Our Mobile Earth," Charles Scribner's Sons, New York (1926).

Davis, W. M.: The Basin Range Problem, *Nat. Acad. Sci. Proc.*, vol. 11, pp. 387–392 (1925).

——: Mountain Ranges of the Great Basin, *Museum Comp. Zool. Harvard*, vol. 42 (1933).

DeLury, J. S.: Compressional Creep of Rubber and Rock, *Jour. Geology*, vol. 50, pp. 189–199 (1942).

Demorest, M.: Critical Structural Features of the Bighorn Mountains, Wyoming, *G.S.A. Bull.*, vol. 52, pp. 161–176 (1941).

De Terra, H.: Structural Features in Gliding Strata, *Am. Jour. Sci.*, 5th ser., vol. 21, pp. 204–213 (1931).

Dott, R. H.: Overthrusting in Arbuckle Mountains, Oklahoma, *A.A.P.G. Bull.*, vol. 18, pp. 567–602 (1934).

Eardley, A. J.: Geology of the North-central Wasatch Mountains, Utah, *G.S.A. Bull.*, vol. 55, pp. 819–894 (1944).

——: Strong Relief before Block Faulting in Vicinity of Southern Wasatch Mountains, *Jour. Geology*, vol. 41, pp. 243–267 (1933).

——: "Structural Geology of North America," Harper & Brothers, New York (1943).

——: Structure and Physiography of the Wasatch-Great Basin Region, *G.S.A. Bull.*, vol. 50, pp. 1277–1310 (1939).

Engeln, O. D. von: "Geomorphology, Systematic and Regional," The Macmillan Company, New York, (1942).

Evans, J. W.: Regions of Tension, Presidential Address to Geological Society, *Geol. Soc. London Quart. Jour.*, vol. 81, p. lxxx (1925).

Fath, A. E.: The Origin of the Faults, Anticlines and Buried "Granite Ridge" of the Northern Part of the Mid-Continent Oil and Gas Field, *U.S.G.S. Prof. Paper* 128(c) (1921).

Fuller, R. E., and Waters, A. C.: Nature and Origin of the Horst and Graben Structure of Southern Oregon, *Jour. Geology*, vol. 37, pp. 204–238 (1929).

Gallup, W. B.: Geology of the Turner Valley Oil and Gas Field, Alberta, Canada, *A.A.P.G. Bull.*, vol. 35, pp. 797–821 (1951).

Gardner, L. S.: The Hurricane Fault in Southwestern Utah and Northwestern Arizona, *Am. Jour. Sci.*, vol. 239, pp. 241–260 (1941).

Gianella, V. P., and Callaghan, E.: The Earthquake of December 20, 1932, at Cedar Mountain, Nevada, and Its Bearing on the Genesis of Basin Range Structure, *Jour. Geology*, vol. 42, pp. 1–22 (1934).

Gill, J. E.: Fault Nomenclature, *Royal Soc. Canada, Proc. and Trans.* 3d ser., sec. 4, vol. 35, pp. 71–85 (1941).

——: Normal and Reverse Faults, *Jour. Geology*, vol. 43, pp. 1071–1079 (1935).

Gilluly, J.: Basin Range Faulting along the Oquirrah Range, Utah, *G.S.A. Bull.*, vol. 39, pp. 1103–1130 (1928).

Gonzalez de Juana, C.: Elements of Diastrophic History of Northeastern Venezuela, *G.S.A. Bull.*, vol. 58, pp. 689–702 (1947).

Goodman, A. J.: Structure of the Turner Valley Gas Fields, Alberta, *Canadian Inst. Min. Metallurgy Trans.*, vol. 34, pp. 307–356 (1932).

———: Tectonics of East Side of Cordillera in Western Canada, *A.A.P.G. Bull.*, vol. 35, pp. 783–796 (1951).

Goubkin, I. M.: Tectonics of Southeastern Caucasus and Its Relation to Producing Oil Fields, *A.A.P.G. Bull.*, vol. 18, pp. 603–671 (1934).

Gray, K. W.: A Tectonic Window in Southwestern Iran, *Geol. Soc. London Quart. Jour.*, vol. 105, part 2, pp. 189–223 (1949).

Gregory, J. W. (ed.): "Structure of Asia," Methuen & Co., Ltd., London (1929).

Gutenberg, B.: Earthquakes and Structure in Southern California, *G.S.A. Bull.*, vol. 54, pp. 499–526 (1943).

———: Mechanism of Faulting in Southern California Indicated by Seismograms, *Seismol. Soc. America Bull.*, vol. 31, pp. 263–302 (1941).

Haddock, M. H.: "Disrupted Strata," Crosby Lockwood & Son, Ltd., London, 2d ed. (1938).

Hake, B. F., Willis, R., and Addison, C. C.: Folded Thrust Faults in Foothills of Alberta, *G.S.A. Bull.*, vol. 53, pp. 291–334 (1942).

Harrington, J. W.: Structural Analysis of the West Border of the Durham Triassic Basin, *G.S.A. Bull.*, vol. 62, pp. 149–157 (1951).

Heck, N. H.: Earthquakes and the Western Mountain Region, *G.S.A. Bull.*, vol. 49, pp. 1–22 (1938).

——— and Neumann, F.: Earth Motions in Vicinity of a Fault Slip, *G.S.A. Bull.*, vol. 53, pp. 179–194 (1942).

Heritsch, F.: "The Nappe Theory of the Alps," Methuen & Co., Ltd., London, (1929).

Hewett, D. F.: The Heart Mountain Overthrust, Wyoming, *Jour. Geology*, vol. 28, pp. 536–557 (1920).

———: Late Tertiary Thrust Faults in the Mohave Desert, California, *Nat. Acad. Sci. Proc.*, vol. 14, pp. 7–12 (1928).

Honess, C. W.: Geology of the Southern Ouachita Mountains of Oklahoma, *Oklahoma Geol. Survey Bull.* 32, 278 pp. (1923).

Horberg, L., Nelson, V., and Church, V.: Structural Trends in Central Western Wyoming, *G.S.A. Bull.*, vol. 60, pp. 183–216 (1949).

Hubbert, M. K.: A Suggestion for the Simplication of Fault Descriptions, *Jour. Geology*, vol. 35, pp. 264–269 (1927).

Hudson, F. S., and White, G. H.: Thrust Faulting and Coarse Clastics in Temblor Range, California, *A.A.P.G. Bull.*, vol. 25, pp. 1327–1342 (1941).

Hume, G. S.: Overthrust Faulting and Oil Prospects of the Eastern Foothills of Alberta between Bow and Highland Rivers, *Econ. Geology*, vol. 26, pp. 258–273 (1931).

———: Turner Valley Oil Area, Alberta, *Canada Geol. Survey Summary Rept.*, part B, pp. 8–14 (1926).

Jeffreys, H.: On the Mechanics of Faulting, *Geol. Mag.*, vol. 79, pp. 291–295 (1942).

Keith, A.: Outlines of Appalachian Structure, *G.S.A. Bull.*, vol. 34, pp. 309–380 (1925).

Kelsey, M. A.: Studies in Fault Detection with the Reflection Seismograph, *Geophysics*, vol. 14, pp. 21–28 (1949).

King, P. B.: Geology of the Marathon Region, Texas, *U.S.G.S. Prof. Paper* 187 (1937).

————: Tectonic Framework of Southeastern United States, *A.A.P.G. Bull.*, vol. 34, pp. 635–671 (1950).

————: "Tectonics of Middle North America," Princeton University Press, Princeton, N.J. (1951).

————: Tectonics of Northern Mexico, *Proc. Eighth Am. Sci. Cong.*, vol. 4, pp. 395–398 (1942).

Lahee, F. H.: "Field Geology," McGraw-Hill Book Company, Inc., New York, 5th ed., pp. 209–252 (1952).

Lees, G. M., and Richardson, F. D. S.: The Geology of the Oil-field Belt of Southwest Iran and Iraq, *Geol. Mag.*, vol. 77, pp. 227–252 (1940).

Lehman, R. P.: Thrust Faulting in Arbuckle Mountains, Oklahoma, *A.A.P.G. Bull.*, vol. 29, pp. 187–209 (1945).

Link, T. A.: Interpretations of Foothills Structures, Alberta, Canada, *A.A.P.G. Bull.*, vol. 33, pp. 1475–1501 (1949).

Locke, A., Billingsley, P., and Mayo, E. B.: Sierra Nevada Tectonic Pattern, *G.S.A. Bull.*, vol. 51, pp. 513–540 (1940).

Longwell, C. R.: Geology of the Muddy Mountains, Nevada, *U.S.G.S. Bull.* 798 (1928).

————: Megabreccia Developed Down Slope from Large Faults, *Am. Jour. Sci.*, vol. 249, pp. 343–355 (1951).

————: Sedimentation in Relation to Faulting, *G.S.A. Bull.*, vol. 48, pp. 433–442 (1937).

————: Structure of the Northern Muddy Mountain Area, Nevada, *G.S.A. Bull.*, vol. 60, pp. 923–968 (1949).

————: Tectonic Theory Viewed from the Basin Ranges, *G.S.A. Bull.*, vol. 61, pp. 413–434 (1950).

Louderback, G. D.: Faults and Earthquakes, *Seismol. Soc. America Bull.*, vol. 32, pp. 305–330 (1942).

————: Morphological Features of the Basin Range Displacements in the Great Basin, *California Univ., Dept. Geol. Sci. Bull.*, vol. 16, p. 1–42 (1926).

Lovering, T. S.: Field Evidence to Distinguish Overthrusting from Underthrusting, *Jour. Geology*, vol. 40, pp. 651–663 (1932).

Ludlum, J. C.: Structure and Stratigraphy of Part of Bannock Range, Idaho, *G.S.A. Bull.*, vol. 54, pp. 973–986 (1943).

McCoy, A. W., and others: Types of Oil and Gas Traps in Rocky Mountain Region, *A.A.P.G. Bull.*, vol. 35, pp. 1000–1037 (1951).

Melton, F. A.: Fracture Systems in Texas, in Geology of Texas: II, Structural and Economic Geology, *Univ. Texas Bur. of Econ. Geology Bull.* 3401 (1935).

Meyer, W. G.: Grabens in Gulf Coast Anticlines and Their Relation to Other Faulted Troughs, *A.A.P.G. Bull.*, vol. 28, pp. 541–553 (1944).

Miller, W. J.: Some Features of Faulting in Southern California, *Jour. Geology*, vol. 48, pp. 385–420 (1940).

————: Studies for Students: Recognition of Faults in Southern California, *Jour. Geology*, vol. 49, pp. 87–100 (1941).

Miser, H. D.: Structure of Ouachita Mountains of Oklahoma and Arkansas, *Oklahoma Geol. Survey Bull.* 50 (1929).

Nugent, L. E., Jr.: Genesis of Subordinate Conjugate Faulting in Kern River Salient, *Jour. Geology*, vol. 50, pp. 900–913 (1942).

Page, B. M.: Basin-range Faulting of 1915 in Pleasant Valley, Nevada, *Jour. Geology*, vol. 43, pp. 690–707 (1935).

Pardee, J. T.: Late Cenozoic Block Faulting in Western Montana, *G.S.A. Bull.*, vol. 61, pp. 359–406 (1950).

Peach, B. N., and Horne, J.: "Chapters in the Geology of Scotland," Oxford University Press, New York (1930).

Perry, E. L.: Flaws and Tear Faults, *Am. Jour. Sci.*, 5th ser., vol. 29, p. 112 (1935).

Pierce, W. G.: Heart Mountain and South Fork Thrusts, Park County, Wyoming, *A.A.P.G. Bull.*, vol. 25, pp. 2021–2045 (1941).

Powers, S.: Structural Geology of Northeastern Oklahoma, *Jour. Geology*, vol. 39, pp. 117–132 (1931).

Price, P. H.: The Appalachian Structural Front, *Jour. Geology*, vol. 39, pp. 24–44 (1931).

Price, W. A.: "Role of Diastrophism in Topography of Corpus Christi Area, South Texas–Gulf Coast Oil Fields," American Association of Petroleum Geologists, Tulsa, pp. 205–238 (1936).

Quirke, T. T.: Concerning the Process of Thrust Faulting, *Jour. Geology*, vol. 28, pp. 417–438 (1920).

Reed, R. D.: "Geology of California," American Association of Petroleum Geologists, Tulsa (1933).

Reeves, F.: Origin and Mechanism of Thrust Faults Adjacent to the Bearpaw Mountains, Montana, *G.S.A. Bull.*, vol. 57, pp. 1033–1048 (1946).

————: Shallow Folding and Faulting around Bearpaw Mountains, *Am. Jour. Sci.*, 5th ser., vol. 10 (1925).

Reid, H. F.: The Geometry of Faults, *G.S.A. Bull.*, vol. 20, pp. 171–196 (1909).

———— Davis, W. M., Lawson, A. C., and Ransome, F. L.: Report of the Committee on the Nomenclature of Faults, *G.S.A. Bull.*, vol. 24, pp. 163–186 (1913).

Rettger, R. E.: Experiments on Soft-rock Deformation, *A.A.P.G. Bull.*, vol. 19, pp. 271–292 (1935).

Rich, J. L.: Fault-block Nature of Kansas Structures Suggested by Elimination of Regional Dip, *A.A.P.G. Bull.*, vol. 19, pp. 1540–1543 (1935).

————: Mechanics of Low-angle Over-thrust Faulting as Illustrated by the Cumberland Thrust Block, Virginia, Kentucky and Tennessee, *A.A.P.G. Bull.*, vol. 18, pp. 1584–1596 (1934).

————: Origin of Compressional Mountains and Associated Phenomena, *G.S.A. Bull.*, vol. 62, pp. 1179–1222 (1951).

Rodgers, J.: Evolution of Thought on Structure of Middle and Southern Appalachians, *A.A.P.G. Bull.*, vol. 33, pp. 1643–1654 (1949).

————: Mechanics of Appalachian Folding as Illustrated by Sequatchie Anticline, Tennessee and Alabama, *A.A.P.G. Bull.*, vol. 34, pp. 672–681 (1950).

Scott, J. C.: Folded Faults of the Rocky Mountain Foot Hills of Alberta, *A.A.P.G. Bull.*, vol. 35, pp. 2316–2347 (1951).

Selk, E. L.: Types of Oil and Gas Traps in Southern Oklahoma, *A.A.P.G. Bull.*, vol. 35, pp. 582–606 (1951).

Sellards, E. H., Baker, C. L., and others: Geology of Texas: II, Structural and Economic Geology, *Univ. Texas Bur. Econ. Geology Bull.* 3401 (1934).

Shand, S. J.: Mylonite, Slickensides and the Great Glen Fault, *Geol. Mag.*, vol. 88, pp. 423–428 (1951).

Sharp, R. P.: Basin-range Structure of the Ruby–East Humbolt Range, Northeastern Nevada, *G.S.A. Bull.*, vol. 50, pp. 881–920 (1939).

Sharpe, C. F. S.: "Landslides and Related Phenomena," Columbia University Press, New York (1938).

Sheets, M. M.: Diastrophism during Historic Time in Gulf Coastal Plain, *A.A.P.G. Bull.*, vol. 31, pp. 201–226 (1947).

Sherrill, R. E.: Some Problems of Appalachian Structure, *A.A.P.G. Bull.*, vol. 25, pp. 416–423 (1941).

Stamp, L. D.: Britain's Structure and Scenery, William Collins Sons & Co., Ltd., London, (1947).

Stevens, E. H.: Inertia as a Possible Factor in the Mechanics of Low-angle Thrust Faulting, *Jour. Geology*, vol. 43, pp. 729–736 (1935).

Stille, H.: Upthrust of the Salt Masses of Germany, *A.A.P.G. Bull.*, vol. 9, pp. 417–441 (1925).

Suess, E.: "The Face of the Earth," Oxford University Press, New York, 5 vols. (1904–1924).

Suter, H. H.: Relations between Kinds of Well Data and Apparent Faulting, *A.A.P.G. Bull.*, vol. 30, pp. 1910–1917 (1946).

Taber, S.: Fault Troughs, *Jour. Geology*, vol. 35, pp. 577–606 (1927).

———: The Great Fault Troughs of the Antilles, *Jour. Geology*, vol. 30, pp. 89–114 (1922).

Thom, W. T., Jr.: Relation of Deep-seated Faults to the Structural Features of Central Montana, *A.A.P.G. Bull.*, vol. 7, pp. 1–13 (1923).

Tomlinson, C. W.: Odd Geologic Structures of Southern Oklahoma, *A.A.P.G. Bull.*, vol. 36, pp. 1820–1840 (1952).

Tromp, S. W.: The Age and Origin of the Red Sea Graben, *Geol. Mag.*, vol. 87, pp. 385–392 (1950).

Van Gundy, C. E.: Faulting in East Part of Grand Canyon of Arizona, *A.A.P.G. Bull.*, vol. 30, pp. 1899–1909 (1946).

VerWiebe, W. A.: Geosynclinal Boundary Faults, *A.A.P.G. Bull.*, vol. 20, pp. 910–938 (1936).

Wallace, W. E., Jr.: Structure of South Louisiana Deep-seated Domes, *A.A.P.G. Bull.*, vol. 28, pp. 1249–1312 (1944).

Weaver, C. E.: Geology of the Coast Ranges Immediately North of the San Francisco Bay Region, *G.S.A. Mem.* 35, pp. 1–242 (1949).

Weeks, A. W.: Balcones, Luling and Mexia Fault Zones in Texas, *A.A.P.G. Bull.*, vol. 29, pp. 1733–1737 (1945).

White, W. A.: Blue Ridge Front, a Fault Scarp, *G.S.A. Bull.*, vol. 61, pp. 1309–1346 (1950).

Willis, B.: Normal Fault Structures and Others, *A.A.P.G. Bull.*, vol. 30, pp. 1875–1887 (1946).

———: San Andreas Rift, California, *Jour. Geology*, vol. 46, pp. 793–827 (1938).

——— and Willis, R.: "Geologic Structures," 3d ed., McGraw-Hill Book Company, Inc., New York, (1934).

Willis, R.: Development of Thrust Faults, *G.S.A. Bull.*, vol. 46, pp. 409–424 (1935).

CHAPTER 6

JOINTS AND FRACTURES

It is generally recognized that open joints and fractures, when they occur in productive petroleum reservoirs, are extremely important in both petroleum geology and petroleum engineering. In many highly productive oil and gas fields, the permeability of the unfractured reservoir is too low to permit commercial production. Hence the great production from these fields owes its existence entirely to the open fractures. Unfortunately there is no satisfactory well-logging method for recording the presence of open fractures; this is a handicap both in locating the producing horizons and in studying the nature and origin of the fractures. Petroleum geologists in general do not pay a great deal of attention to joints or fractures outside of producing reservoirs. Possibly more use could be made of them than is generally done. Certainly they are in some cases useful for finding and interpreting faults and folds.

DEFINITIONS

Both joints and faults are fractures. A joint differs from a fault in the absence of relative movement parallel to the plane of the fracture. Far below the surface, the walls of joints are generally in contact, and the joints may be planes of weakness rather than actual cracks. As the rocks weather at the surface, these planes of weakness form definite, visible cracks, the walls of which may become slightly separated. Joints which have opened up in this manner may be called open in contrast to the closed joints which generally occur underground.

Most joints found at the surface generally form part of a group having approximately the same dip and strike. Such a group is called a joint set. Joints whose strike is parallel to the strike of the associated strata are called strike joints. If the strike of the joints is parallel to the dip of the associated strata, they are called dip joints. In well-bedded sediments, particularly those in which the strata are thin and hard, joints are usually perpendicular to the plane of stratification. Fracture cleavage consists in closely spaced joints, generally less than an inch apart. This causes the rock to split into thin plates. Fracture cleavage is rarely found in association with oil fields.

The terms "joint" and "fracture" are not synonymous. All joints are fractures, but not all fractures are joints. Joints are rather smooth and tend to approximate plane surfaces, at least for short distances. They are generally at right angles to the bedding, and in many cases occur in two sets which are perpendicular to each other. Some rocks that have been affected by structural deformation contain a network of irregular cracks with no definite trend. These cracks may be open, but more commonly they are cemented with quartz or carbonates. Fractures of this type are clearly not joints. Faults constitute another type of fractures which are not joints.

USES AND GEOLOGICAL RELATIONS OF JOINTS

Relation to Stresses That Produce Joints. Joints are produced by stretching or by shearing. The stretching that produces joints may proceed far enough to produce actual tension, or it may simply reduce the compressive stress in one direction without reducing it to zero. Joints produced by stretching are found in lava flows and sills. The hot, solid igneous rock shrinks as it cools. Joints produced in this manner are at right angles to the tension or stretching. Joints produced by shearing are at an oblique angle to the major stresses that produce them. A given set of joints may be produced in so many different ways that it is commonly very difficult or impossible to determine just how it has formed. This is the reason why joints have not more frequently been used successfully in making mechanical analyses of structural problems. This subject has been discussed by Bailey Willis and Robin Willis,[1] Billings,[2] Forrester,[3] Cloos,[4] Bucher,[5] Wager,[6] and Sheldon.[7] Joints due to shearing are reported to be straighter and smoother than those due to tension, although not all geologists agree with this conclusion. The published work on the relations of joints to stresses does not appear to be of much practical value to petroleum geologists.

[1] Bailey Willis and Robin Willis, "Geologic Structures," McGraw-Hill Book Company, Inc., New York, pp. 114, 120, 126–27, 327 (1934).

[2] Marland P. Billings, "Structural Geology," Prentice-Hall, Inc., New York, pp. 11, 86, 108, 112, 122–125, 130–132 (1946).

[3] James D. Forrester, "Field and Mining Geology," John Wiley & Sons, Inc., New York, pp. 26, 50–52 (1946).

[4] Ernst Cloos, Feather Joints as Indicators of the Direction of Movements on Faults, *Nat. Acad. Sci. Proc.*, vol. 18, pp. 387–395 (1932).

[5] Walter Bucher, Mechanical Interpretation of Joints, *Jour. Geology*, vol. 28, pp. 707–730 (1920); vol. 29, pp. 1–28 (1921).

[6] L. R. Wager, Jointing in the Great Scar Limestone of Craven and Its Relation to the Tectonics of the Area, *Geol. Soc. London Quart. Jour.*, vol. 87, pp. 392–424 (1931).

[7] Pearl Sheldon, Some Observations and Experiments on Joint Planes, *Jour. Geology*, vol. 20, pp. 53–79 (1912).

Relation to Regional Alteration. Joints are absent in very weak, plastic, or unconsolidated rocks, and become more prominent as the rocks become harder and more indurated. Ordinarily joints are not conspicuous in shales unless the shale has some special composition which makes it more rigid, or unless the shale is well compacted, cemented, or altered. The black, organic Chattanooga and Woodford shales are conspicuously jointed even in regions of slight alteration. This is because the organic matter of the shale increases its rigidity, and possibly because of the uniform character of the rock. If ordinary clay shales display conspicuous or closely spaced jointing over a limited area, the presence of some structural disturbance in the vicinity is suggested. If this type of jointing occurs over a wide region, it may indicate a degree of incipient regional alteration that is unfavorable for oil production, though of course other evidence should be sought.

Relation to Local Structures. In some places it may be observed that joints have a definite relation to the local structural features of a region. The joints in the portions of an area devoid of well-defined folding may be of random strike or poorly developed. Near pronounced anticlines well-defined joints may be formed parallel to the strike of the axial plane of the anticline. In some areas there are belts of closely spaced parallel joints which presumably mark zones of shearing. As mentioned on page 120, joints and fractures near faults may aid in tracing them. In hard or brittle rocks such as limestones, dolomite, quartzite, and chert, fractures are produced by pronounced sharp folding. These fractures are commonly filled by veins of carbonates in limestone and dolomite, and by veins of quartz in sandstone, quartzite, and chert. It may be observed that the sharper the folding the greater the relative volume of the rock occupied by these fillings or fractures. Most of the fractures observed at the surface are filled with cement and apparently have no permeability. Obviously the fractures must be left open and uncemented if they are to serve as reservoir rocks. However, study of the vein-filled fractures at the surface throws light on the origin of the open fractures in reservoir rocks, which were formed in a similar manner, but for some reason were not filled with vein material.

Relation to Regional Structure. In some cases the most prominent joint set either has the same orientation over great distances, or over a great area it radiates from a common center. In cases such as these the joints are related to regional rather than to local structures. Ver Steeg[1] and Parker[2] have described the joints of eastern Ohio and central New

[1] Karl ver Steeg, Jointing in the Coal Beds of Ohio, *Econ. Geology*, vol. 37, pp. 503–509 (1942).

[2] John M. Parker III, Regional Systematic Jointing in Slightly Deformed Sedimentary Rocks, *G.S.A. Bull.*, vol. 53, pp. 381–408 (1942).

York State. These joints radiate from the convex side of the great bend in the Appalachian folds to the south and southeast. Melton[1] has described the joints which radiate from the convex side of a similar bend in the Ouachita belt of deformation in Oklahoma. These joints cut formations as young as the middle of the Oklahoma Permian section, but are not found in the Cretaceous beds of the Ouachita region. These relations suggest that the Ouachita deformation was at least in part as late as the youngest Permian beds affected by the joints.

Role in the Migration of Oil and Gas. Although the importance of migration of oil and gas along joints is not known, there is no question that during the course of geologic time great quantities of oil and gas can move through minute fractures, provided that their walls are continuously separated. This migration through joints and fractures may permit the escape of oil and gas to the surface, and thus destroy oil and gas pools or prevent their formation. Joints may permit oil and gas to escape from source rocks to reservoir rocks, or from one reservoir to another.

McNaughton[2] has found that in California the occurrence of oil in fractures in the basement is not related to the levels of the oil-water contacts in reservoirs composed of sedimentary rocks. On the contrary, oil is found in fractures in the basement rocks where the sediments in contact with the basement contain oil, even though the elevation of the oil in the fractures is far below the level of the oil-water contacts in sedimentary reservoir rocks. This suggests that the oil in the fractures in the basement migrated directly downward from the sediments.

Fractures as Reservoir Rocks

Economic Importance. Most of the oil and gas of the world is produced from reservoirs in which open fractures, if present at all, do not have much effect on the production. The oil and gas are contained in intergranular pores or solution cavities and move through these to the wells. On the other hand, fractures play a part in the production of many fields, some small and some of great size. The great oil fields of Iraq and Iran produce from fractured limestones. In California hundreds of millions of barrels of oil have been produced from fractured cherts or from fractures in the basement rocks. In West Texas, oil is produced from fractured limestones and cherts and from fractured Permian Spra-

---

[1] Frank A. Melton, A Reconnaissance of the Joint Systems of the Ouachita Mountains and Central Plains of Oklahoma, *Jour. Geology*, vol. 37, pp. 729–746 (1929); Age of the Ouachita Orogeny and Its Tectonic Effects, *A.A.P.G. Bull.*, vol. 14, pp. 57–72 (1930).

[2] Duncan A. McNaughton, Dilatancy in Migration and Accumulation of Oil in Metamorphic Rocks, *A.A.P.G. Bull.*, vol. 37, pp. 217–231 (1953).

berry sandstones. Fractures due to settling are believed to aid in the production of oil and gas from some limestone and dolomite reefs. The production of gas from some sandstones of low porosity, such as those of the Oriskany formation of New York and Pennsylvania and the Pennsylvanian sandstones of Arkansas, is probably greatly aided by fractures. Fractures probably make possible the gas production from bituminous shales. The Northern or Panuco oil fields of the Tampico region, Mexico, formerly yielded great oil production from fractures in limestone. Other oil fields having fracture production are Rangely, Colo., the Cretaceous formations of the western Maracaibo area, Venezuela, and some of the Uinta Basin fields, Utah.

Stratigraphic Conditions Favoring Production. The stratigraphic conditions are not favorable for oil or gas production if the fractured rocks extend clear to the surface. Under such conditions the oil or gas would doubtless escape. The stratigraphic conditions favoring oil and gas production from fractures therefore consist in a hard or brittle rock which will form open fractures on deformation, overlain by a softer or more plastic rock which will not develop connected fractures under the structural conditions to which it is exposed. The brittle rocks in which the fractures occur may be limestone, dolomite, chert, igneous or metamorphic rocks of the basement, sandstone, or more rarely shales. The overlying rocks which do not fracture may be shale, clay, anhydrite, gypsum, volcanic ash, or salt.

Oil and Gas Production from Basement Rocks. Oil and gas production from fractures in basement rocks has been found in California and Kansas, but there appears to be no important gas production from the basement. The production is obtained from a variety of igneous and metamorphic rocks. In California the basement rocks may be Jurassic or older, but in Kansas the basement is pre-Cambrian. It appears that there is a prospect for obtaining oil from fractures in the basement wherever the sediments just above the basement contain oil. Until recently, very few wells were drilled into basement because oil operators supposed that there was no chance for finding oil in it. Now that the possibilities for finding oil in the upper few hundred feet of the basement are known, more wells will doubtless be drilled into it. In California, oil production is obtained from the basement rocks more than 500 ft below the base of the sediments. According to Walters,[1] oil production from fractures in pre-Cambrian basement rocks has been obtained from 50 or more widely scattered fields in central Kansas. The basement production comes from buried hills in which the top of the basement rises 100 to 500 ft above the general level of its top. The fractures in the basement which produce

[1] Robert F. Walters, Oil Production from Pre-Cambrian Basement Rocks in Central Kansas, *A.A.P.G. Bull.*, vol. 37, pp. 300–313 (1953).

oil in Kansas are thought to have been caused by weathering, but those which produce oil in California are supposed to have been produced chiefly by structural deformation.

Structural Conditions Favoring Production. Fractures develop in brittle rocks because of local structural deformation or as a result of forces of regional extent. Folding in general is likely to produce fractures in the more brittle rocks. As the sharpness of the folding increases, there is also an increase in the number of fractures produced, the degree of interconnection of the fractures, and the percentage of pore space occupied by open fractures. The crest or axis of an anticline is an especially favorable zone for the development of open fractures because of the development of stretching or tension along the axial plane. If a thick, hard, or rigid formation is folded, the convex side of the formation is especially likely to contain open fractures. If one flank of an anticline dips gently, while the other side dips steeply, the steeper side generally contains the larger proportion of fractures. O'Brien[1] has found from studies of air photographs that limestones are more strongly fractured where the axes of the anticlines plunge steeply or change their plunge.

Open fractures which may serve as reservoirs are also commonly developed in brittle rocks along faults. The Gilbertown field, Alabama, described by Current,[2] produced from fractures in the Selma chalk in a long, narrow zone bordering a normal fault. In Caldwell County, Tex., oil production was obtained chiefly from the Edwards limestone along the upthrown sides of large normal faults. Some production was also obtained close to the faults from fractures in the Austin chalk, which lies above the main zone of production. In other cases the fractures in the reservoir rocks are not associated with local structural deformation, but appear to be produced during compaction or in response to stresses of regional extent.

Characteristics of Oil and Gas Production. *Determining Nature of Reservoir.* The production of oil and gas from fractures has certain characteristics which help to distinguish it from the production obtained from intergranular pores. It is of great practical importance to determine the type of reservoir from which the production is coming. The value of the production, the rate of decline, the recovery per acre, the types of secondary methods of recovery needed, and the most desirable well spacing all depend on whether or not the production is coming from fractures. Another important point is whether the oil and gas are

[1] C. A. E. O'Brien, Statement in Discussion of Fractured Reservoir Subjects, *A.A.P.G. Bull.*, vol. 37, pp. 325–326 (1953).

[2] A. M. Current, Gilbertown Field, Choctaw County, Alabama, "Structure of Typical American Oil Fields," American Association of Petroleum Geologists, Tulsa, vol. 3, pp. 1–4 (1948).

entirely contained in the open portions of the fractures, or whether they are chiefly contained in intergranular pores and the fractures merely serve to increase the effective permeability.

Significance of Lithology. Some indications as to the nature of the reservoir rock may be obtained from its lithology. Chert and novaculite, except where they are detrital or affected by weathering, do not have enough porosity and permeability to make reservoir rocks unless they are fractured. As noted by Russell,[1] gas may be stored in coal and probably in the organic matter of bituminous shales without detectable pores. Such rocks can probably not produce gas in commercial quantities unless there are fractures to increase the effective permeability. The production of oil from shales has not been of much importance, but some rather large gas fields have been found in shales. The role of fractures in the production of gas from the Chattanooga shale of eastern Kentucky has been discussed by Hunter and Young.[2]

Lithologic Nature of Reservoirs. The lithologic characteristic which favors the development of open fractures is hardness or brittleness. The same rock type may vary greatly in hardness. Shales, for example, may be either soft and plastic or hard and relatively brittle. Oil and gas have been produced from fractures in most of the common types of sedimentary rocks. The exceptions are evaporites and bentonite. Fracture production is commonest in limestone, dolomite, and chert. The igneous and metamorphic rocks of the basement may also produce, as explained previously. If the sedimentary rocks in an area are fractured at all, it is generally the hardest and most brittle rocks in the section which are most fractured. Ordinarily the shales in the section are too plastic to be suitably fractured, and their role in most fields is to serve as cover rocks. However, according to Reagan[3] about 290,000,000 bbl of oil has been produced from fractured shale reservoirs in California. The shales which produce oil in California are generally siliceous or cherty. In general, shales of ordinary types do not produce oil or gas in large amounts from fractures. The commercial production of oil or gas is commonly obtained from shales which have been stiffened or made hard and brittle by siliceous cement or organic matter.

Production from Both Fractures and Pores. In many fractures the total volume of the open portions is quite small. In such cases if all the oil in the reservoir were in the fractures, the production per acre would be too

---

[1] William L. Russell, "Principles of Petroleum Geology," McGraw-Hill Book Company, Inc., New York, pp. 105–107 (1951).

[2] Coleman D. Hunter and David M. Young, Relationship of Natural Gas Occurrence in Eastern Kentucky (Big Sandy Gas Field) to Joints and Fractures in Devonian Bituminous Shale, *A.A.P.G. Bull.*, vol. 37, pp. 282–299 (1953).

[3] Louis J. Reagan, Jr., Fractured Shale Reservoirs of California, *A.A.P.G. Bull.*, vol. 37, pp. 201–216 (1953).

small to be profitable. Hence most of the oil must be stored in the intergranular pores of the reservoir, and the function of the fractures must be to increase the permeability. The Iranian fields in which production is obtained from the Asmari limestone are of this nature. The Permian Spraberry sandstones of West Texas described by Wilkinson[1] constitute another reservoir in which most of the oil comes from the intergranular pores and the fractures serve to increase the permeability. It appears, however, that the oil production from this reservoir will be unprofitable unless very wide well spacing or some special method for stimulating production is used. Usually the staining of the unfractured portions of the reservoir indicates whether they contain oil. The oil in unweathered chert and novaculite is contained in the fractures only. Limestones and dolomites may contain oil and gas in the fractures alone, or in the intergranular pores as well. As far as is known, the profitable production from fractures in sandstones is limited to cases in which the intergranular pores of the sandstone serve as a reservoir for the oil and gas, and the fractures merely increase the permeability.

Some Characteristics of Fracture Production. In cable-tool wells the production increases gradually as the reservoir is penetrated if the production is from intergranular pores. If the production is from fractures, there is likely to be a sudden increase in the production as a fracture is penetrated. Production from intergranular pores is generally obtained from fairly definite stratigraphic horizons. The production from fractures may be from various stratigraphic horizons in adjacent wells. Commonly no production is obtained on drilling through the producing formation until a suitable fracture is encountered; this may be at variable depths below the top of the formation. In wells drilled with rotaries, a very successful method of completion is to drill through the whole of the formation, cement the casing to the walls of the hole, and gun-perforate by firing bullets through it. Since the bullets might miss the open portions of the reservoir rocks, this method may not be so successful where the production is obtained from a few widely scattered fractures.

Pressure Differences and Interference. In some cases variations in the hydrostatic pressure of the fluids in the reservoir may indicate fracture production. The pressures in the same horizon in adjacent wells may differ considerably, or similar pressures may be encountered in wells in different horizons connected by open fractures. The hydrostatic pressure in the fluids of fractures which are of limited extent may be much higher than normal for the depth. Perhaps the most significant characteristic of fracture production is the interference of wells at great distances and producing from different horizons. The interference may con-

---

[1] Walter M. Wilkinson, Fracturing in Spraberry Reservoir, West Texas, *A.A.P.G. Bull.*, vol. 37, pp. 250–265 (1953).

sist in affecting the rate of production of another well, its pressure, or the type of fluid produced. Wells which happen to be located on the same fracture may show this interference to great distances, while closer wells on different fractures may not be affected. If the fractures are few with wide spaces between them, some of the wells may miss the fractures altogether, with the result that dry holes are interspersed with producing wells. Production of this nature is called spotted.

Rate of Decline. The decline curves, recovery per acre, recovery per acre-foot of reservoir, and production per well may be markedly different in wells which produce from fractures and those which produce from intergranular pores. Since large oil production can come from small fractures, the initial daily production of wells from fractures may be very high. If the fractures connect with one another over a wide area, the wells producing from fractures may continue to produce at a high rate for long periods. If, on the other hand, the fractures are not well connected with one another, only the oil from the fractures close to the well may be obtained. Unless the oil comes from intergranular pores also, the total amount of oil obtainable from fractures of limited extent is generally small, with the result that the production of the well declines rapidly, and it fails to pay for itself. Until a well has been producing for some time it may be very difficult to determine whether the production from fractures will hold up or not.

Estimating Recovery. By studying cores of formations producing from intergranular pores, petroleum engineers can estimate fairly closely the production per acre-foot of pay and the production per acre. Unfortunately, core studies may be meaningless where the production is coming from fractures. The cores may miss the fractures, or the fractures, if present, may not be preserved in the cores. Diamond-drill cores, however, are said to show very good core recoveries of fractural reservoirs. The thicknesses of the pay may have little significance, for a highly fractured formation 10 ft thick may produce more oil per acre than a poorly fractured formation 100 ft thick. The character of the fractures may vary so rapidly from place to place that previous experience may not be a reliable guide. Secondary methods of recovery have been extremely successful where production is from intergranular pores, but as far as is known there has been no successful secondary recovery operation where production comes from fractures. A very favorable feature of fracture production is that it may permit very wide well spacing. The high permeability of open fractures enables the oil to come to a well from much greater distances than where the production is from intergranular pores. Hence high recoveries per well and profitable production may be obtained from fractured reservoirs where the production per acre is very low.

ADDITIONAL REFERENCES

Baker, C. L.: Panuco Oil Field, Mexico, *A.A.P.G. Bull.*, vol. 12, pp. 395–441 (1928).

Barton, D. C.: The Surface Fracture System of South Texas, *A.A.P.G. Bull.*, vol. 17, pp. 1194–1212 (1933).

Braunstein, J.: Fracture-controlled Production in Gilbertown Field, Alabama, *A.A.P.G. Bull.*, vol. 37, pp. 245–249 (1953).

Brown, A. B., and Kew, W. S. W.: Occurrence of Oil in Metamorphic Rocks of San Gabriel Mountains, Los Angeles County, California, *A.A.P.G. Bull.*, vol. 16, pp. 777–785 (1932).

Chamberlin, R. T.: The Strain Ellipsoid and Appalachian Structures, *Jour. Geology*, vol. 36, pp. 85–90 (1928).

DeFord, R. K.: Surface Structure, Florence Oil Field, Fremont County, Colorado, "Structure of Typical American Oil Fields," American Association of Petroleum Geologists, Tulsa, vol. 2, pp. 75–92 (1929).

Eggleston, W. S.: Summary of Oil Production from Fractured Rock Reservoirs in California, *A.A.P.G. Bull.*, vol. 32, pp. 1352–1355 (1948).

Gibson, H. S.: Oil Production in Southwestern Iran, *World Oil*, vol. 128, no. 1, pp. 271–280; vol. 128, no. 2, pp. 217–226 (1948).

Hanna, M. A.: Fracture Porosity in Gulf Coast, *A.A.P.G. Bull.*, vol. 37, pp. 266–281 (1953).

Hills, E. S., and Thomas, D. E.: Fissuring in Sandstones, *Econ. Geology*, vol. 40, pp. 51–61 (1945).

Horberg, L., Nelson, V., and Church, V.: Structural Trends in Central Western Wyoming, *G.S.A. Bull.*, vol. 60, pp. 183–216 (1949).

Hubbert, M. K.: Direction of Stresses Producing Given Geologic Strains, *Jour. Geology*, vol. 36, pp. 83–84 (1928).

Hunter, C. D., and Young, D. M.: Relationship of Natural Gas Occurrences and Production in Eastern Kentucky (Big Sandy Gas Field) to Joints and Fractures in Devonian Bituminous Shale, *A.A.P.G. Bull.*, vol. 37, pp. 282–299 (1953).

Kendall, P. F., and Briggs, H.: The Formation of Rock Joints and the Cleat of Coal, *Proc. Roy. Soc. Edinburgh*, vol. 53, pp. 164–187 (1933).

King, P. B.: The Geology of the Southern Guadalupe Mountains, Texas, *U.S.G.S. Prof. Paper* 215 (1948).

Lahee, F. H.: "Field Geology," McGraw-Hill Book Company, Inc., New York, 5th ed., pp. 253–267 (1952).

Levin, S. B.: Conjugate Sets of En Echelon Tension Fractures in the Athens Limestone at Riverton, Virginia, *G.S.A. Bull.*, vol. 61, pp. 509–518 (1950).

Lewis, J. V.: Fissility in Shale and Its Relations to Petroleum, *G.S.A. Bull.*, vol. 35, pp. 557–590 (1924).

Lovering, T. S.: The Fracturing of Incompetent Beds, *Jour. Geology*, vol. 36, pp. 709–717 (1928).

Marshall, J. W.: Spraberry Reservoir of West Texas, *A.A.P.G. Bull.*, vol. 36, pp. 2189–2191 (1952).

Melton, F. A.: Fracture Systems in Texas, "Geology of Texas," vol. 2, Structural and Economic Geology, *Univ. Texas Bur. Econ. Geology Bull.* 3401 (1935).

Pincus, H. J.: Statistical Methods Applied to the Study of Rock Fractures, *G.S.A. Bull.*, vol. 62, pp. 81–129 (1951).

Pirson, S. J.: Performance of Fractured Oil Reservoirs, *A.A.P.G. Bull.*, vol. 37, pp. 232–244 (1953).

Regan, L. J., Jr.: Fractured Shale Reservoirs of California, *A.A.P.G. Bull.*, vol. 37, pp. 201–216 (1953).

Swanson, C. O., On Stress, Strain and Joints, *Jour. Geology*, vol. 35, pp. 193–233 (1927).

White, J. L.: The Schist Surface of the Western Los Angeles Basin, *California Dept. Nat. Resources, Div. Oil and Gas, Thirty-second Ann. Rept.*, pp. 3–13 (1946).

Winterburn, R.: Wilmington Oil Field, *California Dept. Nat. Resources, Div. Mines Bull.* 118, pp. 301–305 (1943).

CHAPTER 7

UNCONFORMITIES

Unconformities are of importance to petroleum geologists in several different ways. They produce the traps in which a number of oil fields occur. They may improve the prospects for oil and gas in a region, but they may also render the structure maps of surface or shallow beds worthless for interpreting the structure of the deeper formations. Thus, unless the effect of unconformities in the section is known and allowed for, the value and oil prospects of structures cannot be properly appraised. Unconformities have an important bearing on the geologic history of an area. Serious errors in interpretations of the structure and stratigraphy may occur if the unconformities which are present are not recognized, or if they are mistaken for structures of other types.

DEFINITIONS AND TYPES

Unfortunately there is much variation in the usage of the terms relating to unconformities. Not only are different meanings attached to the same terms, but different terms are used for the same thing. The remedy is not to introduce new terms or to drop the old ones. Usually the best plan is to adopt the generally accepted terms and to define them according to the manner in which they are commonly used.

Unconformity. An unconformity is a surface separating two rocks which differ notably in age. The younger of these rocks is nearly always of sedimentary origin, and must have been deposited on the surface of the older. Generally an unconformity implies erosion between the time of formation of the two rocks and indicates that the younger rock lies on an eroded surface. It is possible, however, that the time gap between the deposition of the two rocks represents merely nondeposition with no erosion. This might occur, for example, if in a very stable area the bottom of a shallow sea were built up by deposition until it reached a level at which erosion and deposition were in balance. There would then be no additional deposition until the conditions changed.

Where the water is permanently stagnant, or where the currents are always very weak, great thicknesses of strata may be laid down with no breaks in deposition. Such conditions may occur in the bottoms of deep lakes or nearly landlocked seas and in the deeper parts of the oceans.

During the deposition of most terrestrial and shallow-water deposits, deposition and erosion are likely to succeed each other many times during the accumulation of a thick series of sediments. At each surface of erosion a feature is produced which resembles a true unconformity in some respects. However, these erosion surfaces differ from unconformities in that the time between the deposition of the strata above and below the break is geologically short—much shorter than that necessary for the deposition of a formation. The thickness of strata eroded is also considerably less than that comprising a formation in the same area. Minor breaks in deposition involving less time than is needed for the deposition of a formation are termed diastems. The relations between two formations are said to be unconformable if significant erosion took place between the times of their deposition.

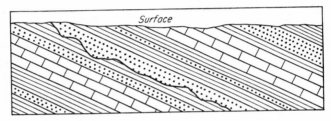

FIG. 7-1. Cross section showing a disconformity.

Disconformity and Angular Unconformity. The strata on both sides of a disconformity dip at essentially the same angle, aside from the initial dips formed during deposition. This means that there has been no appreciable tilting of the older formation before the deposition of the younger. Cross-bedding, delta formation, and deposition in channels and on uneven slopes may cause the strata on the two sides of a disconformity to differ locally in dip. Such differences in dip are due to the manner of deposition and do not indicate the presence of an angular unconformity. If there has been structural deformation involving tilting between the times of deposition of the two formations, their dips are generally different at all horizons and the unconformity is angular. The strata of two formations are rarely if ever exactly parallel; the distinction in this case is whether the difference in dip is appreciable, is readily observed, or has any important consequences. Since an angular unconformity must represent enough time for the erosion of an appreciable thickness of tilted strata, it signifies the lapse of an appreciable amount of geologic time; probably the time interval is usually greater than in the case of a disconformity. However, there are some disconformities which signify a time gap of hundreds of millions of years. Fig. 7-1 shows a disconformity, and Fig. 7-2 shows an angular unconformity.

Nonconformity. A nonconformity is an erosional surface separating sediments from rocks formed far beneath the earth's surface, such as plutonic igneous and metamorphic rocks. If sediments were deposited on granite schist or gneiss, the surface at the base of the sediments would

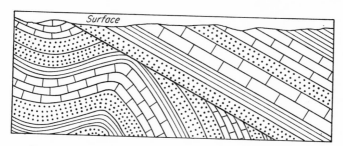

Fig. 7-2. Cross section showing an angular unconformity.

be a nonconformity. If, however, the sediments were deposited on volcanic rocks such as lava flows or ash beds, the contact would not be considered a nonconformity, because these igneous rocks were not formed at considerable depths below the surface. The rocks beneath a nonconformity were deeply buried when formed. The great thickness of

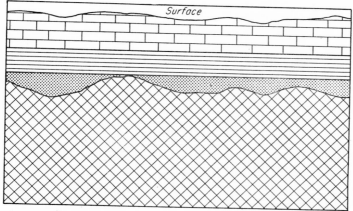

Fig. 7-3. Cross section showing a nonconformity.

overburden must have been eroded away before the sediments could have been deposited in their present position. In many cases this involves the erosion of a mile or two of rock, and in some cases much more. Clearly, therefore, a nonconformity marks the passage of a great period of time, usually much more than is indicated by a disconformity. Fig. 7-3 shows a sketch of a nonconformity.

Channeling and Local and Regional Unconformities. Unconformities vary greatly in the size of the areas they cover. Some are of vast extent and may be termed regional; others, of small extent, are called local. A local unconformity may cover only a single anticline or a valley or channel. It may happen that deposition is fairly continuous in an area except in the channel or valley of a river or tidal estuary. In the channel or valley itself perhaps 20 to 200 ft of strata found beyond its banks may be eroded. Later the channel may be filled with shale, sand, or gravel. If these deposits are associated with sediments of marine origin, the sands and gravels may be the reservoir rocks of oil pools.

Intraformational Conglomerates. During the many brief intervals of erosion which commonly occur during the deposition of a thick series of shallow-water deposits, the strata just deposited may be broken up and incorporated in the overlying beds. If these fragments are of a different nature from that of the enclosing material, the rock containing them has a close resemblance to a conglomerate. The chief difference is that the pebbles of ordinary conglomerates were generally transported for some distance before being deposited. Moreover, they were usually well consolidated, as otherwise they would not have survived the transportation. The rock fragments of the intraformational conglomerates were rarely transported for any appreciable distance. At the time of their deposition they were shale, clay, peat, sandstone, silt, limestone, or some other material which is fairly coherent when freshly deposited.

Basal Conglomerates. The conglomerates found in the strata immediately overlying unconformities are called basal conglomerates. They may consist of resistant pebbles carried in from great distances, of residual materials such as chert which accumulated at the erosion surface because of their greater resistance to solution, or of blocks and fragments from the rock immediately underlying the unconformity. Most conglomerates are not basal conglomerates, and at many unconformities there are no basal conglomerates. Nevertheless the presence of a conglomerate suggests the presence of an unconformity beneath it. A conglomerate is especially likely to indicate an unconformity if it terminates abruptly downward, and if the termination occurs at a lithologic break.

Hiatus and Time Value. An unconformity has three aspects: the amount of time represented, the period of erosion indicated, and the formations which were eroded at the particular locality in question, but which may remain elsewhere. The time represented by the interval between the formation of the older rock at the unconformity and the stratum immediately overlying it is the hiatus. If the age of these rocks is known accurately, the hiatus is also accurately fixed. It is not affected by the relative amounts of time consumed in erosion and deposition between the time of formation of the two rocks. Erosion was generally in progress during part of the hiatus at an unconformity. The time of erosion is known as the time value of an unconformity. It cannot be longer than the hiatus, and it may be much shorter. Let it be assumed that the youngest rock beneath an unconformity is middle Cambrian, and that the stratum laid down on top of the unconformable surface is upper Permian. The hiatus is from the middle Cambrian to the upper Permian. If deposition took place during the Upper Cambrian, Ordovician, Silurian, Devonian, Mississippian, and Pennsylvanian, but not during the Permian, the time value of the unconformity is represented by the lower and middle Permian, when erosion was taking place. The thickness of the eroded strata absent at a locality but present elsewhere gives an idea of the magnitude of the time and uplift represented by an unconformity. For example, if 10,000 ft of strata are absent at an unconformity at point *A* but present on both sides, the uplift at *A* is at least 10,000 ft.

STRATIGRAPHIC AND STRUCTURAL RELATIONS

To the petroleum geologist perhaps the most important aspects of unconformities are the structural relations of the strata above and below the unconformable surface. These structural relations are typically developed in association with angular unconformities. Traps for the accumulation of oil and gas are also developed in association with disconformities and nonconformities; however, these traps are for the most part associated with buried hills, weathering, or compaction. These features are discussed in Chap. 9.

In order to obtain a clear idea of the relations at unconformities, it is necessary to distinguish carefully between the features above and below the unconformable surface. It is confusing to give the same name to structural or stratigraphic conditions which occur on opposite sides of this surface.

Truncation. Truncation occurs at all angular unconformities. Beneath the unconformable surface the strata rise in their updip direction until they reach the unconformity and are cut off or truncated by it. Further in this direction they were removed by erosion before the unconformity was formed, and older beds lie immediately beneath the unconformable surface. Truncation is shown in Fig. 7-4.

Overlap. The strata above an unconformity may or may not be parallel to its regional or average surface. Where the surface of an unconformity is irregular, the beds above cannot be parallel to its surface at all points, but they may be parallel to a plane formed by averaging in the irregularities at the unconformity. Where this occurs there can be no overlap at the unconformity, though there may be truncation. If, on the other hand, the strata above the unconformity are not parallel to its general surface, there will be a direction in which progressively younger beds immediately overlie the unconformity.   This condition is known as overlap, and refers only to beds above the unconformity.   A younger bed is said to overlap an older one if it covers the unconformity in the area where the older one has been cut out.   Thus each younger bed or formation extends along the unconformity beyond the limit of the next older one.   Overlap is shown above the unconformity in Fig. 7-4.

Strike Overlap.   Fig. 7-4 is unusual in that aside from the traps it may be interpreted as a cross section in a vertical plane, or as an areal map of a horizontal surface.   In the first case the truncation and overlap

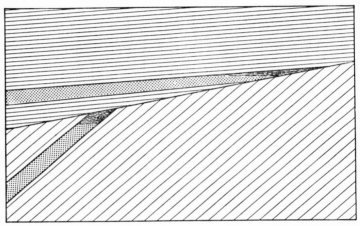

Fig. 7-4. Truncation and overlap at an angular unconformity.   Shaded areas show traps favorable for oil and gas accumulation.

show up on the cross section because of the difference in dip between the unconformity and the formations above and below the unconformity. If the figure is an areal map, the truncation and overlap show up because of differences in strike.   If the strike of the unconformity were the same as the strike of the formations above and below it but the dip of the unconformity were different from the dip of the formations above and below it, the truncation and overlap would not show up on an areal map of a flat surface, but would show up on the vertical cross section at right angles to the strike.

Melton[1] has suggested using the term "strike overlap" to indicate the structural condition which causes the formations below an angular unconformity to strike into the unconformity and appear on areal maps to terminate against it.   According to Melton's definition, "strike overlap"

[1] Frank A. Melton, Onlap and Strike Overlap, *A.A.P.G. Bull.*, vol. 31, pp. 1868–1878 (1947); vol. 32, pp. 2296–2297 (1948).

would not replace "truncation," but would refer to a special case of truncation in which the difference between the strike and dip of the unconformity and that of the beds below it is very slight. It seems to the present writer that the term "strike overlap" should be rejected, because it is easily confused with "overlap." It seems advisable to follow the generally accepted usage by restricting "overlap" of any sort to features above the unconformable surface.

Onlap, Offlap, Transgression, and Regression. The problem of the relations of advances and retreats of the sea to unconformities is an

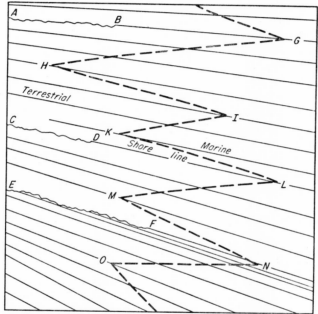

Fig. 7-5. Cross section showing relation of terrestrial and marine transgressive deposits to unconformities.

important one. These fluctuations have a marked influence on the location of oil and gas accumulations. Furthermore, the relations at unconformities are likely to be misinterpreted unless these matters are clearly understood. Fig. 7-5 shows a cross section through sediments which have accumulated in a subsiding area marked by advances and retreats of the shore line. The heavy dashed line indicates the shore line. Terrestrial deposits are deposited to the left of it and marine deposits to the right. As the sediments accumulated, the area to the right subsided slightly faster than the area to the left, with the result that the formations increase slightly in thickness to the right. The straight lines slanting to the right are time lines, and along each one the sediments were deposited simultaneously.   Advances of the shore line toward the land are known as onlaps or transgressive overlaps.   In Fig. 7-5 onlaps are shown by *IH*, *LK*, and *MN*.   Retreats of the shore line toward the sea are known as offlaps or regressive overlaps.   Offlaps are indicated by *HG*, *KI*, *ML*, and *ON*.   These advances or retreats of the shore line are caused by depression or uplift of the land relative to sea level, by variations in the supply of sediments, or by a combination of these.

The sediments shown in Fig. 7-5 are all conformable except for unconformities along *AB*, *CD*, and *EF*.   These unconformities are shown occurring inland from the coast at times of maximum retreat of the shore line.   During the time when the erosion represented by these unconformities was going on, terrestrial deposition continued between the areas which were eroded and the shore line.   Clearly the withdrawal of the sea or uplift of the land does not mean that erosion will produce an unconformity everywhere over the land surface.   On the contrary, this may merely mean that terrestrial deposits will be laid down on the newly formed land instead of in the sea.   However, landward from the zone of terrestrial deposits there must be a belt in which erosion is taking place.   The seaward edge of this zone is likely to advance toward the sea during uplifts, and retreat toward the land during periods of depression.   Thus, although unconformities may mark the periods of retreat of the sea, they are likely to disappear seaward and be replaced by conformable strata.

Where overlap takes place in the strata above an unconformity, there is one direction in which the beds in contact with the unconformable surface become progressively older.   This is the direction in which the unconformity dipped at the time it was being covered by the overlying formations.   Thus in Fig. 7-4 the strata just above the unconformity become progressively older toward the left.   This indicates that the old erosion surface which is now the unconformity sloped to the left while it was being buried.   Overlap does not necessarily mean that sea advanced over the land, or that the sea was present at all in the area where the overlap appears.   The formations which overlap one another may be all terrestrial, all marine, or a combination of marine and terrestrial.

Fig. 7-6, from a paper by Sears, Hunt, and Henricks,[1] shows an example of the effect of advances and retreats of the sea on lithology.   Offshore marine shales are indicated by an absence of pattern.   The sandy strata indicated by the dots were laid down near the shore line.   The cross-hatching and diagonal shading indicate terrestrial beds.   Formations that contain valuable coal beds are shown by crosshatching.   The coals repre-

---

[1] Julian D. Sears, C. B. Hunt, and T. A. Henricks, Transgressive and Regressive Cretaceous Deposits in Southern San Juan Basin, New Mexico, *U.S.G.S. Prof. Paper* 193(*f*) (1941).

sent swamp deposits which accumulated just inland from the shore line. Farther inland in better-drained areas the barren beds were deposited. It should be noted that retreats of the sea did not produce unconformities.

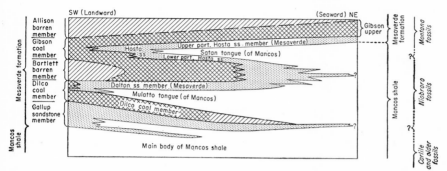

Fɪɢ. 7-6. Cretaceous deposits related to advances and retreats of the sea in southern San Juan Basin, N.Mex. The main body of the Mancos shale is marine. The stippling indicates sandy deposits laid down close to the shore line. Crosshatching indicates formations which accumulated in coastal swamps back of the shore line. They contain carbonaceous shales and valuable coal beds. The diagonal shading shows terrestrial beds which are generally devoid of coal. They were deposited farther back of the shore line than the coal-bearing strata. *(After Sears, Hunt, and Hendricks, U.S. Geological Survey.)*

The various structural relations at unconformities have been discussed by Lowman,[1] Melton,[2] Malkin and Echols,[3] and Swain.[4]

Recognition at the Surface

In the oil-producing regions of the United States more unconformities are doubtless recognized at the present time by subsurface studies than by surface work. However, a knowledge of how unconformities appear at the surface is a great help in finding them underground. Since the conditions of sedimentation are likely to change during the time gap represented by the unconformity, there is commonly an abrupt change in the lithology at an unconformity. Nevertheless, at many unconformities these abrupt changes in lithology are not found; in fact, unconformities occasionally occur in a zone of uniform lithology. The degree of induration or metamorphism of the rocks may also change abruptly at an unconformity, being greater in the older rocks.

[1] S. W. Lowman, Sedimentary Facies in Gulf Coast, *A.A.P.G. Bull.*, vol. 33, pp. 1939–1997 (1949).

[2] Frank A. Melton, Onlap and Strike Overlap, *A.A.P.G. Bull.*, vol. 31, pp. 1868–1878 (1947).

[3] Doris S. Malkin and Dorothy Jung Echols, Marine Sedimentation and Oil Accumulation: II, Regressive Marine Offlap and Overlap-Offlap, *A.A.P.G. Bull.*, vol. 32, pp. 252–261 (1948).

[4] Frederick M. Swain, "Onlap, Offlap, Overstep, and Overlap," *A.A.P.G. Bull.*, vol. 33, pp. 634–636 (1949).

Any feature which formed before the deposition of the younger rock at an unconformity, but after the older rock, will be truncated at the unconformity. Not only are the strata cut off, but also dikes, faults, and other structures. If the unconformity is angular, the difference in dip is a great help in recognizing it. The surface of the unconformity may be flat and parallel to the strata, or it may be markedly uneven. This irregular surface of erosion is also a great help in recognizing unconformities, though similar irregular surfaces may be produced by erosion which is of short duration but is not sufficient in magnitude to constitute an unconformity.

Conglomerates in the stratigraphic section suggest the possible presence of unconformities at their bases. In general, pebbles of the older rock in the younger constitute evidence of erosion and may mark an unconformity. The pebbles of a basal conglomerate may be derived from the immediately underlying rock, or they may consist of resistant rocks which have been transported for long distances. In some places various resistant or insoluble materials may accumulate at the surface during the period of erosion represented by the unconformity. If composed of gravel-sized fragments, they are called lag gravels. The relatively insoluble cherts occurring in limestones and dolomites may accumulate at the surface during the period of erosion, and may be buried by the younger sediments at an unconformity. Gravels and conglomerates formed in this manner have been called chat. In central Kansas chat forms the reservoir rock of several oil pools.

In some cases evidences of weathering may indicate an unconformity. These evidences may consist in disintegrated, discolored, or decomposed rock, or in fossil soils. In a few places the caliche or duricrust which is formed at or near the surface may mark an unconformity.

Nonconformities may be indicated by the nature of the rock in contact with the sediments. A nonconformity is always formed by the deposition of sediments on the eroded surface of a plutonic or metamorphic rock. Hence if these rocks crop out close to sediments, a nonconformity must be present if it can be shown that the contact is not faulted or intrusive igneous.

RECOGNITION ON AREAL MAPS

Many unconformities can best be recognized and studied by means of geologic or areal maps. However, it is generally only angular unconformities which show up on areal maps. Since the formations above and below a disconformity have the same dip and strike, they are expressed on the areal map by parallel bands, and no sign of the disconformity appears on the map. It is true that the presence of an unconformity is indicated by the occurrence in contact with each other of formations which differ appreciably in age. However, the evidence for this is not provided by the distribution of the outcrops on the map, but by fossils, correlations with distant localities, or other lines of evidence which do not show up on local maps.

The areal map shown in Fig. 7-7 indicates three angular unconformities. The formations grow progressively younger from A to Z and from 1 to 5. There is an angular unconformity at the base of formations S, 1, and 5.

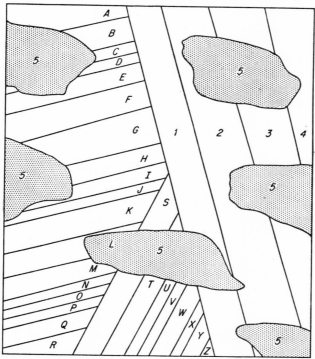

Fig. 7-7. Sketch showing how angular unconformities may appear on areal maps. Three angular unconformities are indicated. One is at the base of bed S, another at the base of bed 1, and a third at the base of bed 5.

By studying a map of this type it is possible to obtain a great deal of information about the geologic history of an area. Evidently formations A to R were tilted and eroded before the deposition of formation S. Formations S to Z and the older strata were again tilted to the right and eroded before the deposition of bed 1. The whole area was tilted to the right before the deposition of formation 5. If the thickness of formations 1 to 5 is known, the angle of the present regional dip may be determined. If it is assumed that the effects of the topography are negligible, the direction of the contacts gives the strike in the formations older than 5.

In some cases the expression of faults and angular unconformities on areal maps may be easily distinguished; in other cases it is difficult or impossible to determine positively which is present. If the formations are offset, a fault is definitely indicated. Repetition of the outcrops may be produced by faulting or by folding. It is certain that neither offsetting nor repetition can be caused by unconformities. On the other hand, the omission of the outcrop of a formation on an areal map could be produced by faulting or by an unconformity.

Usually a fault may be easily distinguished from an angular unconformity on areal maps if the strike of the fault is markedly different from

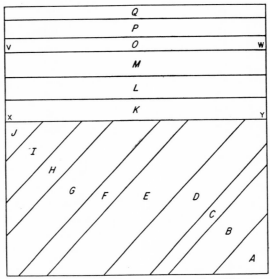

Fig. 7-8. Areal map showing how faults and angular unconformities may be distinguished.

the strike of the associated formations. On the other hand, faults and unconformities which strike in nearly the same direction as the younger beds with which they are associated may be difficult to distinguish from each other. Fig. 7-8 illustrates some problems of this type which may occur. Let it be assumed that each letter on the areal map designates a formation, and that formation N, which is generally present between M and O, is missing along the line VW. This omission could be due to a strike fault or to an unconformity, and the areal map does not indicate which is present. However, whether the line XY would be interpreted as a fault or as an angular unconformity would depend on whether the formations grow progressively younger from A to Q or from Q to A. If A is the youngest formation, then the formations strike into the contact at a high angle. Since this is not likely to occur at an unconformity, the line XY is probably a fault. If, on the other hand, the youngest formation is Q, the strike of the younger formations along XY is parallel to the line. This is generally a characteristic of angular unconformities on areal maps, but is much less likely to occur along faults. It should be understood, however, that only the probabilities can be determined in such cases. It is only where the formations are offset or repeated that we can be absolutely sure that an unconformity is not responsible.

RECOGNITION OF SUBSURFACE UNCONFORMITIES

Many of the methods used in recognizing subsurface unconformities are very much like those used in finding them at the surface. Information as to age relations, basal conglomerates, and sharp breaks in lithology may be obtained from well logs or samples. Cross sections in various directions may show that there is local relief or buried topography at the contact between two formations. Detailed correlations between wells may indicate that formations or groups of strata are missing in certain areas. Correlations may also demonstrate that the interval between the horizons varies considerably from place to place. The question then arises as to whether these conditions are caused by faulting, folding during deposition, flowage during folding, or angular unconformities. Usually flowage of the strata sufficient to produce marked thinning of the formations occurs only in regions of very high dips. Moreover, thinning due to this cause occurs on the flanks of folds, with thickening near the axial planes. Local unconformities may exist near the crests of supratenuous folds, and it may require detailed correlations to show whether the thinning of intervals near the crests of these folds is due to folding with continuous deposition, or whether erosion has removed some beds from the crests.

RELATION TO TRAPS FOR OIL AND GAS ACCUMULATION

Several different kinds of traps for oil and gas occur at unconformities. Most of the traps at disconformities and some of those at nonconformities are associated with buried hills or compaction; the discussion of these features is reserved for Chap. 9. Three types of traps are associated with angular unconformities. Oil and gas rising up the dip through a porous, permeable formation beneath an angular unconformity may be trapped at the angular unconformity, provided that the formations are impervious on all sides of the reservoir at its termination. The East Texas oil field is the best-known example of an accumulation in this type of trap. Oil and gas may also be trapped where reservoir rocks above an angular unconformity thin out against it owing to overlap up the dip. The beds overlying and underlying the reservoir at its updip end must be impervious if the trap is to remain sealed. Ideal examples of traps of this nature are shown in Fig. 7-4.   Truncated anticlines and bald-headed structures are special cases of truncations.   Furthermore, a bald-headed anticline is a special base of a truncated anticline.   Fig. 7-9, from a paper by Tomlinson,[1] shows a truncated and bald-headed anticline.   A truncated anticline is simply an anticlinal fold which has been planed off by erosion, and then buried by deposits laid down after the folding.   The cross section through the Fox-Graham field, shown in Fig. 7-9, indicates that the anticline was planed off before the deposition of the basal Deese. A bald-headed structure is an anticline which is planed off at an angular unconformity, and from which a reservoir rock present on the flanks has

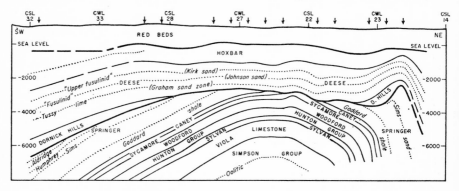

SECTION THROUGH THE FOX-GRAHAM OIL FIELD T2S, R3W
CARTER COUNTY, OKLAHOMA
VERTICAL AND HORIZONTAL SCALES THE SAME
Vertical arrows at top indicate location of wells

FIG. 7-9. Cross section through Fox-Graham field, Okla., a "bald-headed" anticline.   (*After Tomlinson, published by permission of the American Association of Petroleum Geologists.*)

been eroded near the crest.   The Sims sand has been eroded from the crest of this anticline, and it is therefore "bald-headed" with respect to this sand.

A third type of trap at an angular unconformity consists in lenticular or variable reservoir rocks overlying tilted beds which furnish a source of the oil or gas.   If the permeable strata in the formation overlying the angular unconformity are persistent, the oil and gas entering them will rise up the dip until they either escape at the surface or accumulate in a structural trap.   If, on the other hand, these permeable beds are non-persistent, the oil and gas will be trapped in them before moving far and will remain to form oil or gas pools.

Many important oil and gas fields occur along unconformities, and in a great number of smaller fields the unconformity is responsible for the

[1] C. W. Tomlinson, Odd Geologic Structures of Southern Oklahoma, *A.A.P.G. Bull.,* vol. 36, p. 1828 (1952).

trap. Among the larger fields at unconformities may be mentioned Panhandle, Tex., and Monroe and Richland, La. Cunningham and Kleinpell[1] have described the relations of the Coalinga and Midway-Sunset fields to unconformities. In the Coalinga field the Temblor (Miocene) is the main producing horizon. The Kreyenhagen shale (Eocene) lies beneath the Temblor with marked angular unconformity, and is believed to be the source of the Temblor oil. In some cases oil is trapped in the sands of the Temblor, where they thin out by overlap against the Kreyenhagen shale. In the Sunset-Midway field many individual traps of various types have combined to give one continuous field. In this field there is an important angular unconformity between the Miocene and the Pliocene. Oil is trapped in Miocene sands where they are truncated at this unconformity. Oil is also found in Pliocene sands where they thin out by overlap against the unconformity. It also accumulates in lenticular beds above the unconformity. According to Canfield,[2] the Santa Maria Field, California, which has produced half a billion barrels of oil, is in a trap produced by overlap at an unconformity. The great Bolivar Coastal Field, Venezuela, is a large area of accumulation produced by a number of traps of different types. Some of the oil occurs in anticlines in the Eocene, but much is found in Miocene sands above the unconformity with the Eocene in lenticular reservoirs and in areas where the Miocene sands terminate up the dip because of overlap against the unconformity.

Fig. 7-10, from a paper by Borger,[3] is a cross section through the Quiriquire field, Venezuela. The producing reservoir is outlined by diagonal shading. It is of Plio-Pleistocene age, and occurs a short distance above a marked angular unconformity. The relations suggest that the chief source of the oil is from the strata beneath the angular unconformity. Probably oil from these strata rose up into the Plio-Pleistocene beds above the angular unconformity and was trapped in the lenticular and variable sands.

Effect on Oil and Gas Prospects

The effect of unconformities on oil and gas prospects may be either favorable or unfavorable. It may happen that an unconformity lies

[1] George M. Cunningham and W. D. Kleinpell, The Importance of Unconformities to Oil Production in the San Joaquin Valley, Calif., "Problems of Petroleum Geology," American Association of Petroleum Geologists, Tulsa, pp. 785–805 (1934).

[2] Charles R. Canfield, Subsurface Stratigraphy of the Santa Maria Valley Oil Field and Adjacent Parts of Santa Maria Valley, California, A.A.P.G. Bull., vol. 23, pp. 45–81 (1939).

[3] H. D. Borger, Case History of the Quiriquire Field, Venezuela, A.A.P.G. Bull., vol. 36, fig. 18, p. 2322 (1952).

between unaltered sediments and rocks which are too highly altered for oil production.   In such a case the unconformity may be regarded as unfavorable, since it marks the lower limit of the zone having oil prospects.   An angular unconformity may mean that the structure in the beds above the unconformity is entirely different from the structure in the strata beneath.   While this is unfavorable for the possibilities of each individual structure, it is not unfavorable for the general prospects in

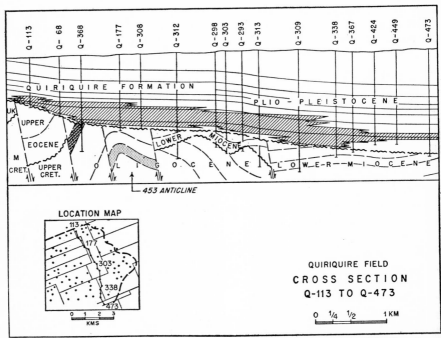

Fig. 7-10. Cross section through the Quiriquire field, Venezuela.   Diagonal shading shows the oil reservoir in the Plio-Pleistocene beds above the truncated older rocks.   (*After Borger, published by permission of the American Association of Petroleum Geologists.*)

the formations underlying the unconformity, because other structures will doubtless be present.

The occurrence of unconformities has a favorable bearing on oil and gas prospects in a number of ways.   Traps of various types occur in association with unconformities.   Furthermore, if there is folding in the strata beneath an angular unconformity which does not occur in the beds above it, an angular unconformity may mean that good structures are present at depth although none appear in the surface exposures.   Usually the presence of several unconformities in the sedimentary sections is considered distinctly favorable.

ADDITIONAL REFERENCES

Bailey, T. L.: Origin and Migration of Oil into Sespe Redbeds, California, *A.A.P.G. Bull.*, vol. 31, pp. 1913–1935 (1947).

Ball, M. W., and others: Possible Future Petroleum Provinces of North America, *A.A.P.G. Bull.*, vol. 35, pp. 141–498 (1951).

Barrell, J.: Rhythms in the Measurement of Geologic Time, *G.S.A. Bull.*, vol. 28, pp. 745–904 (1917).

Blackwelder, E.: The Valuation of Unconformities, *Jour. Geology*, vol. 17, pp. 289–299 (1909).

Bloesch, E.: Unconformities in Oklahoma and Their Importance in Petroleum Geology, *A.A.P.G. Bull.*, vol. 3, pp. 253–285 (1919).

Bridge, J., and Dake, C. L.: Initial Dips Peripheral to Resurrected Hills, *Missouri Bur. Geology and Mines, Biennial Rept. State Geologist (1927–1928)*, pp. 93–99 (1929).

Bucher, W. A.: Geologic Structure and Orogenic History of Venezuela, *G.S.A. Mem.* 49, pp. 1–113 (1952).

Caribbean Petroleum Co. Staff: Oil Fields of Royal Dutch-Shell Group in Western Venezuela, *A.A.P.G. Bull.*, vol. 32, pp. 517–628 (1948).

Gardner, F. J.: Relationship of Unconformities to Oil and Gas Accumulation, *A.A.P.G. Bull.*, vol. 24, pp. 2022–2031 (1940).

Jacobsen, L.: Structural Relations on East Flank of Anadarko Basin, Cleveland and McClain Counties, Oklahoma, *A.A.P.G. Bull.*, vol. 33, pp. 695–719 (1949).

Krumbein, W. C.: Criteria for Subsurface Recognition of Unconformities, *A.A.P.G. Bull.*, vol. 26, pp. 36–62 (1942).

Lahee, F. H.: "Field Geology," McGraw-Hill Book Company, Inc., New York, 5th ed. (1952).

———: Overlap and Non-conformity, *A.A.P.G. Bull.*, vol. 33, p. 1901 (1949).

Levorsen, A. I.: Pennsylvanian Overlap in United States, *A.A.P.G. Bull.*, vol. 15, pp. 113–148 (1931).

———: Relation of Oil and Gas Pools to Unconformities in the Mid-Continent, "Problems of Petroleum Geology," American Association of Petroleum Geologists, Tulsa, pp. 761–784 (1934).

McClellan, H. W.: Subsurface Distribution of Pre-Mississippian Rocks of Kansas and Oklahoma, *A.A.P.G. Bull.*, vol. 14, pp. 1535–1556 (1930).

McCoy, A. W., III, and others: Types of Oil and Gas Traps in Rocky Mountain Region, *A.A.P.G. Bull.*, vol. 35, pp. 1000–1037 (1951).

McGee, D. A., and Jenkins, H. D.: West Edmond Oil Field, Central Oklahoma, *A.A.P.G. Bull.*, vol. 30, pp. 1797–1829 (1946).

Malkin, D. S., and Jung, D. A.: Marine Sedimentation and Oil Accumulation on Gulf Coast: I, Progressive Marine Overlap, *A.A.P.G. Bull.*, vol. 25, pp. 2010–2020 (1941).

Moore, R. C.: Pennsylvanian Cycles in the Northern Mid-Continent Region, *Illinois Geol. Survey Bull.* 60, pp. 247–257 (1931).

Reeves, F.: Status of German Oil Fields, *A.A.P.G. Bull.*, vol. 30, pp. 1546–1584 (1946).

Selk, E. L.: Types of Oil and Gas Traps in Southern Oklahoma, *A.A.P.G. Bull.*, vol. 35, pp. 582–606 (1951).

Sharp, R. P.: Ep-Archean and Ep-Algonkian Erosion Surfaces, Grand Canyon, Arizona, *G.S.A. Bull.*, vol. 51, pp. 1235–1270 (1940).

Siever, R.: The Mississippian-Pennsylvanian Unconformity in Southern Illinois, *A.A.P.G. Bull.*, vol. 35, pp. 542–581 (1951).

Silver, C.: Jurassic Overlap in Western New Mexico, *A.A.P.G. Bull.*, vol. 32, pp. 68–81 (1948).

Stephenson, L. W.: Unconformities in the Upper Cretaceous Series of Texas, *A.A.P.G. Bull.*, vol. 13, pp. 1323–2134 (1929).

Swesnik, R. W., and Green, T. H.: Geology of Eola Area, Garvin County, Oklahoma, *A.A.P.G. Bull.*, vol. 34, pp. 2176–2199 (1950).

Symposium on Major Unconformities in the Texas Geologic Section, *Univ. of Texas Bur. Econ. Geology Bull.* 3501, Section III, pp. 113–149 (1935).

Tulsa Geological Society Research Committee: Relationship of Crude Oils and Stratigraphy in Parts of Oklahoma and Kansas, *A.A.P.G. Bull.*, vol. 31, pp. 92–148 (1947).

Twenhofel, W. H.: Marine Unconformities, Marine Conglomerates, and Thicknesses of Strata, *A.A.P.G. Bull.*, vol. 20, pp. 677–703 (1936).

Walters, R. F.: Buried Pre-Cambrian Hills in Northeastern Barton County, Central Kansas, *A.A.P.G. Bull.*, vol. 30, pp. 660–710 (1946).

Wanless, H. R., and Shepard, F. P.: Sea Level and Climatic Changes Related to Late Paleozoic Cycles, *G.S.A. Bull.*, vol. 47, pp. 1177–1206 (1936).

Weller, J. M.: Cyclical Sedimentation of the Pennsylvania Period and Its Significance, *Jour. Geology*, vol. 38, pp. 97–135 (1930).

———: Pennsylvanian Overlap in the United States (Discussion), *A.A.P.G. Bull.*, vol. 15, pp. 704–707 (1931).

———: Sedimentary Cycles of the Pennsylvanian Strata, a Reply, *Am. Jour. Sci.*, 5th ser., vol. 21, pp. 311–320 (1932).

Wheeler, H. E., and Beesley, E. M.: Critique of the Time-stratigraphic Concept, *G.S.A. Bull.*, vol. 59, pp. 75–86 (1948).

Wilson, I. F.: Buried Topography, Initial Structures and Sedimentation in Santa Rosalia, Baja California, Mexico, *A.A.P.G. Bull.*, vol. 32, pp. 1762–1807 (1948).

CHAPTER 8

SALT DOMES

IMPORTANCE AND VALUE

Salt domes are of considerable importance, owing to the great value of the mineral products obtained from them. Billions of barrels of oil and extensive accumulations of natural gas have been found on them. They are the source of most of the sulfur produced in the United States, and a number of salt mines are located in them. However, even if salt domes had no economic value, they would still be of great interest to geologists, for they illustrate the mechanics of intrusion of one sedimentary rock into another. Furthermore, study of the logs of wells drilled on salt domes has furnished useful information regarding the problems of faulting and folding.

Petroleum geologists in the United States are especially interested in the salt domes of the Gulf Coast. These salt domes produce more oil than those of any other area, and more petroleum geologists work in the Gulf Coast than in any other salt-dome region. Moreover, there is more available information about Gulf Coast salt domes than about the salt domes of other areas. For these reasons, this chapter deals chiefly with the salt domes of the Gulf Coast. However, the study of foreign domes aids in understanding those of the Gulf Coast, and should not be entirely neglected even by those solely interested in this region.

GEOGRAPHIC DISTRIBUTION

Salt domes are known in a number of widely scattered regions in North America, Europe, and Asia. They occur in groups confined to areas having thick sediments underlain by a salt bed. In the Gulf Coast the most important area of salt domes extends in a belt from Corpus Christi to southern Mississippi. Outside this belt three domes are known in southwest Texas. Salt domes far north of the coast are known as interior domes. Eighteen interior domes are known in the East Texas syncline west of the Sabine uplift, and eleven are known in Louisiana east of the Sabine uplift. These figures refer only to domes in which the salt comes close to the surface, and do not include broad, gentle uplifts in which the top of the salt lies at great depth. The shallow interior salt domes are in general unproductive. Of the 18 interior salt domes of Texas

185

only one, Boggy Creek, has produced oil. Nevertheless, in the same region great oil fields are located on large, low-dip uplifts which are believed to be produced by flowage of the salt. According to Carsey,[1] salt has actually been encountered in 190 domes on land in the Gulf Coast region. The leases taken on the continental shelf of Texas and Louisiana suggest that 120 structures have been found there by geophysics. However, these may not all be salt domes.

According to Longwell,[2] there is evidence of eight salt domes in the valley of the Virgin River in southeastern Nevada. On the Colorado Plateau in Colorado and Utah, there are several long, narrow anticlines underlain by abnormal thicknesses of gypsum and salt. Prommell and Crum[3] have described some anticlines in southeastern Utah which may be underlain by salt domes. In Europe salt domes are found in Germany, Denmark, Rumania, Transylvania, and Russia. In Rumania about 200 salt domes and salt anticlines are found, many of which have produced oil. Oil production has also been obtained from the salt domes of Germany. In Russia about 110 salt domes have been found in the area north of the Caspian Sea, and in Iran about 110 salt domes occur in the area north of the Persian Gulf. Oil production is also obtained from traps associated with salt domes in the Isthmus of Tehuantepec, Mexico.

HISTORY OF DEVELOPMENT

Salt was mined from the salt domes of Louisiana by the Indians, and white men have mined it for about 100 years. However, the large-scale exploitation of salt domes began with the drilling of the Spindletop gusher in 1901. As Clark and Halbouty[4] have pointed out, the opening up of this field not only marked the beginning of oil development on the Gulf Coast, but had an important influence on the oil industry of the United States. The original gusher flowed about 100,000 bbl of heavy oil per day from the cap rock at a depth of 1,020 ft. The field was located on a low hill with surface indications of gas. The discovery of this field initiated the first stage in the exploration for salt domes—locating them by their topographic expression or surface indications. The production was obtained from cap rock or from shallow sands over the domes. The second stage in Gulf Coast exploration involved searching for oil in the

[1] J. Ben Carsey, Geology of Gulf Coastal Area and Continental Shelf, *A.A.P.G. Bull.*, vol. 34, pp. 365, 385 (1950).

[2] Chester R. Longwell, Geology of the Boulder Reservoir Floor, *G.S.A. Bull.*, vol. 47, pp. 1393–1476 (1936).

[3] H. W. C. Prommel and H. E. Crum, Salt Domes of Permian and Pennsylvanian Age in Southeastern Utah and Their Influence on Oil Accumulation, *A.A.P.G. Bull.*, vol. 11, pp. 373–393 (1927).

[4] James A. Clark and Michel T. Halbouty, "Spindletop," Random House, New York (1952).

upturned sands along the margins of the salt domes below their crests. This search became active with the discovery of prolific flank production at Spindletop in 1925, and has continued to the present time. The third stage, which also still continues, consists in drilling for production in gently dipping, broad anticlines over very deep salt uplifts. It was initiated by the discovery of Conroe in 1932.

TYPES

Salt domes may be classified in several ways. The classification according to depth gives shallow, intermediate, and deep domes. At present it appears that a dome in which the top of the salt is a few thousand feet or less in depth would be classed as shallow, one about a mile in depth as intermediate, and one more than two miles in depth as deep. Another classification is based on whether or not the salt cuts across the sedimentary strata. If it does, the dome is piercement. If the contact between the salt and the sediments is parallel to the strata, the dome is concordant. Unfortunately there is a general tendency to use "piercement" as synonymous with "shallow." This would imply that the domes which are not shallow are concordant, which is presumably not the case. Salt domes might be classed according to their origin as compressional and gravitational.

SALT STOCK

The most essential feature of the piercement salt dome is a great column of salt which rises from the deep source salt layer. On the Gulf Coast this column is generally at least 3 to 5 miles high, and may be much higher. The diameter of the salt stock is usually at least 1 mile, and may be as much as 7 miles. The average diameter of the upper portion on the Gulf Coast is probably about 2 or 3 miles. In the Gulf Coast the portion of the salt stock which is accessible to observation is generally cylindrical, with a cross section that approximates a circle. However, in some cases one diameter is greater than the others and where this is the case the longest diameter is generally parallel to the coast. Many of the foreign domes are markedly elongated, with the longer diameter parallel to the axes of the associated anticlinal folds. In many very shallow domes the top of the salt is flat, probably because of solution. In a number of domes the top of the salt is rounded or domal. In the upper portions of domes which are accessible to observation, the diameter of the salt stock may increase with depth, or it may decrease, forming the overhang which is discussed below. In some domes the walls of the upper part of the salt stock seem to be nearly vertical.

The salt is traversed by thin, dark bands which contain a larger proportion of anhydrite than the lighter portions. These bands are original sedimentary strata, and by means of them the structure of the salt may be worked out in the salt mines.   The salt of the stocks is intensely folded. Isoclinal folds with vertical axes predominate in the inner portions of the salt.   The strata in the outer portions of the stock are vertical and parallel to the edge of the stock.   The steep folds in the salt are cut off abruptly at the base of the cap rock.   It has been suggested that some salt stocks taper below and either are cut off entirely from the source salt layer or have a smaller diameter at depth.   However, generally very little is known about the nature of the salt stocks at great depth.   It is not certain that any of them are disconnected from the source layer.

Overhang

In a number of domes the sides of the salt stock project outward and are underlain by sediments.   This is called overhang or mushrooming.

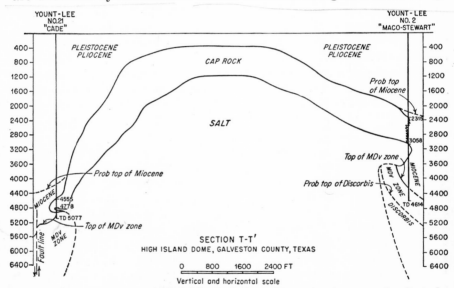

Fig. 8-1. Cross section through High Island salt dome, Texas, showing cap rock, salt stock, and overhang.   (*After Halbouty, published by permission of the American Association of Petroleum Geologists.*)

Oil is quite commonly produced from the sands beneath the overhang. These strata beneath the overhang generally dip at high angles, and in some places are nearly vertical or slightly overturned.   If a well near the margin of a salt dome encounters salt, it is evident that it still has possibilities of producing oil, for it may continue through the salt and enter sediments beneath an overhang.   The presence of overhang is proved only by drilling.   If a number of wells have been drilled and no overhang has been found, this does not mean that there is none, for no salt dome has been so thoroughly tested that all possibilities of overhang have been completely eliminated. For this reason, it is not known what percentage of salt domes have overhang.

Most of the known cases of overhang occur near the top of the salt dome, but this may be partly because of lack of knowledge about the deeper portions. Two possible explanations of overhang have been suggested. The density of the lower part of the cap rock is 2.7 or 2.8, while that of the salt varies from about 2.15 to 2.2. Furthermore, the upper portion of a salt stock which approaches close to the surface is generally denser than the associated sediments, if these sediments have never been deeply buried. Hence near the surface there is a tendency for the rising salt to expand laterally into the sediments instead of raising the heavy cap rock. Another possible explanation of the overhang is that the salt is dissolved near the contact of water-bearing sands with the salt plug. The saturated salt solution may be carried away by currents in the reservoir rock, or it may settle down the dip into the rim syncline because it is heavier than the unsaturated solution. The confining pressure due to the overlying rock would force the plastic sediments into the void produced by solution.

Fig. 8-1, from a paper by Halbouty,[1] shows a good example of salt overhang in the High Island dome. The steep dip of the sediments under the overhang should be noted. The cap rock is typical of many shallow salt domes.

Source Salt Layer

All the regions of salt domes are underlain by a thick layer of sedimentary salt. It is known that in Germany this layer is of Permian age. It is suspected but not known definitely that in Iran the source salt layer is of Cambrian age. In the Gulf Coast region it is known to underlie upper Jurassic deposits. Its age may be Jurassic, though some geologists believe it to be as old as Permian. The source layer has been penetrated by the drill updip from the salt domes in East Texas, Louisiana, and Arkansas. The depth of the layer near the coast is not known, but it is believed to be at least 4 or 5 miles. One way of estimating the thickness of the source salt layer is by observing the depths of the rim synclines. As explained below, these rim synclines are probably formed by the thinning of the salt layer as the salt is forced upward. If this is the case, the salt layer must be at least as thick as the maximum depth of the rim synclines. However, geologists are not agreed as to what features constitute rim synclines. If the Mineola Basin referred to on pages 212–215 is a rim syncline, the source salt layer must be at least 8,000 ft thick in this area. If, on the other hand, this basin is formed by ordinary folding, it gives no indication of the thickness of the source salt layer. It

[1] Michel T. Halbouty, Geology and Geophysics Showing Cap Rock and Salt Overhang of High Island Dome, Galveston County, Texas, *A.A.P.G. Bull.*, vol. 20, pp. 560–611 (1936).

should be noted that the depth of the rim syncline increases with the age of the strata and is greatest in the formations just above the source layer. In younger strata only minimum thicknesses are given.

MARGINAL UPTURNING AND UPLIFT

The structure of the strata near a salt dome is profoundly affected by the movement of the salt mass. Aside from the cap rock, the traps which cause the localization of the oil and gas pools associated with the salt domes are produced by the deformation of the sediments by the salt. Above the dome the sediments may be thrown into an anticlinal structure, with the crest of the anticline over the center of the salt stock. If this overlying dome is steep, it is commonly faulted, as is described below. The amount of uplift generally decreases upward above the top of the cap rock. If the dome is deeply buried, the strata thousands of feet above the top of the stock may show no uplift. On the other hand, a number of salt structures show an anticlinal structure at the surface though the top of the salt is probably about 3 miles or more below the surface. The amount of uplift varies from a few feet to thousands of feet. Some of the uplift over deep salt domes may be due to differential compaction occurring as the domes are buried. The dips away from the crest of the dome vary similarly, from a few feet to the mile to more than 60°. The largest oil fields associated with salt structures have been found on broad, rather gentle uplifts in which the salt lies at great depths.

The sediments around the margin of the salt stock dip away from it at a rather steep angle. Generally there is a gouge zone separating the salt from the sediments. The steep angle of dip diminishes rather rapidly away from the edge of the dome. However, these outward dips may continue to the bottom of the rim syncline, if there is one. The dip away from the salt stock is produced by the frictional drag of the salt on the sediments. It is to be expected, therefore, that plastic sediments like shales and relatively unconsolidated sandstones would show more marginal upturning than relatively competent rocks such as limestones and dolomites. The amount of dip away from the salt stocks ranges from 0 to 90°, and the uplift of the beds may be hundreds or thousands of feet. Generally the strata near the salt stock are cut by numerous faults. As a result of steep dips, faulting, and flowage of plastic beds, the structure around the periphery of salt stocks is generally extremely complex.

RIM SYNCLINES

It seems reasonable to suppose that the salt squeezed into the salt stock will be withdrawn from the portions of the source salt layer nearest the base of the stock. The source salt layer will therefore be thinnest in a circular area surrounding the salt stock. Since the overlying formations settle as the top of the salt layer drops, dips toward the salt dome are produced. Nearer the salt dome the dip is away from the salt stock at a steep angle because of frictional drag. The combination of these dips toward and away from the dome should produce a rim syncline with a circular axis surrounding the dome. Rim synclines would be expected to die out upward where the extrusion of the salt into the stock occurred during the deposition of the sediments. Conversely, if the depth of a rim syncline remained the same through a series of sediments, the extrusion of salt should have taken place after the deposition of the sediments. However, the latter condition has not been reported.

No rim synclines should be present at the horizons of strata level with the top of the dome, because all the extrusion of the salt should have taken place previously. Presumably rim synclines should not be expected around salt domes in which the intrusion of the salt is due to lateral pressure.

The field evidence for the occurrence of rim synclines varies considerably with the conditions. It is difficult to find clear geologic evidence of rim synclines on the salt domes near the coast of the Gulf of Mexico. The formations penetrated by the drill in this area are relatively young, and a large part of the development of the rim syncline may have occurred before these strata were deposited. Good key beds are scarce or absent in the shallower beds. Furthermore, since a syncline is an unfavorable place to drill, wells are drilled in rim synclines only by mistake. No doubt reflection seismograph surveys in the vicinity of salt domes have furnished some information on the occurrences of rim synclines around coastal domes, but this information is apt to be considered too confidential to publish. However, Nettleton[1] states that geophysical work has shown partial or complete synclines surrounding many salt domes on the Gulf Coast. On the southeastern side of the Moss Bluff salt dome, for example, reflection seismograph surveys show a dip toward the dome of 1,000 ft in a few miles just outside the edge of the salt stock.

Geologic field evidence for rim synclines is easier to obtain in the region of the interior salt domes. One reason for this is that the interior domes have been eroded more deeply, and therefore the rim synclines are better developed in the strata available for examination. Furthermore, in these strata there are good key horizons for mapping structure.

CAP ROCK

Nature and Distribution. Many but not all salt domes are covered by a layer of anhydrite, gypsum, or calcite that is known as the cap rock, a typical example of which is shown in Fig. 8-1. The thickness of the cap rock varies from a few feet to over 1,000 ft. The salt domes of Rumania and Iraq do not have cap rocks. Where cap rock is present on

[1] L. L. Nettleton, Recent Experimental and Geophysical Evidence of Mechanics of Salt Dome Formation, *A.A.P.G. Bull.*, vol. 27, p. 58 (1943).

German salt domes, it is thin compared to the cap rocks of the Gulf Coast. Nearly all the salt domes of the Gulf Coast have cap rock, though even in this area some are without it. Cap rock is absent or thin on the Five Islands salt domes of Louisiana, where the salt comes very close to the surface. In some domes the base of the cap rock is nearly level. In other domes the cap rock bends or dips toward the margin, forming a dome-shaped structure. In general, the cap rock is thicker on the shallower domes than on those at greater depth.

Generally the cap rock consists of three layers or zones. At the base there is a portion composed of anhydrite, which usually comprises the thickest zone. At the bottom of this zone there may be a thin, porous anhydrite sand, but the rest of the anhydrite portion of the cap is devoid of porosity or permeability. Above the anhydrite cap there is a zone composed of gypsum. This in turn may be overlain by a cap composed of limestone or calcite. Aside from the anhydrite sand at the contact with the salt, the calcite cap is the only part of the cap rock which is commonly porous and permeable. The calcite cap may have large openings which give it a high permeability. Sulfur

False Cap. The sediments over the cap rock in some domes are cemented so that they are unusually hard and nonporous. These rocks are known as false cap. They may be distinguished from the true cap by the fact that they consist of clastics with a cement of carbonates or sulfates. The true cap, on the other hand, contains little clastic material. The cementation which affects the rocks of the false cap may render sandstones which ordinarily make good reservoir rocks too impervious to produce oil. According to Halbouty[1] there is a false cap from 200 to 1,300 ft thick on the High Island salt dome. This false cap contains indurated, well-cemented sandstones. In this field many cavities are found in both the false and the true cap rock. However, such thickness of false cap is unusual. Most of the descriptions of salt domes do not mention the existence of a false cap.

Origin. Cap rock and its origin have been discussed by Brown,[2] Goldman,[3] Barton,[4] Hanna,[5] Hanna and Wolf,[6] and Taylor.[7] In the

[1] *Op. cit.*, p. 581 (1936).

[2] Levi S. Brown, Cap-rock Petrography, *A.A.P.G. Bull.*, vol. 15, pp. 509–522 (1931).

[3] Marcus I. Goldman, Origin of the Anhydrite Cap Rock of American Salt Domes, *U.S.G.S. Prof. Paper* 175-(d), pp. 83–114 (1933).

[4] Donald C. Barton, Review of Goldman's Publication, *A.A.P.G. Bull.*, vol. 18, pp. 269–271 (1934).

[5] Marcus A. Hanna, Secondary Salt-dome Materials of the Coastal Plain of Texas and Louisiana, *A.A.P.G. Bull.*, vol. 14, pp. 1469–1475 (1930).

[6] Marcus A. Hanna and Albert G. Wolf, Texas and Louisiana Salt-dome Cap-rock Minerals, "Gulf Coast Oil Fields," American Association of Petroleum Geologists, Tulsa, pp. 119–132 (1936).

[7] Ralph E. Taylor, "Origin of the Cap Rock of Louisiana Salt Domes," *Louisiana Dept. Cons. Geol. Bull.* 11, pp. 1–191 (1938).

past some geologists have supposed that the cap rock represented layers of anhydrite, gypsum, and limestone which before uplift rested on the source salt layer. This was assumed to have been forced upward to the surface by the intrusion of the salt stock. At present very few, if any, geologists familiar with salt domes believe that the cap rock was formed in this manner. It is doubtful if such a layer could be preserved intact as the top of the salt column rose. One would think that portions of the cap would be forced into the sediments on the way up, but if such fragments occur they are extremely uncommon. The intense folding of the salt stocks and the abrupt truncation of the folds at the bottom of the anhydrite layer of the cap rock constitute evidence against this theory.

The general opinion of those who have studied cap rock is that it is a concentration of the less soluble matter in the salt stock. As the salt rises into the zone of solution, its top is gradually dissolved away, with the concentration of the relatively insoluble portions. The relatively insoluble matter in the salt stocks is strikingly similar to the cap-rock materials. The depth at which this solution of the salt stock takes place is probably at least 100 ft, and possibly 1,000 ft or more. The solution of the salt forms the anhydrite cap. This absorbs water and becomes the gypsum portion of the cap. Reactions between the calcium sulfate of the gypsum cap and hydrocarbons present in the sediments may cause the formation of the calcite cap rock. Sulfur may be formed in the same reaction.

FAULTING

Nature of Faults. On the Gulf Coast most salt domes are faulted, and some are intensely faulted. All or nearly all the faults are normal, with the dips of most fault planes ranging from 40 to 70°. This development of normal faulting may have a bearing on the origin of the domes; normal faults appear to be less prominent in the salt structures associated with evidences of compression, such as those of Rumania. The throws of the faults range from less than a foot to more than 1,000 ft, and their lengths up to about 5 miles. Of course, faults are known in the Gulf Coast which are much longer than 5 miles, but there is some doubt that they are produced by the uplift of the domes. As far as is known, the faults are predominantly dip slip. Reverse drag is in many places well developed on the downthrown side of the faults, but if it is developed on the upthrown side it is much less in evidence. Near the faults there is in some places a narrow zone in which the sandstones have been cemented by the deposition of opal or other forms of silica. This cementation is for the most part very irregular and nonpersistent.

Pattern of Faulting. When plotted on a map, the faults over salt domes tend to show a characteristic pattern. In some salt domes a central graben is the dominant feature, in others a radial pattern. These patterns develop over more or less circular domes of a piercement nature, where the sediments over the salt stock are sharply domed.   There are other uplifts believed to be underlain by salt masses of abnormal thickness in which the faults are roughly parallel, and all have their throws in the same direction.   The Cayuga structure is of this type.   Fig. 8-2, from a paper by Bader,[1] is a cross section through the Anahuac field, Texas.   It shows the nature of the faulting over very deep salt uplifts.

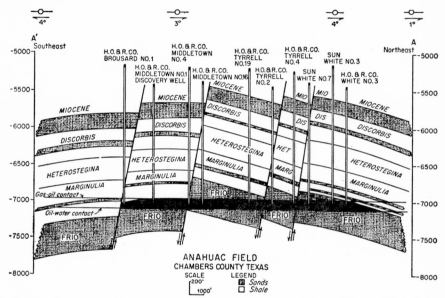

FIG. 8-2. Cross section through Anahuac field, Texas, showing relation of faults to oil, gas, and water zones.   (*After Bader, published by permission of the Society of Exploration Geophysicists.*)

It should be noted that in this case the downthrown sides of the faults are all in the same direction.   Faults showing a parallel alignment and with their downthrown sides in the same direction may develop over very deeply buried salt ridges.   It is by no means certain that all the faults in the vicinity of a salt dome are caused by the uplift of the dome. Wallace[2] shows a number of faults of parallel alignment which occur in the general region of the salt domes and salt anticlines but are apparently not caused by the uplift of the domes.   Faults of this system occurring

[1] Glenn E. Bader, Geophysical Case History of the Anahuac Oil Field, Chambers County, Texas, "Geophysical Case Histories," Society of Exploration Geophysicists, p. 72 (1949).

[2] W. E. Wallace, Jr., "South Louisiana Fault Trends," *Second Ann. Meeting Gulf Coast Assoc. Geol. Societies*, pp. 63–67 (1952).

by chance in the vicinity of a salt dome would be likely to be mistaken for faults produced by the uplift of the dome.

Time of Faulting. Since the faults associated with salt domes are generally produced by the uplift of the salt mass, it is to be expected that the times of faulting and salt uplift would coincide. If a fault takes place during the deposition of a formation, the throw of the fault decreases upward through the formation, and isopach maps show that the formation is thicker on the downthrown side. By applying these principles to the faults over salt domes on the Gulf Coast, it has been determined that the faults in general were formed simultaneously with the sediments they cut. One would expect that faulting over the domes would cease with the uplift of the domes. However, the faults forming the graben over the Millican salt dome, Brazos County, Tex., displace the base of the Catahoula, though the base of the Catahoula shows no uplift. Evidently there are some unsolved problems relating to the faults of this region.

Gouge Zone, Breccia. Between the salt stock and the sediments there is in many places a gouge zone consisting of crushed and shattered sediments. This gouge zone is very much like an ordinary fault gouge. A salt stock may be considered to be a horst bounded by a cylindrical fault. The marginal upturning of the sediments near the edge of the salt stock would therefore correspond to the drag along a fault. According to Voitesti,[1] around the salt cores of the Rumanian salt domes there is a breccia which consists of fragments of the rocks the salt has penetrated. Enormous blocks of Jurassic limestone have been found in this breccia, and schists and granites are occasionally found in it. Some of the fragments of limestone and sandstone are polished by friction.

Origin of Faulting. In the Gulf Coast region the radial and peripheral faults associated with round or oval salt domes, whether deep or shallow, are clearly produced by the relative uplift of the domes. It might be said, therefore, that there is no problem about what causes them. The case is quite different, however, with the faults which occur outside the vicinity of the domes. The larger of these tend to be parallel to the coast, and some of them occur in zones many miles long. They have been discussed by Wallace[2] and by Quarles.[3] Explanations that have been proposed for these faults are that they are produced by the stretching during the depression of the Gulf Coast geosyncline and that they are produced by the large-scale slumping of these deposits into the Gulf along certain

---

[1] I. P. Voitesti, Geology of the Salt Domes in the Carpathian Region of Roumania, *A.A.P.G. Bull.*, vol. 9, pp. 1165–1206 (1925).

[2] *Op. cit.*

[3] Miller W. Quarles, Jr., Salt-ridge Hypothesis on Origin of Texas Gulf Coast Type of Faulting, *A.A.P.G. Bull.*, vol. 37, pp. 489–508 (1953).

stratigraphic zones which permitted easy gliding. Quarles rejects these theories and favors the idea that these faults are produced by structural adjustments over salt ridges at great depths. His conclusions are based on the study of large numbers of seismograph cross sections, one of which is shown in Fig. 8-3. This figure suggests that the fault emerges from

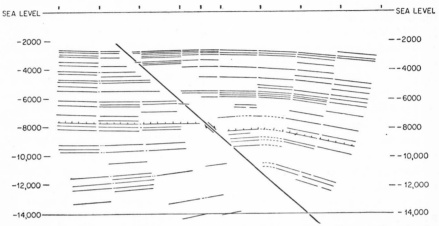

FIG. 8-3. Seismograph cross section showing possible relation of a fault at shallow depths to a salt anticline at great depths. (*After Quarles, published by permission of American Association of Petroleum Geologists.*)

an anticline at great depths. In this area an anticline is generally underlain and caused by a salt ridge or enlargement of the source salt layer.

TOPOGRAPHIC EXPRESSION AND SURFACE INDICATIONS

The topographic expression of salt domes varies greatly not only from one region to another, but also within the same area. Many of the salt domes known on the Gulf Coast have no surface expression or recognizable surface indications whatever. On the other hand, some of the domes near the Gulf Coast are overlain by low, rounded hills. On the flat, marshy land near the coast a hill only 15 or 20 ft high may be a conspicuous feature. These hills indicate very recent uplift of the salt. Probably in some cases uplift has taken place within late Pleistocene or Recent time. The hills in these cases are clearly produced by uplift, and not by differences in the rate of erosion of various formations. Spindletop, Barbers Hill, and the Five Islands are some of the best-known salt domes marked by these topographic highs. The Five Islands are a group of five salt domes in southern Louisiana which are all marked by conspicuous hills, and on all of which the salt is found at very shallow depths.

The topographic expression of domes more than 100 miles inland from the Gulf Coast is generally of a different nature. Any topographic indications which are found seem to be produced either by the differences in the resistance of the formations to erosion, or to solution of the underlying salt. The topographic expression of the interior salt domes of Texas and Louisiana has been described by Powers[1] and Spooner.[2] Some of these domes are overlain by mounds or hills. Some are surrounded by a circular valley called a race track. In other cases a circular topographic low occurs over the dome. Some domes are marked by marshes, swamps, lakes, or ponds.

The most striking topographic expression of salt domes is found in southwestern Iran. These domes have been described by Lees[3] and by Harrison.[4] The salt domes have an average diameter of 4 miles and are circular to elongate. Some emerge on anticlines, and some seem to have no relation to surface structure. Massive limestones around the salt plugs are little disturbed, but the softer sediments are sharply upturned. Mountains of bare, glistening salt rise to heights of 5,000 ft above the surrounding plains. Furthermore, salt glaciers flow by gravity to distances of as much as 3 miles from the salt domes. These glaciers and salt mountains indicate that the movement of the salt continues at present. These great outcrops of salt are able to maintain themselves because of the hot, arid climate with an average annual rainfall of only a few inches. Salt also crops out on the salt domes of Rumania. No salt crops out in the Gulf Coast salt domes, though it comes within 18 ft of the surface in the Five Islands. The calcite and gypsum portions of the cap rock do, however, crop out on the Gulf Coast.

Many salt domes on the Gulf Coast are marked by gas seeps, and there are some oil seeps over them. Salt or acid soils are other surface indications. Occurrences of salt water and sulfur water in springs or at unusually shallow depths are also associated with salt domes. In many areas sulfur water seems to result from chemical reactions associated with lignite in the sediments, and in such cases it is not a reliable indication of the domes. Near the coast, where lignite in the sediments is rare, the occurrence of sulfur water may be more significant.

A substance known as paraffin dirt has been reported to occur over a number of salt domes. It appears to be a clay with some organic content and elastic or resilient behavior. In other words, when deformed

---

[1] Sidney Powers, Interior Salt Domes of Texas, "Geology of Salt Dome Oil Fields," American Association of Petroleum Geologists, Tulsa, pp. 209–268 (1926).

[2] W. C. Spooner, Interior Salt Domes of Louisiana, "Geology of Salt Dome Oil Fields," American Association of Petroleum Geologists, Tulsa, pp. 269–344 (1926).

[3] G. M. Lees, Geology of the Oilfield Belt of Iran and Iraq, "Science of Petroleum," vol. 1, Oxford University Press, New York, p. 142 (1938).

[4] J. V. Harrison, Salt Domes in Persia, *Jour. Inst. Petroleum* (London), vol. 17, pp. 303–315 (1931); The Geology of Some Salt Plugs in Laristan (Southern Persia), *Geol. Soc. London Quart. Jour.*, vol. 86, pp. 463–522 (1930).

and released it tends to regain slowly its original shape. A plausible theory for the origin of paraffin dirt is that it is formed by the action of certain kinds of bacteria on hydrocarbon gases seeping slowly through moist clay or soil. If paraffin dirt is formed in this manner, it should be regarded as a surface indication of salt domes, for seeps of natural gas are common over them.

The various surface indications described above were very important in the early prospecting for salt domes on the Gulf Coast during the years from 1901 to 1910. At present surface indications are not used in prospecting in this region, though they are of historic and scientific interest.

GEOLOGIC EXPRESSION

Some salt domes are expressed at the surface by abnormal outcrop patterns. The most common expression is an inlier. The older rocks brought up by the uplift may crop out in an area which is more or less circular, or which is irregular in shape because of the effects of topography or faulting. The faulting itself may be an indication of the presence of a salt dome at depth. If the faults in an area are unusually numerous, the presence of a salt dome is suggested; if the faults show the characteristic pattern that is found over salt domes, the indications are stronger. Steep local dips are also suggestive of the presence of a dome. These dips may be produced by the uplift over the dome, by the tilting of the fault blocks, or by slumping due to the subsurface solution of the salt. It should be noted, however, that dips due to cross-bedding, delta formation, and contemporaneous slumping are fairly common in the salt-dome region and have been confused with local dips associated with the salt domes.

RESIDUAL HIGHS AND OTHER SALT STRUCTURES

Types of Salt Structures. In addition to the salt domes in which salt has been encountered in drilling, there are a large number of uplifts which are believed to be caused by movements of salt, though no salt has actually been detected. Some of these structures are so similar to the salt domes in which salt has been encountered that no one doubts that they are true salt domes. Other uplifts have some but not all of these typical features of salt domes. In order to classify these structures satisfactorily it is necessary to arrive at some idea of the essential features of salt domes and salt structures. The term "salt dome" may refer to any uplift produced by flowage of salt. The salt must be thicker beneath the dome than in the region surrounding it, but the salt does not have to cut across the strata in its contacts with the sediments. "Salt anticline" has approximately the same meaning, except that a salt dome is rounded or oval, while a salt anticline may be long and narrow. Both salt domes and salt anticlines may be produced by flowage of the salt without any compressional folding. However, compressional folding may also cause or initiate the flowage of the salt which caused the structure. Salt domes and salt anticlines may or may not be underlain by anticlines in the strata older than the source salt layer. The general opinion of Gulf Coast geologists seems to be that nearly all of the uplifts of the coastal region are caused by flowage of salt and underlain by abnormally thick salt masses. These structures are generally marked by gravity minima. This occurrence of gravity minima seems to be the chief criterion for considering that they are salt uplifts.

The types of salt structures which occur or may occur in the Gulf Coast region are piercement salt domes in which the salt has been penetrated by drilled wells, piercement salt domes in which the top of the salt lies at great depths and has not yet been drilled, nonpiercement salt domes, salt anticlines, salt ridges, residual highs, and anticlines on the downthrown sides of faults. Although there is some evidence for the existence of all these types of structures, it is quite possible that some of them do not exist on the Gulf Coast. Certainly the opinions of geologists familiar with the Gulf Coast differ as to the importance of residual highs.

Very Deep Piercement Salt Domes. It seems probable that there are a number of very deep domes of the piercement type in which the salt has not yet been penetrated by the drill. If the source salt layer is 5 miles or more in depth near the coast, as it seems to be, piercement salt uplifts could rise for miles into the sediments and still be too deep to be encountered by the deepest wells on the domes. However, it would presumably be very difficult in the case of such deep structures to distinguish the piercement from the nonpiercement types.

Nonpiercement Domes. Some of the very broad salt structures on the Gulf Coast may be of the nonpiercement type, particularly those in the region of the interior salt domes. The large area of these uplifts suggests low, flat structures in which the salt would not be likely to break across the strata. Possibly Van, Hawkins, and Opelika are of this nature. However, in the absence of definite evidence the exact nature of these structures is a matter of speculation.

Salt Anticlines and Salt Ridges. A long narrow uplift underlain by an abnormally thick mass of salt may be called a salt anticline. The salt anticline may be either a concordant swelling of the source salt layer or a piercement intrusion. A salt ridge is overlain by an anticline in the same manner as a salt dome. In fact, the terms "salt ridge" and "salt anticline" have very nearly the same meaning. However, a salt anticline may be merely a normal anticline in which the salt layer has thickened by flowage near the axis. In this type of structure the anticline would be

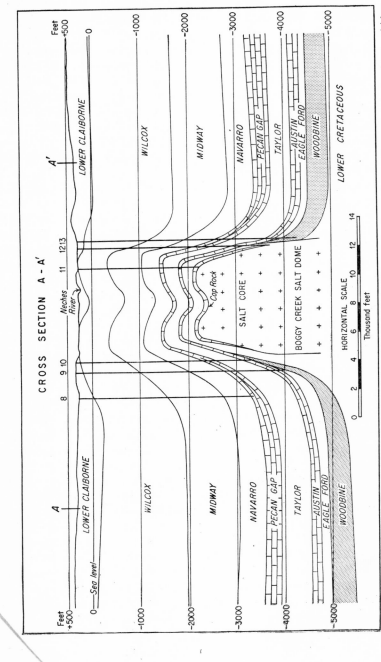

CROSS SECTION A - A'

FIG. 8–4. Cross section through Boggy Creek salt dome, Texas, showing thinning of the formations as they pass over the dome. (*After Eaton, Texas Bureau of Economic Geology and East Texas Geological Society.*)

present both above and below the salt layer, whereas presumably no anticline would be present beneath a salt ridge.

There is no sharp distinction between long, relatively narrow salt domes and salt ridges. Any long, narrow salt uplift is presumably underlain by a salt ridge at great depths. The Boggy Creek dome is a salt dome or salt uplift about 1½ miles in maximum width and 7 or 8 miles long. Aside from its shape, it seems to be a typical interior salt dome. It can also serve as an example of a salt ridge. About 5 million barrels of oil have been produced from the sharply upturned Woodbine sand on its southeast flank. Fig. 8-4, from a paper by Eaton,[1] shows a cross section across this dome. The Boggy Creek structure is called a salt dome because it penetrates close to the surface. If it were deeply buried, it might be considered a salt ridge.

Residual Highs. It is reasonable to expect that the salt of the salt stock is derived to a considerable extent from the area close to the base of the stock rather than from greater distances. If this is the case, the salt layer must be thinner near the base of the stock than in the areas at some distance from the nearest stocks. As the source layer thins around the stock and remains of greater thickness at a distance, the beds immediately above it dip gently toward the base of the stock. Beyond the zone in which the salt layer is thinned, there is an area in which it has normal thickness, and over which the beds have therefore not subsided. If this area of normal thickness is surrounded by rim synclines in which the salt layer is depleted, a broad anticlinal area will be formed between the rim synclines. This type of structure is known as a residual high. The characteristics of a residual high should be gentle dips, compared to salt domes, large area, closure increasing downward, and negative gravity anomalies. Residual highs should be located between the rim synclines of adjacent salt domes. Unfortunately low, broad salt domes and salt anticlines formed by flowage also have these characteristics, and it is very difficult to distinguish these structures from residual highs. The Katy structure in Texas has been cited by Allison[2] as an example of a residual high. Ritz[3] has also discussed the origin and characteristics of rim synclines and residual highs. The great size of the closed areas of these structures makes them of considerable importance, whatever their origin.

[1] R. W. Eaton, Boggy Creek Field, Anderson and Cherokee Counties, Texas, in Occurrence of Oil and Gas in Northeast Texas, *Univ. Texas Bur. Econ. Geol. Pub.* 5116, p. 33 (1951).

[2] A. P. Allison and others, Geology of the Katy Field, Waller, Harris and Fort Bend Counties, Texas, *A.A.P.G. Bull.*, vol. 30, pp. 157–180 (1946).

[3] C. H. Ritz, Geomorphology of Gulf Coast Salt Structures and Its Economic Application, *A.A.P.G. Bull.*, vol. 20, pp. 1413–1438 (1936).

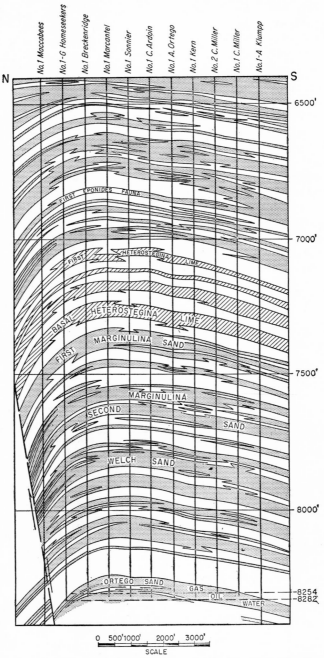

FIG. 8-5. Cross section through Tepetate structure, Louisiana. (*After Bornhauser and Bates, published by permission of the American Association of Petroleum Geologists.*)

Anticlines on the Downthrown Side of Faults. In the Gulf Coast region the strata on the downdip side of many of the larger faults dip toward the fault plane. This feature has been called reverse drag because it is in the opposite direction to the true drag nearer the fault plane. If the downthrown side of the fault is toward the coast, the dip toward the fault plane is in the opposite direction to the normal dip, and an anticline and reversal are produced. A number of these anticlines on the downthrown sides of faults are known, and important oil and gas production is obtained from them. The general trend of both the faults and the anticlines is parallel to the coast line.

Anticlines on the downthrown sides of faults may be called Tepetate or Amelia-type structures, from two of the typical structures of this type which have been described. Fig. 8-5, from a paper by Bornhauser and Bates,[1] shows a cross section through the Tepetate field and anticline. The steep dip into the fault plane on its downthrown side should be noted. Another interesting feature is that although the fault dips to the right, the axial plane of the anticline is nearly vertical. The only feature indicating that anticlines of this type should be classed as salt structures is the reported occurrence of negative gravity anomalies on them. These anomalies suggest that they are underlain at great depths by salt anticlines or salt ridges produced by the flowage of the salt. However, there is no general agreement as to the mechanism which caused the fault outcrop to appear on the updip side of the anticline. Quarles's explanation of this type of structure is discussed on pages 121–124.

Salt Domes Associated with Compressional Folds

In the Gulf Coast region folds clearly due to compression seem to be rare, at least in the zones where the structure is accurately known. Folds caused by compression may possibly be more common at great depths. A few folds which may be due to compression have been described, but these folds might also be caused by the flowage of salt without compression. One such fold is the Mineola basin, described below. An anticline, which has been described by Fisk,[2] is associated with the Five Islands salt domes in southern Louisiana. In some other regions there is ample evidence that salt domes occupy the cores or spring from the crests of anticlines formed by compression. The salt domes of Rumania and Germany in particular are commonly associated with folds that have been formed by compression. The salt domes of these countries have

[1] Max Bornhauser and Fred W. Bates, Geology of the Tepetate Oil Field, Acadia Parish, Louisiana, *A.A.P.G. Bull.*, vol. 22, p. 298 (1938).

[2] Harold N. Fisk, "Geological Investigation of the Alluvial Valley of the Lower Mississippi River," conducted for the Mississippi River Commission (War Department, Corps of Engineers, U.S. Army), p. 65 (1944).

been described by a number of geologists.[1] The salt anticlines of the Colorado Plateau may also be of this nature. In an intensely compressed fold any formation that is relatively plastic or incompetent may be forced upward through the overlying formations. Shale, clay, anhydrite, gypsum, and salt are some of the formations that are in a number of cases sufficiently plastic to behave in this manner. A compressional fold with an intrusive core of sedimentary rock is known as a diapir fold. If the intrusive core is of salt, the structure may also be called a salt dome. However, many salt domes appear to be produced entirely or largely because of the lower specific gravity of the salt compared to that of the adjacent sediments. It is not altogether clear whether such structures should be called diapir folds.

Fig. 8-6, from a paper by Stille,[2] illustrates various stages in the development of piercement-type salt domes. These cross sections suggest that the piercement-type German domes develop from salt anticlines.

EXPERIMENTS

The value and possible uses of model studies of salt domes are the same as in the case of other structures. These studies of salt domes might conceivably throw light on the origin of the domes, or might suggest new interpretations of the associated structures. As mentioned in Chap. 3, it is only when careful consideration is given to the effect of differences between the model and the field structures that significant results are obtained. The earlier experimenters on salt domes did not realize the importance of these considerations, and for this reason their experiments are of doubtful value. One type of salt dome experiments is intended to duplicate the compressional folds in which a plastic substance is forced by lateral pressure through the overlying layers. The other type imitates the Gulf Coast type of salt dome in which the salt

---

[1] Donald C. Barton, The American Salt-dome Problems in the Light of the Roumanian and German Salt Domes, *A.A.P.G. Bull.*, vol. 9, pp. 1227–1268 (1925).

Frederick G. Clapp, Notes on the Natural Gas Fields of Rumania, *A.A.P.G. Bull.*, vol. 9, pp. 202–211 (1924).

Walter Kauenhowen, The Oil Fields of Germany, *A.A.P.G. Bull.*, vol. 12, pp. 1041–1047 (1930).

S. L. Mason, Rumanian Oil Fields, *A.A.P.G. Bull.*, vol. 9, pp. 145–157 (1925).

J. F. M. De Raaf, Notes on the Geology of the Southern Rumanian Oil District with Special Reference to the Occurrence of a Sedimentary Laccolith, *Geol. Soc. London Quart. Jour.*, vol. 101, pp. 111–134 (1945).

Frank Reeves, Status of German Oil Fields, *A.A.P.G. Bull.*, vol. 30, pp. 1546–1584 (1946).

I. P. Voitesti, Geology of Salt Domes in the Carpathian Region of Roumania, *A.A.P.G. Bull.*, vol. 9, pp. 1165–1206 (1925).

[2] Hans Stille, Upthrust of the Salt Masses of Germany, "Geology of Salt Dome Oil Fields," American Association of Petroleum Geologists, Tulsa, p. 150 (1926).

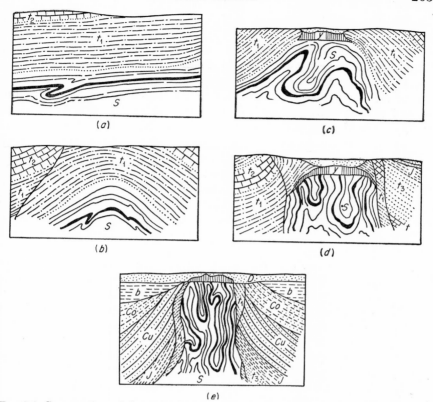

Fig. 8-6. Cross sections of German salt structures showing stages in the development of a typical intrusive salt stock. These stages are (*a*), a minor fold in the source salt layer; (*b*), a salt anticline; (*c*) a salt anticline with the salt strongly folded and a gypsum cap rock; (*d*) transition from a salt anticline; (*e*) a typical piercement salt stock. The symbols have the following significance: *D*, Diluvium; *b*, Tertiary; *CO*, Upper Cretaceous; *CU*, Lower Cretaceous, *J*, Jurassic; t_3, Upper Triassic; t_2, Middle Triassic; t_1, Lower Triassic; *Y*, residual gypsum cap rock; *S*, salt formations with potash beds in heavy black lines. (*After Stille, published by permission of the American Association of Petroleum Geologists.*)

rises through the sediments because of its buoyancy. Experiments of the latter type have been performed by Dobrin,[1] Nettleton,[2] Nettleton and Elkins,[3] and Parker and McDowell.[4] Parker and McDowell used

[1] Milton B. Dobrin, Some Quantitative Experiments on a Salt Dome Model and Their Geological Implications, *Am. Geophys. Union Trans.*, vol. 22D, pp. 528–542 (1941).

[2] L. L. Nettleton, Fluid Mechanics of Salt Domes, *A.A.P.G. Bull.*, vol. 18, pp. 1175–1204 (1934); Recent Experimental Evidence of Mechanics of Salt Dome Formation, *A.A.P.G. Bull.*, vol. 27, pp. 51–63 (1943).

[3] L. L. Nettleton and Thomas A. Elkins, Geologic Models Made from Granular Materials, *Am. Geophys. Union Trans.*, vol. 28, pp. 451–466 (1941).

[4] Travis J. Parker and A. N. McDowell, Scale Models as a Guide to Interpretation of Salt Dome Faulting, *A.A.P.G. Bull.*, vol. 35, pp. 2076–2086 (1951).

asphalt beneath a layer of plastic baroid mud of high specific gravity but sufficiently coherent to fault. The asphalt, being lighter than the mud, rose through it under the right conditions to form domes with fault patterns much like those of actual salt domes.

According to Parker,[1] it was found during the experiments that reverse faults were formed by forcing a plug upward through sand or mud fluid. If, on the other hand, the asphalt layer beneath the mud fluid rose through it because of its buoyancy, normal faults were found on the resultant domes and rim synclines were developed. This suggests that possibly the development of rim synclines has some connection with the development of normal faults on the domes. It was also found that where a large rim syncline is formed by the depletion of the asphalt layer, secondary domes may start to form at the outer edge of the rim syncline suggesting an interpretation of the Mineola syncline discussed on pages 212–215.

TIME OF FORMATION

The evidence as to the time of formation of Gulf Coast salt domes is derived chiefly from well logs. However, geophysics, surface structure, and topography contribute some information. As already mentioned, the low hills over some domes close to the Gulf Coast show that the ground surface over the domes has in some cases been uplifted during the past few thousand years. The salt glaciers and mountains of bare salt found in association with the salt domes of Iran show that the salt in that region must still be rising up through the sediments.

The time of formation of salt domes may be indicated by variations in the thicknesses of intervals and formations, changes in the throws of faults in rising in the section, and differences in sedimentary facies between deposits laid down over and around the dome and at a distance from it. The best way to determine the time of formation is to construct isopach maps of each formation or interval. If the intervals between two beds are less over the dome, uplift during the time interval between the deposition of the two beds is indicated. The amount of thinning is approximately equal to the amount of uplift. The decrease of throw of the faults upward may also indicate the time of formation of the dome, provided that it is assumed that the uplift and faulting were contemporaneous. Isopach maps of various formations cut by the faults over domes generally reveal which faults were active during the deposition of these formations. If the facies of a formation or bed is different over the dome and away from it, uplift of the dome during deposition is indicated, provided that the apparent relations are not due to chance. Uplift of the dome during deposition is likely to cause the deposition of

---

[1] Travis J. Parker, "Model Studies as a Guide to Salt Dome Tectonics," unpublished dissertation for degree of Doctor of Philosophy, University of Texas (1952).

coarser-grained or more sandy sediments over it. There may also be a change in the nature of the fossil content of the beds over the dome, compared with equivalent strata off it. Possibly the shallower water over the growing dome would be more favorable for reef development; if this is the case, reefs should be more common over the domes. Local unconformities covering only the area of the dome are also evidence of uplift between the time of deposition of the beds immediately above and below the unconformity. The thickness of the strata removed by erosion is a measure of the amount of uplift.

The cross section of the Boggy Creek salt dome, shown in Fig. 8-4, illustrates well the continued growth of the salt domes. Every formation shown in this cross section is thinner over the dome, indicating continued uplift during the deposition of the formations. It should be noted that the Woodbine sand thins out against the flank of the dome and is absent over its higher portions. Evidence as to the growth of the dome during the deposition of formations older than the Woodbine must be sought in changes in facies, variations in thickness, and the presence of local unconformities in the upturned beds along the flanks of the dome. These beds in this and other domes are so deformed, contorted, subject to flowage, and faulted that it may be very difficult to decide whether any changes in these formations near the dome are caused by deformation during deposition or at a later date.

Direct evidence of the uplifted sediments over salt domes indicates that during the deposition of these sediments the uplift was in some cases continuous and in others intermittent. Indirect evidence may be obtained from the study of rim synclines, since salt was rising in the salt core during the period when its rim syncline was growing deeper. The questions of the time of initiation of dome growth, and of whether it has been continuous since it started, are related to the theories of origin, which are discussed in the next section.

Origin

Roles of Compression and Buoyancy. It seems clear that two processes have operated to produce salt domes. One is the production of salt domes or salt anticlines by lateral pressure. A fold is formed by compression, and the lateral pressure eventually squeezes the plastic salt up through the overlying rocks. The other process produces the domes by means of the buoyancy of the salt compared to the sediments. The density of the salt with included impurities may be 2.15 to 2.2. The density of the associated sediments at a considerable depth below the surface may be 2.4 to 2.6. However, the density of the sediments within a few thousand feet of the surface may range from 1.8 to 2.4. These statements regarding density are made on the assumption that the sediments are deposited in a subsiding basin or geosyncline, and that they consist of clastic deposits. If the deposits are limestone or dolomite, or if the surface rocks have once been buried to considerable depths, high densities may continue to the surface. If the sediments are more dense than the salt, there will be a pressure causing the salt to flow into the base of an incipient salt dome and flow up through the sediments. The magnitude of this pressure in pounds per square inch is equal to the differences in density times the height in feet of the salt column above the top of the salt layer, times 0.43. Clearly this pressure becomes effective only where there is a projection of the salt above the top of the salt layer.

Distinguishing Features. Salt domes due to compression are associated with folds caused by compression. These folds are steep, and they affect formations at a distance from the salt stocks. The upturned beds near salt domes formed by buoyancy do not extend far from the domes which produce them. Rim synclines are likely to be present near salt domes produced by buoyancy, but they probably do not occur around domes produced by compression. The faulting associated with salt domes caused by compression is likely to be reverse or thrust; faulting associated with domes caused by buoyancy is generally of the normal type. The compressional folds associated with domes resulting from lateral pressure extend beneath the source salt layer. The salt domes due to buoyancy do not affect beds below the source salt layer. However, salt domes of this type may spring from the crests of folds due to compression. In this case there would be an anticline beneath the salt layer in the general area of the domes in the formations overlying the source salt layer. Salt domes started by compressional forces may continue to rise because of buoyancy. The salt domes of Rumania appear to be good examples of domes produced chiefly by tectonic forces. The salt domes of the Gulf Coast are apparently produced chiefly by buoyancy.

Initiation of Salt Domes Produced by Buoyancy. It is clear that the forces tending to cause salt to rise through the sediments because of its buoyancy are very weak before the salt stock or incipient salt dome has risen appreciably above the source salt layer. In regions such as Rumania, where the salt is squeezed up by compression or springs from folds produced by compression, there is no difficulty in explaining how the domes are initiated. Two theories have been proposed to explain the development of salt domes produced by the combination of gravity and the low density of the salt compared to the sediments. One theory, outlined by Dobrin,[1] is based partly on the fact that the upper portion of freshly deposited clastic rocks is less dense than salt. According to

[1] Milton B. Dobrin, Some Quantitative Experiments on a Salt Dome Model and Their Geological Implications, *Am. Geophys. Union Trans.*, vol. 22D, pp. 528–542 (1942).

Dobrin, the salt would therefore not start to rise until several thousand feet of sediments had been deposited. The opposite idea has been expressed by Parker[1] as a result of scale-model studies. In his experiments on mud and asphalt, Parker found that domes failed to form if the overburden became greater than a certain critical depth before the domes started to rise. This suggests that gravitational salt domes would not develop unless incipient domes or irregularities in the top of the surface of the source salt layer formed before it was deeply buried.

When the source salt layer has been buried by a small thickness of sediments, a number of conditions may produce the slight forces necessary to cause the roof of the salt layer to rise in some places and sink in others. Among these causes may be mentioned slight initial variations in the elevation of the top of the salt layer, caused by facies changes, solution of the top of the salt, and slumping. Variations in the density and thickness of the overlying strata and topographic irregularities in the surface may produce the same effect. These factors could produce irregularities in the top of the salt layer regardless of whether the salt was more or less dense than the overlying sediments, though of course the irregularities would not have a large relief until the sediments became more dense than the salt. Moreover, anhydrite, dolomite, and limestone may be more dense than salt when freshly deposited. Once the irregularities in the top of the salt layer have been formed, they may continue to grow upward as the overlying sediments are deposited.

Fig. 8-7, from a paper by Spencer and Peters,[2] is a seismograph cross section through a structure that may constitute the first stage in the development of a salt dome. The dotted line shows the normal elevation of the top of the salt in the area. In the center of the section the top of the salt and the overlying Smackover limestone rise several hundred feet, but the base of the salt and the formations near the surface do not show this rise. These conditions suggest that the anticline and the adjacent syncline are due to flowage of the salt before it was deeply buried. It seems reasonable to expect that under slightly different conditions the top of the anticline would continue to rise until a salt dome was formed.

Mechanism of Salt-dome Emplacement. The theory that salt domes developed contemporaneously with deposition and burial has been termed "down building" by Barton.[3] According to this theory, the top of the

[1] Travis J. Parker, "Model Studies as a Guide to Salt Dome Tectonics," unpublished dissertation for degree of Doctor of Philosophy, University of Texas (1952).

[2] L. C. Spencer and Jack W. Peters, Geophysical Case History of the Magnolia Field, Columbia County, Arkansas, "Geophysical Case Histories," Society of Exploration Geophysicists, p. 459 (1949).

[3] Donald C. Barton, Mechanics of Formation of Salt Domes with Special Reference to Gulf Coast Salt Domes of Texas and Louisiana, *A.A.P.G. Bull.*, vol. 17, pp. 1025–1083 (1933).

salt domes stayed near the surface as the great thickness of sediments accumulated on the source salt layer. In view of this possibility, it should be understood that any statements made in this book about uplifts and depressions of the salt and sediments associated with salt domes are generally merely relative, and do not imply that any features actually went up or down with reference to sea level.

A salt dome is a great cylinder 1 to 7 miles in diameter and probably 3 to 9 miles high. Was the volume of this cylinder occupied by sediments before the formation of the dome, and, if so, what became of the sediments? This is one of the most important problems relating to the

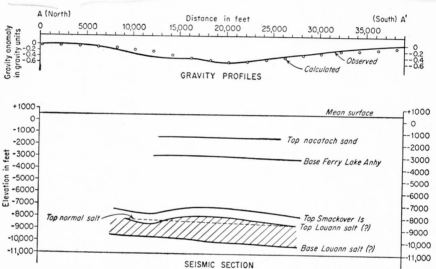

Fig. 8-7. Cross section through Magnolia field, Ark. (*After Spencer and Peters, published by permission of the Society of Exploration Geophysicists.*)

origin of salt domes. It seems that there are five possibilities: These sediments may never have existed because they were never deposited; they may have been forced to the surface and removed by erosion; they may have been forced into the rocks at the side of the salt dome as a series of irregular masses, probably bounded by faults; the original sediments may have been parted and pushed aside by the rising salt; or they may have flowed downward to fill the potential void produced by the displacement of the salt from the source salt layer into the dome. If the domes rise as the sediments accumulate, the problem is greatly simplified, for the layer of sediments to be pushed upward would always be thin. Moreover, if there was a topographic high over the dome, some of the sediments present around the dome may never have been deposited directly over it. Blocks of sediments which have been driven into the rocks surrounding the domes do not appear to be as numerous as would be expected if the sediments in the volume now occupied by the dome had been displaced in this manner. Furthermore, folds and reverse faults do not appear to be as common in the strata surrounding the salt domes as would be expected if the sediments were thrust aside laterally to make room for the salt dome. It seems mechanically impossible or very unlikely that a salt dome starting at great depths could drive a great cylindrical plug of sediments upward before it clear to the surface. Accordingly, if gravitational salt domes do start growing at great depths, it is likely that the sediments displaced by the salt flow downward into the potential void left by the removal of the salt from the source salt layer.

At least three essential conditions must be present for the formation of gravitational salt domes. In the first place, the salt must be of lower specific gravity than the overlying sediments. Second, the source salt layer must have a certain minimum thickness. Third, the viscosity and strength of the salt and overlying sediments must be sufficiently low. A fourth condition may be the presence of sufficiently large irregularities in the top of the salt layer, or the commencement of dome formation before deep burial. It is probably the lack of one or more of these conditions that explains the absence of salt domes in great areas underlain by salt in the northern Appalachian region, Michigan, Kansas, Oklahoma, and western Texas.

Central Subsidence. Subsidence of strata over salt domes occurs occasionally because of solution of the salt in the subsurface waters. This solution generally takes place on the top of the salt mass or around its edges, and is easily explained. Another type of subsidence occurs over the central portion of the domes and is more difficult to explain. Lahee[1] has described the subsidence in the Chestnut dome. This condition is well illustrated by the Clay Creek salt dome, which has been described by Ferguson and Minton,[2] Lahee,[3] and Parker and McDowell.[4] In the Clay Creek salt dome there is a central syncline or area of subsidence, surrounded by a circular anticline over the outer portion of the dome. Solution is a possible explanation of this structure, but one would expect that the effects of subsidence due to solution would be observed around the outer edges of the dome rather than over its center. Parker and McDowell explain the central structural depression as the result of

[1] Frederic H. Lahee, Chestnut Dome, Natchitoches Parish, Louisiana, *A.A.P.G. Bull.*, vol. 15, pp. 277–278 (1931).

[2] William Boyd Ferguson and Joseph W. Minton, Clay Creek Dome, Washington County, Texas, *A.A.P.G. Bull.*, vol. 20, pp. 68–90 (1936).

[3] Frederic H. Lahee, Discussion, *A.A.P.G. Bull.*, vol. 15, pp. 279–283 (1931).

[4] Travis J. Parker and A. N. McDowell, Scale Models as Guide to Interpretation of Salt Dome Faulting, *A.A.P.G. Bull.*, vol. 35, p. 2086 (1951).

faulting produced by the stretching of the strata over the dome. Another possibility is that the subsidence is due to changes in the stresses affecting the salt at depth.

SHAPES AND MUTUAL RELATIONS

The shapes of salt domes are greatly influenced by their mode of origin. Salt domes and salt anticlines formed primarily by compression tend to be rather long and narrow; usually the longer axes of these structures are more or less parallel to the axial planes of the compressional folds of the area. The salt domes of Rumania and the salt anticlines of the Colorado Plateau are examples of these shapes and alignments. Salt domes produced primarily by differences in specific gravity are generally nearly circular in cross section. Thus most of the salt domes of the Gulf Coast are roughly cylindrical. However, detailed maps of salt domes on the Gulf Coast show that a number of them are slightly longer in one direction than another. Where this is the case, the longest axis is generally parallel to the nearest coast line and also parallel to the regional strike of the formations. If the salt dome commences with a salt anticline like the Magnolia, Ark., structure, the direction of elongation of the shallow domes may be determined by the direction of the axes of these initial structural features at great depths.

As already mentioned, salt domes formed primarily by compression show a marked alignment—that is, they are located in rows which tend to be parallel. The longer axes of the domes are parallel to the rows. It is well known that the Gulf Coast salt domes show no well-marked alignment. If the domes are plotted on a map, their arrangement resembles the random pattern of raindrops on a dusty road. About the only definite linear arrangement that can be detected is shown by the Five Islands domes in southern Louisiana. According to Fisk[1] these domes are parallel to an anticline in Quaternary deposits. The alignment of the Five Islands domes does not stand out prominently on a map showing all the domes of the region. However, these domes are all very shallow and are marked by prominent hills. The fact that five domes of such similar characteristics are arranged in a line probably indicates that there is some deep-seated cause which also acts along a line.

MINEOLA BASIN

The Mineola Basin in east Texas has been described by Eaton.[2] This basin is a synclinal structure which subsided as the sediments were

---

[1] *Op. cit.*

[2] R. W. Eaton, Preliminary Notes on the Geology of the Mineola Basin, Smith and Wood Counties, Texas, *Second Ann. Meeting of Gulf Coast Assoc. of Geol. Societies,* pp. 164–180 (1952).

deposited in it. Fig. 8-8 shows the structure on the base of the Upper
Cretaceous Austin chalk. The structure map on the base of the Austin
chalk shows that the basin is about 3,000 ft deep. However, the cross
section of the basin shown in Fig. 8-9 indicates that, because of the thickening of the intervals basinward, the structure of the Lower Cretaceous

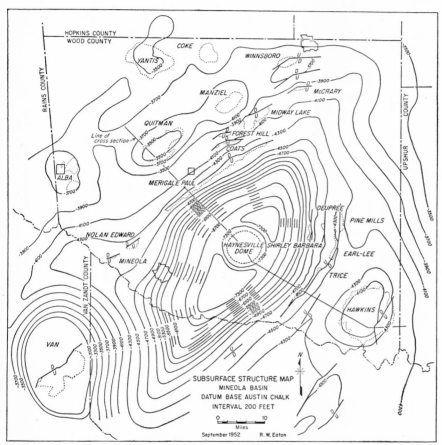

FIG. 8-8. Structure map of Mineola Basin, in east Texas. Dotted lines show boundaries of
oil and gas fields. (*After Eaton, published by permission of Gulf Coast Association of Geological Societies.*)

Travis Peak shows a basin about 8,000 ft deep. In addition to the
basin itself, structures of three types are shown. One type is the piercement Haynesville salt dome, which is not productive of oil or gas. The
broad, low-dip anticlines around the margins of the basin, such as the
Van, Alba, Quitman, Manziel, Winnsboro, and Hawkins uplifts, represent
the second structural type. These anticlines are known to have been

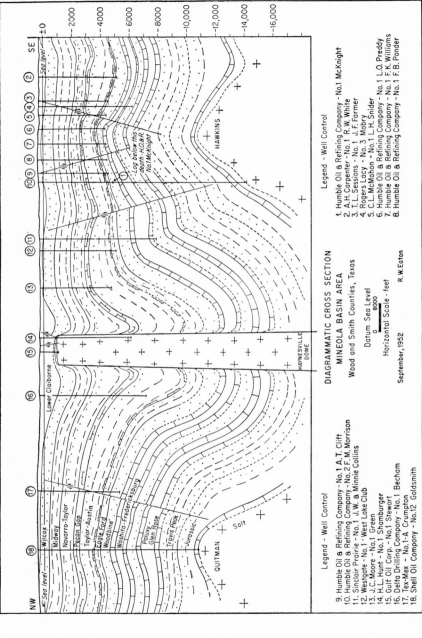

FIG. 8-9. Cross section through Mineola Basin, in east Texas. (After Eaton, published by permission of Gulf Coast Association of Geological Societies.)

DIAGRAMMATIC CROSS SECTION
MINEOLA BASIN AREA
Wood and Smith Counties, Texas

Datum Sea Level

Horizontal Scale - feet

September, 1952   R.W.Eaton

Legend - Well Control

1. Humble Oil & Refining Company - No.1 McKnight
2. A.H. Carpenter - No.1 R.W. White
3. T.L. Sessions - No.1 J.F. Farmer
4. Rogers Lacy - No.3 Mabry
5. C.L. McMahon - No.1 L.H. Snider
6. Humble Oil & Refining Company - No.1 L.O. Preddy
7. Humble Oil & Refining Company - No.1 F.K. Williams
8. Humble Oil & Refining Company - No.1 F.B. Ponder

Legend - Well Control

9. Humble Oil & Refining Company - No.1 A.T. Clift
10. Humble Oil & Refining Company - No.2 F.M. Morrison
11. Sinclair Prairie - No.1 J.W. & Minnie Collins
12. Westgate - No.1 - West Lake Club
13. J.C. Moore - No.1 Green
14. H.L. Hunt - No.1 Shamburger
15. Gulf Oil Corp. - No.1 Stewart
16. Delta Drilling Company - No.1 Becham
17. Tex-Mex - No.1-A Crumpton
18. Shell Oil Company - No.12 Goldsmith

214

uplifted in both Upper and Lower Cretaceous time.   Large oil fields are found on these anticlines.   Van and Hawkins each have an estimated oil production of about half a billion barrels.   The third type of structure consists in closures along strike faults upthrown toward the basin. As shown in Fig. 8-8, many structures of these last two types contain oil fields.   All these types of structures are clearly related to the Mineola Basin.

There are two possible explanations of the Mineola Basin and its associated structural features.   One is that it is a large fold in which the formations thicken toward the synclinal axis.   The Haynesville salt dome sprang from the bottom of the syncline, presumably after it was partly or wholly formed.   Eaton advocates this theory.   However, it is difficult to see why a salt dome starting from the bottom of the syncline would develop faster than the salt uplifts on its margins, when the greater elevation of the top of the salt on the margins would give the domes starting there a great mechanical advantage.   The other theory is based on the scale-model experiments of Parker and McDowell, who found that secondary salt domes rise from the margins of the rim synclines developed around the primary domes.   According to this theory, the Haynesville salt dome formed first and the Mineola Basin is the rim syncline around it. The broad anticlines around the margin of the basin are the secondary domes.   This theory explains why the Haynesville dome is in the center of the basin.

It should be noted that according to the first theory the salt layer would probably be thicker in the bottom of the basin than in the area around it, while according to the second theory the source salt layer would be at least 8,000 ft thinner in the bottom of the basin than in the area around it.   Possibly reflection seismograph or gravimeter surveys can determine which changes in thickness are actually present.   If the Mineola Basin is a rim syncline, a large enough volume of salt must have been squeezed from the source salt layer into the dome to account for the subsidence.   Rough calculations suggest that the volume of salt now in the Haynesville salt dome is only about one-tenth as much as would be needed to account for the subsidence of the basin.   However, it is reasonable to suppose that 10 times as much salt as is now in the dome could have been removed by solution near the surface.   The mile-high mountains of salt over some of the salt domes of Iran show that great quantities of salt may be extruded or removed by solution near the surface.

OIL AND GAS PRODUCTION

Several types of traps for the accumulation of oil and gas are associated with salt domes.   Aside from cap-rock production, the traps associated with salt domes are of the same general type as those which contain oil and gas elsewhere.   Important oil production is obtained from the anticlines over the domes, from fault traps over and around the domes, and from the steeply upturned beds around the margins of the salt stocks. The total cap-rock production was about 200 million bbl; it was obtained from only a few salt domes where the salt occurred at shallow depths, and came from the uppermost or calcite portion of the cap rock.   Although the cap-rock production was responsible for starting the oil industry on the Gulf Coast, it was important only for the first decade or two of oil production in this region.   As already mentioned, many great oil and gas fields, covering 5,000 to 25,000 acres, lie on broad, gentle uplifts over very deep domes.   Large production is also obtained from the fault traps associated with domes, and from anticlines on the downthrown sides of faults.   The production per acre from many salt-dome oil fields is very high.   Large production per acre may be obtained from the anticlines over the domes because the combination of large closure, multiple producing horizons, and thick reservoir rocks results in very thick producing zones.   The producing areas of the pools in the upturned sands on the margins of salt domes generally do not cover a large area.   However, the production per acre is also likely to be very large.   This is because of the thickness of the productive sections and because production may be obtained from many sands.   Production has been obtained in this type of trap to depths of over 17,000 ft, and it is probable that large volumes of oil remain to be found in traps of this nature.

EFFECT OF FAULTING ON PRODUCING RESERVOIRS

The effect of faulting on the producing reservoir rocks and fluid contacts associated with salt domes depends on the throws of the faults and on the thicknesses of the reservoir rocks.   If the reservoir rock is found on both sides of a fault at the same level, the fault plane is not a barrier to the migration of oil and gas across it.   Accordingly, if the throw of the fault is not sufficiently large to separate the productive reservoir into disconnected sections, the oil-water and gas-oil contacts are generally at the same levels on both sides of the fault planes.   Fig. 8-2 illustrates this condition.   If, on the other hand, the throw of the fault is much greater than the thickness of the productive sandstone, the reservoir will be cut up into disconnected segments.   If the fault plane is impervious to the movement of oil and gas parallel to it, as is frequently the case, the oil-water and gas-oil contacts may be at entirely different levels on the two sides of the fault.

DISCOVERY METHODS

At present the three important methods for finding salt domes on land are subsurface studies, gravimeter measurements, and reflection seismograph surveys.   In general, the gravimeter is used as a reconnaissance tool to find the promising areas to be covered in detail by seismograph work.   The structure of the gently dipping anticlines over salt domes may in a number of cases be mapped with reasonable accuracy by the reflection seismograph.   However, the structure of salt domes with steep dips and complex faulting cannot be mapped accurately by any geophysical method.   Studies of well records are also an important means of finding domes.   Subsurface indications of salt domes may consist in uplifts, steep dips, faults, thinning of intervals, or the presence of local unconformities.

Salt Domes on Continental Shelf

It has long been known that many salt domes must underlie the continental shelf off Texas and Louisiana.   Salt domes are distributed more or less at random clear up to the shore line.   The coast line has migrated inland and seaward extensively during the geologic past; its present position has nothing to do with the occurrence of salt domes in the strata at depth.   The location of these domes was determined long before the shore line reached its present position.   Moreover, the Mississippi River has built its delta most of the way across the shelf.   Domes occur extensively in the portion of the shelf covered by the delta, as they doubtless do in the adjacent portions of the shelf now covered by water.

Exploration for salt domes on the continental shelf is guided by geophysics.   The topography of the submerged ocean bottom may also be used as a guide in certain areas.   However, the topography of the inner portion of the shelf may be determined by depositional features and may have no connection with the underlying structure.   As Weaver[1] has mentioned, near the outer margin of the shelf there are many circular or oval hills of considerable relief.   It has been suggested that these features are produced by salt domes; however, they could also be reefs or features produced by large-scale slumping.   Samples may be obtained of the material at the bottom of the ocean, and cores up to more than 50 ft in length may be taken in soft deposits.   At present the information derived from these samples does not appear to be directly useful for finding salt domes on the inner margin of the shelf.

The geophysical problems involved in exploration on the inner portion of the continental shelf appear to have been solved in a satisfactory manner.   Both the gravimeter and the reflection seismograph have been found effective for this work.   In order to take a gravimeter reading, it is necessary to stop the ship and lower the instrument to the bottom.

[1] Paul Weaver, Variations in History of Continental Shelves, *A.A.P.G. Bull.*, vol. 34, pp. 351–360 (1950).

Seismograph surveys, on the other hand, can be made while the ship from which surveys are made continues on its course.

ADDITIONAL REFERENCES

Balk, R.: Structure of Grand Saline Salt Dome, Van Zandt County, Texas, *A.A.P.G. Bull.*, vol. 33, pp. 1791–1829 (1949).

Barnes, R. B.: Plasticity of Rocksalt and Its Dependence upon Water, *Phys. Rev.*, vol. 44, pp. 898–902 (1933).

Bates, F. W.: Geology of Eola Oil Field, Avoyelles Parish, Louisiana, *A.A.P.G. Bull.*, vol. 25, pp. 1363–1395 (1941).

———— and Wharton, J. B., Jr.: Anse la Butte Dome, St. Martin Parish, Louisiana, *A.A.P.G. Bull.*, vol. 27, pp. 1123–1156 (1943).

Bloomer, R. O.: A Tectonic Intrusion of Shale in Rockbridge County, Virginia, *Jour. Geology*, vol. 55, pp. 48–51 (1947).

Dane, C. H.: Geology of the Salt Valley Anticline and Adjacent Areas, Grand County, Utah, *U.S.G.S. Bull.* 863 (1935).

DeGolyer, E.: Discovery of Potash Salts and Fossil Algae in Texas Salt Dome, "Geology of Salt Dome Oil Fields," American Association of Petroleum Geologists, Tulsa, pp. 781–782 (1926).

————: Origin of North American Salt Domes, *A.A.P.G. Bull.*, vol. 9, pp. 831–874 (1925).

Eardley, A. J.: Petroleum Geology of Aquitaine Basin, France, *A.A.P.G. Bull.*, vol. 30, pp. 1517–1545 (1946).

"Geology of Salt Dome Oil Fields," American Association of Petroleum Geologists, Tulsa (1926).

Goldman, M. I.: Bearing of Cap Rock on Subsidence on Clay Creek Salt Dome, Washington County, Texas, and Chestnut Dome, Natchitoches Parish, Louisiana, Discussion, *A.A.P.G. Bull.*, vol. 15, pp. 1105–1113 (1931).

"Gulf Coast Oil Fields," American Association of Petroleum Geologists, Tulsa (1936).

Halbouty, M. T., and Hardin, G. C., Jr.: Types of Hydrocarbon Accumulation and Geology of South Liberty Salt Dome, Liberty County, Texas, *A.A.P.G. Bull.*, vol. 35, pp. 1939–1977 (1951).

Hanna, M. A.: Evidence of Erosion of Salt Stock in Gulf Coast Salt Plug in Late Oligocene, *A.A.P.G. Bull.*, vol. 27, pp. 85–86 (1943).

————: Geology of the Gulf Coast Salt Domes, "Problems of Petroleum Geology," American Association of Petroleum Geologists, Tulsa, pp. 629–678 (1934).

Harrison, T. S.: Colorado-Utah Salt Domes, *A.A.P.G. Bull.*, vol. 11, pp. 111–132 (1927).

Hazzard, R. T., Spooner, W. C., and Blanpied, B. W.: Notes on the Stratigraphy of the Formations Which Underlie the Smackover Limestone in South Arkansas, *Shreveport Geol. Soc. 1945 Reference Rept.*, vol. 2 (1947).

Heath, F. E., Waters, J. A., and Ferguson, W. B.: Clay Creek Salt Dome, Washington County, Texas, *A.A.P.G. Bull.*, vol. 15, pp. 43–60 (1931).

Henninger, W. F.: Occurrence of Sulphur Waters in Gulf Coast of Texas and Louisiana and Their Significance in Locating New Domes, *A.A.P.G. Bull.*, vol. 9, pp. 35–37 (1925).

Hoylman, H. W.: Seismograph Evidence on Depth of Salt Column, Moss Bluff Salt Dome, Texas, *Geophysics*, vol. 11, pp. 128–134 (1946).

Imlay, R. W.: Jurassic Formations of the Gulf Region, *A.A.P.G. Bull.*, vol. 27, pp. 1407–1533 (1943).

Lahee, F. H.: Clay Creek Salt Dome, Washington County, Texas, Discussion, *A.A.P.G. Bull.*, vol. 15, pp. 1113–1116 (1931).

Lees, G. M.: Salt; Some Depositional and Deformational Problems, *Jour. Inst. Petroleum (London)*, vol. 17, pp. 259–280 (1931).

Link, T. A.: Experiments Relating to Salt-dome Structures, *A.A.P.G. Bull.*, vol. 14, pp. 483–508 (1930).

McDowell, A. N.: The Origin of the Structural Depression over Gulf Coast Salt Domes with Particular Reference to Clay Creek Salt Dome, M.S. thesis, Texas A. & M. College (1951).

Meyer, W. G.: Grabens in Gulf Coast Anticlines and Their Relation to Other Faulted Troughs, *A.A.P.G. Bull.*, vol. 28, pp. 541–553 (1944).

Michaux, F. W., Jr., and Buck, E. O.: Conroe Oil Field, Montgomery County, Texas, *A.A.P.G. Bull.*, vol. 20, pp. 736–799 (1936).

Miller, J. C.: Well Spacing and Production Interference in West Columbia Field, Brazoria County, Texas, *A.A.P.G. Bull.*, vol. 26, pp. 1441–1466 (1942).

Minor, H. E.: Chemical Relations of Salt Dome Waters, "Geology of Salt Dome Oil Fields," American Association of Petroleum Geologists, Tulsa, pp. 777–780 (1926).

Nettleton, L. L., and Elkins, T. A.: Geologic Models Made from Granular Materials, *Am. Geophys. Union Trans.*, vol. 28, pp. 451–466 (1947).

Olcott, D. P.: Amelia Field, Occurrence of Oil in Texas, *Univ. Texas Bur. Econ. Geology Progress Rept.*, pp. 43–47 (1949).

Reedy, F., Jr.: Stratigraphy of Frio Formation, Orange and Jefferson Counties, Texas, *A.A.P.G. Bull.*, vol. 33, pp. 1830–1858 (1949).

Roach, C. B.: Subsurface Study of Jennings Field, Acadia Parish, Louisiana, *A.A.P.G. Bull.*, vol. 27, pp. 1102–1122 (1943).

Rogers, G. S.: Intrusive Origin of the Gulf Coast Salt Domes, *Econ. Geology*, vol. 13, pp. 447–485 (1918).

Romanes, J.: Salt Domes of North Germany, *Jour. Inst. Petroleum, (London)*, vol. 17, pp. 252–258 (1931).

Snider, L. C.: A Suggested Explanation for the Subsurface Subsidence in the Goose Creek Oil and Gas Field, Texas, *A.A.P.G. Bull.*, vol. 11, pp. 729–745 (1927).

Steig, M. H., and others: Geology of Erath Field, Vermilion Parish, Louisiana, *A.A.P.G. Bull.*, vol. 35, pp. 943–987 (1951).

Stenzel, H. B.: The Geology of Leon County, Texas, *Univ. Texas Pub.* 3818 (1938).

Stille, H.: The Upthrust of the Salt Masses of Germany, *A.A.P.G. Bull.*, vol. 9, pp. 417–441 (1925).

Swartz, C. A.: Seismograph Evidence on the Depth of the Salt in Southern Mississippi, *Geophysics*, vol. 8, pp. 1–2 (1943).

Symposium on Salt Domes, *Jour. Inst. Petroleum (London)*, vol. 17 (1931).

Teas, L. P.: Natural Gas of Gulf Coast Salt-dome Area, "Geology of Natural Gas," American Association of Petroleum Geologists, Tulsa, pp. 683–740 (1935).

Thomas, E. P.: Mississippi Structures and Their Relation to Oil Accumulation, *A.A.P.G. Bull.*, vol. 34, pp. 1502–1516 (1950).

Torrey, P. D., and Fralich, C. E.: An Experimental Study of the Origin of Salt Domes, *Jour. Geology*, vol. 34, pp. 224–234 (1926).

Van Tuyl, F. M.: Contribution to Salt-dome Problem, *A.A.P.G. Bull.*, vol. 14, pp. 1041–1048 (1930).

Vaughan, F. E.: The Five Islands, Louisiana, "Geology of Salt Dome Oil Fields," American Association of Petroleum Geologists, Tulsa, pp. 356–397 (1926).

Wendlandt, E. A., and Knebel, G. M.: Lower Claiborne of East Texas, with Special Reference to Mt. Sylvan Dome and Salt Movements, *A.A.P.G. Bull.*, vol. 13, pp. 1347–1375 (1929).

———, Shelby, T. H., Jr., and Bell, J. S.: Hawkins Field, Wood County, Texas, *A.A.P.G. Bull.*, vol. 30, pp. 1830–1856 (1946).

Wolf, A.: Refraction Surveying of Salt Domes, *World Oil*, vol. 127, no. 7, pp. 120–125 (November, 1947).

Womack, R., Jr.: Brookhaven Oil Field, Lincoln County, Mississippi, *A.A.P.G. Bull.*, vol. 34, pp. 1517–1529 (1950).

CHAPTER 9

BURIED HILLS AND COMPACTION

The importance of buried hills and of the folds produced over them by differential compaction varies greatly from place to place.   In many areas, such as parts of Oklahoma and Kansas, oil and gas occur commonly in traps associated with buried hills.   This subject is therefore of great importance in the petroleum geology of such regions.   In other areas no production is found in traps of this nature, and little attention is paid to them.   Compaction takes place in all sediments, and this general subject has therefore universal application to sedimentary rocks.

Factors Related to Compaction

The broad problem which is the subject of this chapter has three aspects.   One is compaction itself and the various factors which have a bearing on it.   The second is the production of folds by differential compaction.   The third consists in the study of the traps for oil and gas accumulation which are related to buried hills or to compaction.

Definitions.   Since confusion is likely to arise from some of the terms used in discussing compaction, it seems advisable to give definitions of them at this point.   The meanings of some of these terms have been discussed by Hedberg[1] and by Johnson.[2]

Wet density or natural density is the density of the rock saturated with water.   Probably shales and clays below the surface are generally saturated with water.   Hence the wet density is the actual density of the rock in place.   Bulk density is the weight per unit volume of the rock together with all the fluids it contains.   Dry bulk density is the density of the rock with all the water removed from the pores.   Samples dried in air at room temperature may be called air-dried.   When air-dried samples are heated to about 220°F, water is lost, the density decreases, and the space filled with air increases.   Hence the term "bulk density" is not definite unless it is stated at what temperature the rock is dried. "Porosity" may refer to the percentage by volume of water in the wet

[1] Hollis D. Hedberg, Gravitational Compaction of Clays and Shales, *Am. Jour. Sci.*, 5th ser., vol. 31, pp. 241–287 (1936).

[2] Frank W. Johnson, Shale Density Analysis, "Subsurface Geologic Methods," edited by L. W. LeRoy, Colorado School of Mines, Golden, Colo., pp. 329–343 (1950).

samples, the percentage of air by volume in the air-dried samples, or the percentage of air by volume in samples dried at temperatures around 220°F. This term is not definite unless it is stated which meaning is intended. It has been mistakenly supposed that the porosity of the dried shales and clays is the same as the porosity of the water-saturated rocks. This is not the case, because of the great shrinkage of the porous shales and clays in drying. It is not possible to calculate the porosity of wet samples from tests of dried samples, nor can the porosity of dried samples be determined by measurements of wet samples.

Grain density is the density of the solid portion of the rock. It is the density the rock would have if the porosity were zero.

Porosity and Compaction. Porosity and compaction are obviously closely related, for a sediment which is thoroughly compacted has a very low porosity. Slate is an example of an extremely compacted rock. The porosity of slate is very low, certainly not more than a few per cent. Freshly deposited shales and clays have porosities of more than 50 per cent, and freshly deposited sands may have porosities of around 40 per cent. As sediments are buried under an increasing thickness of overburden, the porosity decreases, at first very rapidly, and then more and more slowly. Except close to the surface, the pore space of sediments is generally saturated with water. As porosity is reduced by compaction, the excess water is squeezed out by the compacting pressure and eventually reaches the surface. Generally no material is added to the sediment during the early stages of compaction, and nothing is lost from its inorganic content except water and the salts dissolved in it. The differences in porosity of shales are likely to be a measure of the compaction. If sediments 1,000 ft thick have decreased 8 per cent in porosity as a result of their compaction, the loss of volume as a result of compaction is 8 per cent, and as a result the top would subside 80 ft.

One important aspect of the porosity of shales and clays must be kept in mind if this subject is to be understood properly. This is that the term "porosity" as applied to shales and clays has no definite or absolute meaning. It has definite meaning only when the processes and conditions of measuring the porosity are precisely defined. This is because there is no sharp boundary between the free water in the pore spaces of the shales and the water which is held so tightly that it is not free. If an ordinary water-saturated sandstone is heated, the water boils off at 212°F, and very little water is driven off at higher temperatures. If, on the other hand, a shale or clay is heated gradually, it is generally found that water continues to be lost as the temperature rises above 212°F. In many cases water is emitted continuously until the rock melts. In some cases there is no abrupt break at 212°F, and the selection of this or any other temperature as the temperature of drying the shale is more or less arbitrary. Furthermore, the methods of testing the porosity of shales and clays vary considerably in their accuracy. Hence the precise meaning of any porosity determinations can be understood only if the methods and conditions of measurement are given. Many papers on the subject do not give this information.

Density. The relation between porosity and density is obviously close. It may be expressed by the equation

$$D_1(1 - P) + D_2P = D_3$$

where D_1 = density of grains or solid constituents of rock

D_2 = density of fluid filling pore space

D_3 = bulk density

P = porosity expressed as a fraction

The density increases as compaction takes place, the rise being at a very rapid rate in the first few feet of freshly deposited sediments, and below

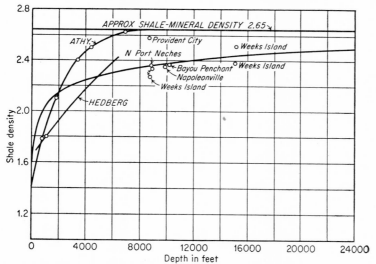

Fig. 9-1. Diagram showing the relations between depth and density in shales, as reported by several investigators. The unlabeled curve is estimated by Dickinson for Gulf Coast shales. (*After Dickinson, published by permission of the American Association of Petroleum Geologists.*)

this at a rate which decreases with depth. If the density of the grains or solid constituents of shales were invariable, the porosity could be estimated accurately from the bulk density. Fig. 9-1 shows graphically some estimates of the relation between density and depth. In the strata associated with oil and gas fields, the density of the solid inorganic contents may not change much during compaction. The solid organic matter, however, probably increases in density during compaction. That this is the case is suggested by the increases in the density of coals as they change from lower to higher rank. The presence of organic matter in shales decreases their density.

Lithology and Compaction. The rate and total amount of compaction are greatly affected by the lithology of the sediments. Limestone reefs and probably limestone and dolomite deposits of other types may be cemented to rigid masses before being deeply buried. As such rigid masses are covered by great thicknesses of overburden, they compact much less than the associated relatively unconsolidated sediments, with the result that anticlines may form over them by compaction. However, even these relatively rigid masses generally have some porosity, and this is likely to be reduced as the overburden increases. Fractures may be developed in these and other rigid limestone masses as a result of the compaction of these rocks themselves, or as a result of the differential compaction of the sediments beneath them. If these fractures remain open, they may greatly increase the permeability. The rate at which limestones and calcareous rocks lose their porosity seems to vary greatly. Chalk is an example of a limestone or calcareous rock which retains considerable porosity in sediments of Cenozoic and Mesozoic age which have been covered by many thousand feet of sediments.

The rate and total amount of compaction in clastic deposits is related to the size of the grains. In general, the finer a clastic deposit, the greater is its porosity when freshly deposited. Very fine clastics such as shales compact more than sandstones, and their compaction is more rapid in the earlier stage. Since sandstones generally compact less than shales, low anticlines may form by differential compaction over sand lenses. In the final stages of compaction sandstones may compact more than shales, for in moderately compacted rocks the sandstones have more porosity than the shales.

Compaction and Overburden. Compaction is produced by compacting pressure, and compacting pressure is approximately proportional to the thickness of overburden. Generally the confining pressure increases at a rate of about 1 lb per ft of depth, and the hydrostatic pressure at a rate of about 0.45 to 0.465 per ft of depth. The difference between the hydrostatic and confining pressures is the compacting pressure. Near the surface freshly deposited shales or clays may have a porosity of around 75 per cent and a wet density of around 1.4. At great depths the porosity is only a few per cent and the wet density approaches 2.6.

If shales had the same lithology from the surface down to great depths, both the porosity and the density would make smooth curves when plotted against depth. If there is an unconformity in the section, a break in these curves would be expected if the thickness of the sediments removed during the period of erosion represented by the unconformity was greater than the depth to which the unconformity was buried by later sediments. This suggests a method for detecting unconformities and for estimating the amount of erosion occurring at them.

Effect of Deformation and Stresses. If two areas are buried to equal depths but one is deformed while the other is not, the degree of compaction of the shales in the deformed area will probably be greater on the average. However, it is difficult to assign quantitative values to the effects produced by deformation or by the stresses that produce it.

Process of Compaction. The process of compaction is partly mechanical. Flexible, platy grains are bent where other grains press against them, and the water between the grains is squeezed out. Some grains may be broken and the fragments may fill the spaces between larger grains. Other particles may rotate or glide over each other so that they occupy less space. Compaction may also be the result of solution, deposition, and recrystallization. According to one theory the grains dissolve where they are under greater stress at their contacts, and the dissolved material is precipitated on the sides of the pores where they are under less stress. According to another theory, the finer particles dissolve first, and their substance is reprecipitated around the larger grains. The net result is the filling up of the pores and increase of density and rigidity. The final stage in this process is a metamorphic rock such as a slate or quartzite. However, by the time this stage is reached new minerals or new crystals have developed in the rock. The loss of porosity of some limestones only a brief time after their deposition and before they have been buried to appreciable depths shows that cementation may take place very early in the history of a sediment. In sandstones and shales, however, cementation is ordinarily not important until after they have been buried to considerable depths.

PRODUCTION OF FOLDS BY DIFFERENTIAL COMPACTION

The factors in the development of folds by differential compaction are the presence of a rigid body surrounded by shales or other rocks that may be compacted by pressure, and the accumulation of enough overburden so that the shales are compacted. The rigid body compacts less than the surrounding sediments. It may consist of a buried hill, a reef of limestone or dolomite, or a sand lens. Reefs and sand lenses compact to some extent as the overburden increases, but in the early stages they compact less than shales. These buried hills may consist of any kind of rock, provided it compacts less than the sediments with which it is covered. Many of the buried hills over which anticlines form by differential compaction are composed of limestone, dolomite, or igneous or metamorphic rocks.

Let it be assumed that a hill of limestone or of granite is being buried beneath an increasing amount of sediments, and that the hill is 100 ft high. Let it also be supposed that a stratum just touches the crest of the hill, and that the shales which bury the hill compact 30 per cent as a result of the weight of overburden. The result is an anticline with 30 feet of closure in the layer which touches the crest of the hill. The size of the fold gradually decreases upward and normally becomes insignificant or imperceptible a mile or so above the buried hill.

If the buried hill itself is so rigid that it does not compact appreciably as the overburden accumulates, the closure of the fold produced by compaction over it is determined by two factors: the compacting ability of the sediments surrounding the buried hill below the level of its top, and the weight of the overburden. The compacting ability of the sediments above the level of the top of the buried hill does not affect the height of the overlying anticline. The largest folds due to differential compaction are produced when the buried hill is surrounded by shale or clay. Sand, lime, or chert in these shales reduces the size of the fold produced by differential compaction.

QUANTITATIVE ASPECTS OF COMPACTION

Tables, Graphs, and Formulas. It is desirable to know how large a structure is produced by compaction a certain distance above a buried hill or reef, and how large a buried hill there must be to produce an anticline of given size a certain distance above it. This subject has been discussed by Athy,[1] Hedberg,[2] Rubey,[3] Trask,[4] and Dickinson.[5] These authors give tables, graphs, or formulas by which the amount of compaction could theoretically be calculated. These quantitative methods are based on measurements of the rate of change of porosity with depth in wells. However, Athy[6] reports that the quantitative methods given by Hedberg and Rubey did not give results in agreement with those he found in north central Oklahoma, and concludes that the rate of change of porosity with depth varies from place to place. Dickinson also concludes that the rate of change of porosity and density with depth varies with the locality and with the age of the deposits.

[1] L. F. Athy, Density, Porosity and Compaction of Sedimentary Rocks, *A.A.P.G. Bull.*, vol. 14, pp. 1–24 (1930).

[2] Hollis D. Hedberg, The Effect of Gravitational Compaction on the Structure of Sedimentary Rocks, *A.A.P.G. Bull.*, vol. 10, pp. 1035–1072 (1926); Discussion, vol. 11, pp. 875–886 (1927).

[3] W. W. Rubey, The Effect of a Gravitational Compaction on the Structure of Sedimentary Rocks, A Discussion, *A.A.P.G. Bull.*, vol. 11, pp. 621–632 (1927).

[4] Parker D. Trask, Compaction of Sediments, *A.A.P.G. Bull.*, vol. 15, pp. 271–276 (1931).

[5] George Dickinson, Geological Aspects of Abnormal Reservoir Pressures on Gulf Coast Louisiana, *A.A.P.G. Bull.*, vol. 37, pp. 410–432 (1953).

[6] *Op. cit.*, p. 14.

Table 9-1 is taken from Hedberg's paper.[1] It should not be supposed that this table is accurate everywhere and for all instances. It is introduced to show how the size of the folds produced by compaction would be calculated in an area where the relation between porosity and

TABLE 9-1. RELATION BETWEEN POROSITY AND OVERBURDEN

Feet of overburden	Percentage porosity
First 100 ft, av.	50
1,000	30
2,000	23
3,000	18
4,000	14.7
5,000	12.2
6,000	10.4
7,000	9
8,000	8

overburden was as shown in this table. A hill 100 ft high would be surrounded by shale with an average porosity of 50 per cent when the sediments just covered the crest of the hill. When the crest of the hill was covered by 3,000 ft of sediments, the average porosity of the shales surrounding the hill would be reduced from 50 to 18 per cent, or by 32 per cent. The closure of the anticline formed in a stratum just touching the crest of the hill would be 100 × .32 or 32 ft. If the hill had been buried to a depth of 8,000 ft, 10 ft of closure would be developed in a horizon 3,000 ft above the top of the hill. If it is known how deeply an area has been buried and how deep the buried hill would be if present, the table may be used to determine how high a buried hill would have to be to produce a given anticline. For example, if an area has been buried to a depth of 5,000 ft, and an anticline with 10 ft of structural relief is present at the surface, at a depth of 3,000 ft a buried hill 100 ft high would be required to produce this anticline by differential compaction.

Fig. 9-1, from Dickinson's paper,[2] shows the depth-density curves of Athy and Hedberg. The third curve is Dickinson's estimate for Gulf Coast shales. Dickinson also points out that older shales generally have a greater density than younger shales found at the same depth.

CORRECTIONS AND ERRORS IN QUANTITATIVE DETERMINATIONS

The tables, formulas, and graphs for making quantitative calculations of differential compaction are based on porosity or density determinations of shales. As already mentioned, porosity as applied to shales has no definite meaning; it is therefore necessary to describe accurately the methods used for determining the porosity in order to give the results

[1] Hollis D. Hedberg, The Effect of Gravitational Compaction on the Structure of Sedimentary Rocks, *A.A.P.G. Bull.*, vol. 10, p. 1058 (1926).
[2] *Op. cit.*, p. 427.

a definite value.   In many cases the methods used to determine porosity have not been mentioned.   Furthermore, in some cases it is not stated whether wet or air-dried samples were used, or at what temperature the samples were dried.

The most accurate results would be obtained by using wet cores. These are cores which have been kept sealed or immersed in water since they were extracted.   If dried samples are used, an error may be produced by the shrinkage in drying.   It should be noted also that some methods of measuring porosity, though they give reliable results on sandstones, may be inaccurate when applied to shales.

The rate of change of porosity with depth is probably affected by variations in the age of the deposits, by the stresses and deformation that have affected them, and by the varying lithology.   These effects appear to have been kept in mind by those writing on this subject.

EXPERIMENTS RELATING TO COMPACTION

Those who have experimented with compaction have had one factor in their favor.   In general, experiments made before the theory of scale models was propounded used materials of too much strength in making their model structures.   In experiments on compaction, however, the general situation practically requires that unconsolidated and very weak substances be used.   As a result these experiments have duplicated the natural structures better than many of the contemporaneous experiments in which stronger materials were used.

Nevin and Sherrill[1] have described some experiments in which structures were produced which closely resemble those found over buried hills in oil fields.   It was found that where compaction takes place over a rigid object that is steeper on one side than on the other, the axial plane of the resultant anticline dips toward the steeper side.

RELATED TYPES OF TRAPS FOR OIL AND GAS ACCUMULATION

It is the occurrence of oil and gas fields in association with buried hills and structures produced by differential compaction that makes them so interesting to petroleum geologists.   The oil fields associated with these features are in some areas very numerous but for the most part not individually very large.   Some great fields, such as the Texas Panhandle oil and gas field, occur in association with buried hills, but in this case the trap is not entirely produced by the buried hills but is in part produced by structural deformation.   Traps over limestone and dolomite reefs are produced by compaction and belong in this classification.   However, they are discussed in Chap. 10 in connection with reefs.

[1] C. M. Nevin and R. E. Sherrill, Studies in Differential Compaction, *A.A.P.G. Bull.*, vol. 13, pp. 1–22 (1929).

Traps within Buried Hills. A buried hill lies beneath an unconformity and must have been exposed to erosion for a long time. The conditions are therefore favorable for the development of porosity and permeability in the buried hills, provided that the rocks of which they are composed are of the right nature. Some rocks, such as sandstones and certain limestones and dolomites, may have been porous and permeable before they were exposed to erosion, while other rocks become porous and permeable only on weathering. If the hills are composed of limestone or dolomite, rain water falling on them before burial will be likely to percolate downward through joints or pores. As it moves through them it may increase the original porosity and permeability by enlarging the openings through which it travels. It is quite common, therefore, to find that buried hills of limestone or dolomite have appreciable permeability. Even igneous and metamorphic rocks may be sufficiently broken up by weathering so that they can form reservoir rocks. However, it is probable that the production obtained from rocks of this nature is generally from fractures produced by structural deformation rather than cavities produced by weathering.

Any porous and permeable rock constituting a buried hill forms a trap for the accumulation of oil and gas when buried by impervious sediments. Nevertheless, the reservoir rock in oil fields in this type of structure is generally limestone or dolomite. The thickness of the reservoir is limited only by the height of the buried hill; hence some of them have thick producing sections.

Traps in Sediments around Buried Hills. Buried hills may be responsible for the accumulation of oil in sedimentary traps associated with them. Oil or gas fields may occur in sands deposited on their flanks and terminating below their tops. These sands generally dip away from the hills, and a trap is formed where they terminate updip against the side of the hill. If the erosion of the hills produces a permeable rock such as a sandstone or granite wash, the reservoir rocks of the oil fields may be derived from the hills. Such rocks may occur in the valleys between the hills.

Traps over Buried Hills. Many oil and gas fields occur in anticlines produced by compaction over the buried hills. These anticlines reflect in a subdued form the topography of the underlying hills. Synclines and anticlinal noses are produced over valleys and minor ridges in the buried hills. The area of the anticlines is about the same as the area of the hills beneath them. The structural relief and closure of these anticlines are always smaller than the height of the hills and diminish upward. The dips on the flanks of these anticlines are less steep than the dips on the hills which cause them, and the dips grow more gentle upward.

Anticlines formed by compaction may be distinguished from those formed by compression in part by their shape. Folds formed by compression are likely to be long, narrow, and parallel to each other. Folds formed by compaction reflect the forms of the topography which cause them, and may be of very irregular configuration. The area, vertical relief, and dips of the folds may show whether they could be caused by compaction or not. If wells have been drilled to the unconformable surface on which the hills occur, it may be possible to determine whether the structures reflect the underlying topography.

Combinations of Buried Hills and Recurrent Folds

In Kansas, Oklahoma, and probably also Missouri and northern Arkansas there are some anticlines which overlie buried hills in the top of the pre-Cambrian surface. Some of these anticlines could not have been produced entirely by compaction because they are larger than could be produced in this manner. The best explanation of these features seems to be that they are caused by recurrent folds with approximately the same axes. The fold first causes a hill by structural uplift. Before the hill is eroded away it is buried by sediments. These sediments are then folded by an anticlinal uplift occurring at about the same location as the original anticline.

Production from Traps Associated with Buried Hills

Some of the oil fields of Kansas furnish excellent examples of the relations between buried hills and oil production. Fig. 9-2, from a paper by Thomas,[1] shows a cross section through two anticlines related to buried hills. The anticline on the right is unproductive, though it has as large a closure as the other anticlines in the area which produce oil. The Elbing oil field is located on the anticline on the left side of the cross section. It produces from the weathered uppermost portion of the Ordovician limestone, just beneath the unconformity. It is evident that this limestone projected above the surface before burial as a buried hill. The angular unconformity is at the base of the Pennsylvanian. The pre-Pennsylvanian surface was clearly of marked relief, and this relief has a close relation to the structure of the pre-Pennsylvanian strata. Every hill in this surface overlies an anticline in the older rocks, and every valley a syncline. Furthermore, the structure of the Pennsylvanian strata above the unconformity reflects the buried topography in a subdued form, the size of the folds gradually decreasing upward. This is characteristic of folds formed by differential compaction.

[1] C. R. Thomas, Flank Production of the Nemaha Mountains (Granite Ridge), Kansas, "Structure of Typical American Oil Fields," American Association of Petroleum Geologists, Tulsa, vol. 1, p. 67 (1929).

Another area in Kansas in which oil production has been found in association with buried hills has been described by Walters,[1] from whose paper Fig. 9-3 is taken. In this area most of the production is obtained from buried topographic highs in the top of the Cambro-Ordovician Arbuckle dolomite at its unconformable contact with the Pennsylvanian beds. Some oil is also obtained from Pennsylvanian limestones in gentle anticlines formed by compaction over the buried hills. These anticlines are indicated on the cross section by the variations in the elevation of the

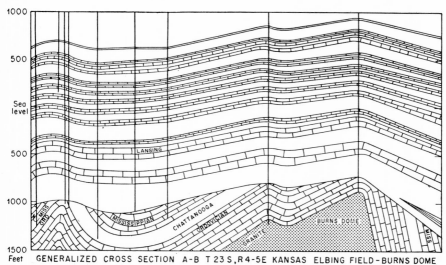

GENERALIZED CROSS SECTION A-B T 23 S, R 4-5 E KANSAS ELBING FIELD-BURNS DOME

FIG. 9-2. Cross section showing the relation of primary anticlines, buried hills, folds produced by compaction, and oil production in an area in Kansas. (*After Thomas, published by permission of the American Association of Petroleum Geologists.*)

top of the Missouri series, which is 200 to 300 ft above the base of the Pennsylvanian. The relatively steep dips on the flanks of the buried pre-Cambrian hill are initial dips due to deposition on inclined slopes. The Stoltenberg field on the right produces from a buried hill in the top of the Arbuckle dolomite. The solution of the dolomite before the deposition of the Pennsylvanian strata produced a karst topography, with numerous sinkholes filled with relatively impervious clay, sand, and chert. Many dry holes between producing wells result from drilling into these sinkholes. In another paper Walters[2] states that oil is produced from fractured pre-Cambrian basement rocks in buried hills in 50 more widely

[1] Robert F. Walters, Buried Pre-Cambrian Hills in Northeastern Barton County, Central Kansas, *A.A.P.G. Bull.*, vol. 30, pp. 660–710 (1946).

[2] Robert F. Walters, Oil Production from Fractured Pre-Cambrian Basement Rocks in Central Kansas, *A.A.P.G. Bull.*, vol. 37, pp. 300–313 (1953).

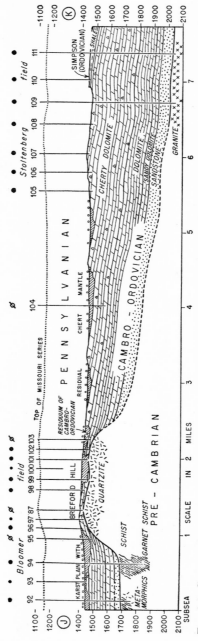

FIG. 9-3. Cross section of an area in central Kansas showing buried karst topography, hills of pre-Cambrian rock, and folds formed by compaction. (*After Walters, published by permission of the American Association of Petroleum Geologists.*)

232

scattered fields in central Kansas. These hills rise from 100 to 500 ft above the general level of the top of the pre-Cambrian basement.

ADDITIONAL REFERENCES

Bridge, J., and Dake, C. L.: Initial Dips Peripheral to Resurrected Hills, *Missouri Bur. Geology and Mines, Biennial Rept. State Geologist* (1927–1928), pp. 93–99 (1929).

Brown, A. B.: Bowers Field, Montague County, Texas, *A.A.P.G. Bull.*, vol. 27, pp. 20–37 (1943).

Fath, A. E.: The Origin of Faults, Anticlines and Buried "Granite Ridge" of the Northern Part of the Mid-Continent Oil and Gas Field, *U.S.G.S. Prof. Paper* 128(c) (1921).

Ferguson, J. L., and Vernon, J.: Relationship of Buried Hills to Petroleum Accumulation, "Science of Petroleum," Oxford University Press, New York, vol. 1, pp. 240–243 (1938).

Gilluly, J., and Grant, U. S.: Subsidence in the Long Beach Harbor Area, California, *G.S.A. Bull.*, vol. 60, pp. 461–529 (1949).

Powers, S.: Reflected Buried Hills and Their Importance in Petroleum Geology, *Econ. Geology*, vol. 17, pp. 233–259 (1922).

Sugden, W.: The Influence of Water Films Adsorbed by Mineral Grains upon the Compaction of Natural Sediments and Notes on Allied Phenomena, *Geol. Mag.*, vol. 87, pp. 26–40 (1950).

Wilson, I. F.: Buried Topography, Initial Structure and Sedimentation in Santa Rosalia Area, Baja California, Mexico, *A.A.P.G. Bull.*, vol. 32, pp. 1762–1807 (1948).

CHAPTER 10

SEDIMENTARY STRUCTURES

DEFINITION

Sedimentary structures are features of some definite or characteristic shape or internal arrangement which are composed of sediments or occur in sediments. These structures were either formed by deposition before burial or developed in the sediments without the aid of structural deformation. However, nearly all were present in the sediments before burial. It is only the minor sedimentary structures of the general type of concretions which develop after burial.

There is no question of the importance of sedimentary structures to the petroleum geologist. They form the traps in which many oil and gas fields occur. These sedimentary structures, generally known as stratigraphic traps, are likely to become more important in the future, owing to the exhaustion of the more easily found structural traps.

CLASSIFICATION

Sedimentary structures might be classified in a number of different ways. They could be classed by their origin, by the agency which deposited them, by their shape, by their size, and according to whether they are produced at the same time as the enclosing deposits or after them. Sedimentary structures produced at the same time as the sediments themselves are primary or contemporaneous; those produced after burial are secondary. The classification according to size gives minor, local, and regional.

MINOR PRIMARY SEDIMENTARY STRUCTURES

Structures Related to Bedding or Layering. All dip and strike measurements are made with reference to the plane of bedding or stratification. Accordingly, stratification or layering is a sedimentary structure of considerable importance in structural geology. This general subject has been discussed by Grabau,[1] Krumbein and Sloss,[2]

---

[1] Amadeus W. Grabau, "Principles of Stratigraphy," 2d ed., A. G. Seiler, New York, pp. 697–699 (1930).

[2] W. C. Krumbein and L. L. Sloss, "Stratigraphy and Sedimentation," W. H. Freeman and Company, San Francisco, p. 97 (1951).

Pettijohn,[1] Shrock,[2] and Twenhofel.[3] A lamina is the thinnest sedimentary unit; it is about 1 cm or less in thickness and may be paper-thin. Each lamina differs from those above and below it in some lithologic character. Fissility is the ability of shales to split along parallel planes into thin plates. According to Lewis,[4] argillaceous rocks do not have this ability to cleave when freshly deposited, but gain it during compaction. If this is the case, fissility is a secondary property, but it is convenient to discuss it along with the stratum and lamina. Unlike lamination, fissility has no relation to differences in composition, but occurs in shales of a uniform character. It is caused by the parallel arrangement of the mica and other platy or elongated mineral grains. Fissility is generally parallel to the laminae and strata.

A stratum is somewhat thicker than a lamina. A unit 1 in. to several inches thick would be called a stratum. A bed may be a few inches or a few feet in thickness. A massive rock is either entirely without bedding and stratification, or the bedding is very thick.

Lamination, stratification, and bedding are produced by variations in the composition, grain size, cementation, hardness, color, or other lithologic property of the rock. These variations are caused originally by the variations in the conditions of deposition. However, the effects of the primary features may be increased in some cases by weathering. In most sediments the laminae, strata, and beds are approximately parallel over considerable vertical intervals. Nevertheless, there is usually some slight departure from parallelism. For this reason, measurements of local dips made with the clinometer have small but unavoidable errors of stratigraphic origin. The size of this error varies with the nature of the deposits. If the exposures are small, it is probably usually a degree or two.

"Face" refers to the direction in sedimentary deposits which was upward when they were laid down. If previously undisturbed strata were tilted 90° toward the north, they would be said to face north.

Graded Bedding. If the details of clastic deposits are studied carefully, abrupt changes in the coarseness will be found in many rocks. Commonly a layer which is relatively very coarse at the base overlies a fine-grained stratum. This coarser deposit becomes progressively finer

[1] F. J. Pettijohn, "Sedimentary Rocks," Harper & Brothers, New York, pp. 129–130, 228 (1949).

[2] Robert R. Shrock, "Sequence in Layered Rocks," McGraw-Hill Book Company, Inc., New York, pp. 5–18 (1948).

[3] W. H. Twenhofel, "Principles of Sedimentation," McGraw-Hill Book Company, Inc., pp. 494–498 (1939); "Treatise on Sedimentation," 2d ed., The Williams & Wilkins Company, Baltimore, p. 83 (1932).

[4] J. Volney Lewis, Fissility of Shale and Its Relations to Petroleum, *G.S.A. Bull.*, vol. 35, pp. 557–590 (1924).

upward, and its top may be the fine material at the base of the overlying coarser layer.   These features are known as graded bedding.   They are very useful for determining the top and base of sediments.

Cross-bedding and Initial Dip.   Another common structural feature of sediments is cross-bedding, also known as false bedding and cross-lamination.   Cross-bedding occurs in crystalline limestones, dolomites, and shales, but is commonest in sandstones.   The feature which characterizes it is the difference in the dip of the cross-bedded strata from the prevailing dip of the beds above and below.   The cause of cross-bedding is deposition on an inclined surface.   This inclined surface may be produced by erosion, or by the sedimentation itself.   Inclined surfaces due to deposition occur, for example, when a pond or depression is filled by sediments coming in from one side.

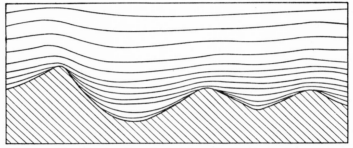

Fig. 10-1. Cross section showing the effect of irregularities in the base of deposition on the attitude of the strata.

Fig. 10-1 shows cross-bedding caused by irregularities in the surface on which the strata are deposited.   Because each layer tends to be slightly thinner on the rises in the surface of deposition and slightly thicker in the depressions, the undulations in the strata produced by irregularities in the surface of deposition gradually die out upward.

Fig. 10-2 shows another type of cross-bedding.   The depression is being filled by sandy sediments coming from the left.   The strong currents which carry the sand drop it as soon as the edge of the depression is reached, with the result that the sand slides or rolls into the depression and comes to rest at a rather steep angle.   According to Twenhofel,[1] the maximum angle of inclination of clastic deposits is about 43°.   The usual angle of dip of cross-bedded strata is much gentler than this, averaging about 20° or less.   Travertine and reef limestones may be deposited at much higher angles, because they may adhere to the surfaces on which they are deposited.

[1] W. H. Twenhofel, "Principles of Sedimentation," McGraw-Hill Book Company, Inc., New York, pp. 495–496 (1939).

Figs. 10-2 and 10-3 show how cross-bedding may be used to determine which side of a steeply dipping deposit is the original top and which is the original base. If currents are filling in a body of water from the side, the conditions may be as shown in Fig. 10-2. The strata marked A, known as the top-set beds, are laid down on top of the steeply dipping

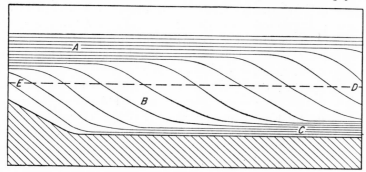

Fig. 10-2. Cross section showing top-set, fore-set, and bottom-set beds.

strata after they have been buried. The steeply dipping strata, B, are known as fore-set beds. They advance progressively over the bottom-set beds, C, and gradually cover them. If the strata remain as in Fig. 10-2, cross-bedding might be difficult to use in determining top and bottom. However, it commonly happens that the currents erode away the top-set beds and the upper part of the fore-set beds. This erosion may cut off the series at the line ED, Fig. 10-2. The bottom-set beds and the

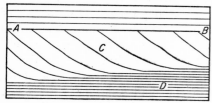

Fig. 10-3. Cross section showing the effect of the erosion of the top-set beds and the upper part of the fore-set beds on typical cross-bedded structures. The line AB is the same as the line ED of Fig. 10-2.

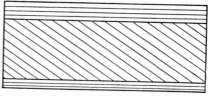

Fig. 10-4. Cross section showing a common type of cross-bedding.

lower part of the fore-set beds are much less likely to be cut off by erosion, because they are at a lower level. The final result is likely to be a structure like that shown in Fig. 10-3. The line AB of Fig. 10-3 is the erosion surface ED of Fig. 10-2. This aspect of cross-bedding permits determining top and base. The significant feature is the curve at the base of the fore-set beds, which is concave upward. Another common type of cross-bedding, shown in Fig. 10-4, does not permit determining top and base.

Fig. 10-2 may also be considered to be a cross section of a delta. A delta may be only a few inches across, or it may extend for hundreds of miles. The description of deltas is given on pages 252–253.

Imbricate Structure and Edgewise Conglomerates. If the pebbles of a conglomerate are flat or disk-shaped, they tend to come to rest with the disks sloping upstream. This arrangement is called imbricate structure. It is likely to give the false impression that the dip is upstream. It should not be confused with the imbricate structure produced by reverse faults. Conglomerates composed of flat pebbles which are nearly vertical are called edgewise conglomerates.

Sedimentary Fabric. If the particles of a sediment have a preferred orientation, the result is sedimentary fabric. This type of structure has been described by Krumbein and Sloss[1] and by Pettijohn.[2] The commonest type of sedimentary fabric is the arrangement of the flakes of platy minerals parallel to the bedding. If the longest dimensions of the grains have a preferred orientation, lineation is produced. The determination of the direction of lineation in oriented cores might possibly be useful for predicting the trend of linear sedimentary deposits such as bars and channel fillings. Aside from determining the plane of stratification, petroleum geologists have made little practical use of sedimentary fabric or lineation. However, it appears that possible uses of fabric and lineation in petroleum geology are a promising field for research.

Cyclic Deposition. In some sediments there is a marked rhythm in the deposition. Certain successions of lithologic types tend to be repeated again and again. Some such alternations are easily explained as being due to annual variations in the conditions of deposition. The varves of glacial lakes and probably the anhydrite-rich bands of some salt deposits are of this nature. Possibly other sedimentary cycles are caused by climatic cycles of longer duration. However, some rhythms in sedimentation cannot be due to climatic variations and must be caused by rhythmic elevations and depressions of the land relative to sea level. Cyclothems are repetitions of a series of characteristic deposits; they are best developed in the Pennsylvanian strata associated with the coal deposits. Cyclothems involve alternations of marine and terrestrial strata, and must therefore involve rhythmic changes in the relative elevations of land and sea. Erosion takes place during the phase of the cyclothem when the land is at its highest. This produces a disconformity which marks the base of each cyclothem. During subsidence sediments accumulate on the unconformable surface. Generally sandstone is the first deposit. Coal is laid down as the land approaches sea level, and

---

[1] *Op. cit.*, p. 84 (1951).

[2] F. J. Pettijohn, "Sedimentary Rocks," Harper & Brothers, New York, p. 59 (1949).

black shales and limestones with marine fossils form while the surface is below sea level. Cyclothems have been described by Shrock,[1] Krumbein and Sloss,[2] and Wanless and Weller.[3]

Markings on Surfaces of Deposition. The top of each layer was once the surface. Before these surfaces were covered by the succeeding layer, various markings and impressions may have been produced on them. Among the more common are rill marks, the swash marks of waves, raindrop impressions, and animal tracks. Beach cusps are triangular ridges of sand, pointing toward the water, 1 to 100 ft apart and an inch to several feet in height. They have been described by Grabau.[4]

Mud Cracks. Mud cracks, also called sun cracks and shrinkage cracks, occur wherever mud dries out. The edges of the polygons between the cracks may curl, and the cracked fragments may be swept along by the currents and included in intraformational conglomerates. In sediments the mud cracks are frequently recognized because the material filling the cracks is of a different nature from the surrounding rock. Mud cracks are generally formed in a terrestrial environment; playa lakes and the flood plains of streams and rivers are especially favorable for their development. They are valuable for indicating the conditions of deposition and for showing which is the top and which the base of the beds.

Clastic Dikes. Clastic dikes appear to be of two types, tectonic and sedimentary. The material of clastic dikes of tectonic origin is intruded into a crack in the sediments by stresses developed in the rocks. The cracks themselves were presumably opened up by folding, faulting, slumping, earthquake vibrations, or other types of tectonic disturbance. If the crack in which the dike now occurs was open to the surface, it may have been filled by normal sedimentary processes. Deep cracks of this nature may be caused by shrinkage on drying, structural deformation, slumping, or earthquake vibrations. If the cracks have been filled by deposits which have been washed or blown into them, the mica flakes tend to be horizontal, as in any sediment. If, on the other hand, the clastic dike is intrusive, the mica flakes near the edge of the dike tend to be parallel to the edge.

Ripple Marks. Ripple marks have been described by Shrock,[5] Twenhofel,[6] and Pettijohn.[7] They consist of parallel ridges in the surfaces

---

[1] *Op. cit.*, pp. 30–40 (1948).

[2] *Op. cit.*, pp. 375–379 (1951).

[3] H. R. Wanless and J. M. Weller, "Correlation and Extent of Pennsylvanian Cyclothems," *G.S.A. Bull.*, vol. 43, pp. 1003–1016 (1932).

[4] *Op. cit.*, p. 708.

[5] *Op. cit.*, pp. 93–94, 103–104.

[6] W. H. Twenhofel, "Principles of Sedimentation," McGraw-Hill Book Company, Inc., New York, pp. 518–527 (1939).

[7] *Op. cit.*, pp. 129–130.

separating strata or beds.   The ridges are generally ½ to 2 in. high and several inches apart.   Ripple marks formed by water are generally made of sand; ripple marks in wind-laid deposits may be made of dust also. In ripple marks formed under water the grains in the troughs are generally coarser than those in the crests.

There are two common types of ripple marks.   Current ripple marks, shown in Fig. 10-5, have steep slopes in the direction toward which the

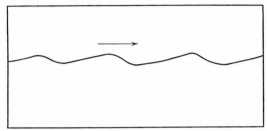

Fig. 10-5. Cross section showing current ripple marks.   Arrow shows direction of the current.

current moves.   The outlines of these ripple marks generally do not indicate which side is top and which is bottom.   Oscillation ripple marks, shown in Fig. 10-6, are caused by waves.   They have sharp crests and rounded depressions.   Thus their shapes indicate the top and bottom of disturbed beds.

Oölites and Pisolites.   Oölites and pisolites are types of concretions. They are not included in the description of concretions in the following

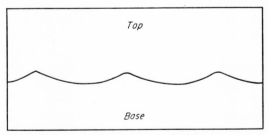

Fig. 10-6. Cross section showing oscillation ripple marks.

section because they formed contemporaneously with the enclosing sediments.   In other words, they were regenerated at the surface before burial.   Oölites and pisolites have a rounded or oval shape and a concentric or radiating structure.   When first deposited they were commonly composed of calcium carbonate.   However, since deposition they may have been altered to dolomite.   Oölites are about the size of shot or the grains of a very coarse sandstone.   Pisolites are about the size of peas.   Oölites and oölitic limestones are important to the petroleum geologist because they are the reservoir rocks of many oil and gas fields. In many oölitic limestones the spaces between the oölites have been cemented so that the porosity and permeability are too low for oil and gas production. Other oölitic limestones and dolomites contain abundant pore space between the oölites and have good permeability. The McClosky horizon in the Mississippian of Illinois and adjacent states is of this nature.

Minor Secondary Sedimentary Structures

Concretions, Septaria, Geodes. General Characteristics. Concretions are of such general occurrence that every geologist is familiar with them. Concretions may occur in most of the common types of sedimentary rock, but there is a tendency for the composition of the concretions to vary with the kind of rock in which they occur. They are usually composed of some minor constituent of the rock. The concretions in shales are likely to be composed of calcite or siderite, those in sandstones of calcite, siderite, or iron oxides, and those in limestones of chert. These are merely the commonest types of concretions; the rarer varieties may be composed of a considerable variety of uncommon minerals.

Concretions generally have rounded outlines, though some of the larger ones have very rough surfaces. They may be spherical, oval, cylindrical, or flat and tabular. The longest dimension of concretions is generally parallel to the stratification. Zones of concretions may follow certain beds. When the bedding is indistinct, these zones may be useful for determining dip and strike. The strata and laminations may curve around concretions, but usually pass through them. Concretions vary in size from small lumps ½ in. or less in length to huge masses 20 ft or more in diameter. Concretions may be structureless, or they may have a concentric or radiating internal structure. Many concretions have at their center a speck or lump of different composition from the rest of the rock. This foreign body served as a nucleus around which the concretion grew. In many cases this nucleus is a fossil. In fact, it is quite common to find richly fossiliferous concretions in sediments otherwise devoid of fossils.

Origin of Concretions. Concretions evidently developed because of the tendency of some mineral widely scattered through the rock in a finely divided state to gather into larger masses. Since all minerals are at least very slightly soluble in water, minute particles scattered through the rock can dissolve in the water in the pores or cracks, migrate short distances by diffusion, and slowly gather into concretions.

Time of Formation of Concretions. Most concretions form after the enclosing rocks have been buried by sediments. However, there is a great deal of controversy as to whether chert concretions and bedded cherts formed before or after burial.   The occurrence of concretions in Recent or late Pleistocene clays shows that they may form within a few thousand years after burial.   The fact that zones of concretions occur beneath unconformities and follow them rather than the enclosing strata indicates that they may form beneath surfaces of erosion.   Doubtless some concretions develop in the zone of weathering or ground-water circulation related to the present surface.   Concretions forming at this late date may be recognized because they follow the land surface rather than the bedding.   Concretions presumably formed after burial if the laminations pass through them without bending.   Between these wide limits little is generally known as to the time of formation of concretions.

Septaria, Geodes.   Septaria are large concretions the outer parts of which are traversed by cracks which grow narrower toward the center. The septaria are commonly composed of limestone, and the cracks may be filled with lighter-colored calcite.   Geodes are concretions, usually rounded, containing central cavities lined with crystals.

Uses of Concretions.   Concretions may be very useful in surface structural and stratigraphic work because they may constitute reliable key horizons.   In thick shale beds such as the Pierre shale of the Great Plains region east of the Rocky Mountains, structural mapping is greatly aided by the zones of concretions.   It is quite common to find that concretions of a given type are confined to a certain horizon.   However, it should not be assumed that any type of concretion is a reliable key horizon unless careful consideration has been given to the evidence favoring all the other possibilities.   These other possibilities include the existence of two or more beds of concretions of the same type, the occurrence of the concretions in patches of irregular distribution at different horizons, the possibility that the zone of concretions is not parallel to the strata, and the possibility that the zone of concretions follows the present surface or an angular unconformity.

In surface structural work it is in some cases found that the zones of concretions make better key horizons than the variations in the lithology of the shales in which they occur.   In areas of slight to moderate relief, outcrops of shales may be very rare.   The concretions, on the other hand, weather out of the shales and are found in the soil below the level of the outcrop of the horizon in which they occur.   The highest occurrence of a concretion of a given type on a hillside may generally be taken to mark the outcrop of the key horizon.   However, in some cases it may be advisable to add a few feet to this elevation, to allow for slumping and soil creep.

The chert concretions of limestones may in many cases be used in a similar manner.   Some limestones may not show suitable lithologic variations for use as key beds, or the exposures of limestone may be too scanty for surface structural mapping. Many areas in which limestone is the bedrock are covered by a thick mantle of red clay containing chert, and exposures of limestone may be very rare. However, even if it has been established that a given type of chert is characteristic of a certain horizon in the limestone, it is necessary to exercise a great deal of caution in determining what elevation to use for structural control points. The highest chert fragments found may be far below the original level of the stratum in the limestone from which the chert came. The red clay occupies a much smaller volume than the limestone from which it was derived. Thus as the limestone is dissolved, the overlying red clay and contained chert slump down greatly. In general, the thicker the red clay beneath a chert occurrence, the greater is the amount of settling.

In subsurface work, it has also been found that chert zones in limestones are very useful for correlation. However, concretions are, in general, much less valuable for correlation in subsurface work than at the surface. This is because the concretions may be missed in the cuttings, because some of the distinctive characteristics of the concretions may be lost in grinding, and because much better information about the lithology of the rocks containing the concretions may be available in subsurface work.

Cone-in-cone. Cone-in-cone consists of calcite in fibrous form, with the fibers in parallel arrangement. The whole is apt to have the shape of imperfect cones, or to break along surfaces which have the shape of cones. Cone-in-cone generally occurs in masses a few inches across. It is common in certain shales but is rare in rocks of other types. In some cases cone-in-cone is developed only in certain horizons. Where the occurrence of cone-in-cone is restricted to certain horizons, it has a limited use as a key bed for surface structural mapping.

Stylolites. Stylolites are partings in limestones which are of limited extent, generally approximately parallel to the bedding, and show sharp irregular, angular, or rectangular bends. They are commonest in limestones and dolomites and very rare in rocks of other types. Along the line of the stylolite there is in many cases a thin seam of clay, which is like the residual clay formed by the solution of the limestone. It is supposed that stylolites are formed by the action of stresses which control the solution of the limestone. These pressures cause the limestone to dissolve along the surface of the stylolite.

Local Sedimentary Structures

Local sedimentary structures are of the greatest importance in petroleum geology, because they form or help to form the traps in which oil and gas occur. The general discussion of these traps is reserved for Chap. 16. In this chapter only those sedimentary features which have a definite shape or internal structure are discussed.   Many traps in which oil and gas may accumulate are permeability zones which have no characteristic shape or structure; the description of all these is given in Chap. 16.

The term "lenticular" is in common use to describe sedimentary units which are nonpersistent.   However, if the true dimensions of most of these are considered, it appears that they are generally about 100 times as wide as they are high.   Evidently they are very thin disks rather than lenses.   The idea that they look like lenses is doubtless suggested by the great vertical exaggeration of the cross sections in which they are shown.

Reefs. *Importance.*   Before 1930 petroleum geologists paid little attention to reefs, but between 1940 and 1950 important reef production was found in many areas.   The discoveries of reef production in West Texas and in Alberta, Canada, were especially noteworthy.   As a result petroleum geologists have become reef-conscious, and reefs are eagerly sought in all the areas of the country where the prospects for this type of production are at all promising.   Reefs buried to the right depth for oil production are difficult but not impossible to find; they may be present even in areas which have been covered by seismograph and gravimeter surveys with negative results.   Consequently it seems likely that reef production will continue to be found for some time to come.

Definitions.   A reef or bioherm is a mass of sedimentary rock of organic origin which at the time of its formation rose above the surrounding surface of deposition in a distinct mound or peak.   In the case of fringing reefs and of some types of barrier reefs of the type shown in Fig. 10-8, the reef rose above the surface of deposition on one side only. On the other side there may have been merely a very slight rise or none at all.   A biostrome is a sediment of organic origin which was deposited as a bed or formation covering a large area.   In other words, it was laid down like any ordinary sedimentary deposit.   A biostrome was laid down as a sheet deposit of rather uniform thickness, while a bioherm is a thick deposit covering a limited area, which caused an elevation in the surface on which the sediments accumulated.

General Characteristics.   The typical features of reefs are shown in Fig. 10-7.   Reefs vary in size from small masses a few feet in diameter to great accumulations 1,000 miles in length and many miles wide.   Some reefs are moundlike and more or less round; others are long and narrow. The reefs which produce oil vary in height from 20 or 30 ft to over 1,000 ft, and in length from a few thousand feet to several tens of miles.   Reefs tend to be triangular in cross section, with flat bases and sharp crests. One side may be much steeper than the other.   Where this occurs the steep side is toward the waves and currents, or toward the most open water.   Slopes of 20 to 30° are not uncommon on the steep sides.   Many reefs have a number of highly irregular peaks and depressions in their upper surfaces.

Relation of Reef Building to Temperature and Depth. The effect of temperature on reef growth varies with the type of organism by which the reefs are formed. Corals require warm waters. Other organisms which build reefs can live in cold water, but the modern reefs are being formed chiefly in the warm waters of the tropics. Reef building is sharply limited by depth. Cloud[1] states that 50 fathoms is the lower limit for reef growth. Cloud also states that a reef 150 ft thick might be formed in 1,000 to 7,500 years.

Types. In the tropics at the present time fringing reefs, barrier reefs, and atolls are found. Fringing reefs border the land; barrier reefs occur some distance out to sea with a shallow bay between the reef and the land. Atolls are circular reefs surrounding a shallow lagoon. The tropical reefs forming at present differ in a number of ways from the reefs in which oil and gas are found. In the first place, the reefs which produce oil generally developed in rather shallow seas more or less surrounded by land. Furthermore, the water surrounding the reefs was shallow to moderately deep and did not drop off abruptly to great depths as is the case with many modern reefs on oceanic islands. The bottoms of the shallow seas in which reefs formed were generally slowly subsiding. In some cases the reefs grew out in the open water and not as a fringe around the land. Some of the reefs in which oil and gas are now found formed parallel to the shore line but at a moderate distance from it. In such cases the sediments laid down between the reef and the land (known as back-reef deposits) were generally quite different from the strata which accumulated in deeper water on the opposite sides of the reefs.

Parts and Attributes. The various parts of reefs are illustrated in Fig. 10-7. The reef core, marked *F* in Fig. 10-7, is the central and most essential feature of reefs. It is generally massive and structureless, but may have a rude bedding. It was commonly a rigid mass even before burial. At the foot of the steep slopes of a reef there may be an accumulation of talus blocks broken by waves from the portion of the reef that extends close to the water level. These talus accumulations, *E* in Fig. 10-7, may extend down to the base of the steep slopes on the flanks of the reef. When originally deposited, reef talus had large open spaces between the fragments, giving the rock a high porosity and permeability. Some of this original porosity and permeability may be retained after consolidation.

Currents may deposit clastic limestone particles broken from the reefs by wave action over a wide area around the reef. Currents developed

---

[1] Preston E. Cloud, Jr., Facies Relationship in Organic Reefs, *A.A.P.G. Bull.*, vol. 36, pp. 2125–2149 (1952).

because of the presence of the reef may also modify the lithology of the sediments near the reef. Since these abnormal deposits may extend many miles from the reef, they are more likely than the reef itself to be encountered by wells. These detrital reef deposits are therefore likely to constitute the first indications of the presence of a reef encountered in subsurface work. They are indicated by D in Fig. 10-7.

Reef-building organisms include corals, algae, bryozoa, sponges, mollusks, and crinoids. In some reefs fossils are rare, possibly because they were destroyed by recrystallization. The rocks composing reefs were originally limestone, but this may have been altered to dolomite. Reefs vary greatly in their porosity and permeability. Many of the reefs

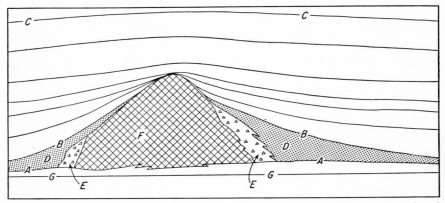

Fig. 10-7. Cross section showing some typical features of reefs. D is the detrital reef material, or sediments the character of which is altered by the presence of the reef; E is the reef talus; and F the reef core.

formed in the geologic past have lost their original porosity and permeability because of cementation and recrystallization. These reefs cannot produce oil or gas unless fractured or unless they have been raised above sea level and have acquired porosity by solution. Where the original porosity is still present it may be retained in a very irregular manner. Some zones and portions of the reef may be porous and permeable, others nonporous. However, since reefs may be as much as 500 to 1,000 ft high, very thick porous zones may occur even in reefs which are largely nonporous.

Barrier Reefs and Facies Changes. Although the reefs in which oil and gas are found did not follow the shore lines of the seas as closely as do the modern fringing and barrier reefs, some of them did form a barrier between sediments of different types. Adams and Frenzel[1] state that

[1] John Emery Adams and Hugh N. Frenzel, Capitan Barrier Reef, Texas and New Mexico, *Jour. Geology*, vol. 58, pp. 289–312 (1950).

the Capitan reef in West Texas grew toward the open water. The upper part of the reef is, in some places, 30 miles in front of the line of its origin. The water in front of the reef was 1,800 ft deep in places, though the top of the reef was approximately at sea level at all times while it was growing. The back-reef deposits consisted of carbonates, anhydrite, salt, and near-shore clastics. A cross section of the Capitan reef is shown in Fig. 10-8.

Divergence and Convergence. If two horizons, one near the base of the reef and one near its top, are traced toward the reef, it is found that they diverge toward the reef. On the other hand, a horizon just touching the top of the reef and one a few hundred feet higher converge toward the reef. This convergence toward the reef is caused by differential compaction over it, as explained in Chap. 9. The reef core, being generally more rigid than the surrounding sediments, compacts less as the overburden increases. Thus a gentle anticline is formed by compaction over the reef. This anticline formed by compaction is especially marked when the reef core is buried by shale. If the reef core is buried by limestone, an anticline may or may not be formed by compaction. Since some reefs are 500 to 1,000 ft high, anticlines of moderate amplitude may form over them by compaction.

The nature of the convergences in the vicinity of reefs is shown in Fig. 10-7. *G* is a horizon just below the reef, deposited just before the reef began to form. *B* is a horizon deposited when the building of the reef was nearly complete. The strata *G* and *B* clearly diverge markedly toward the reef. On the other hand, the strata *B* and *C* and the horizons between them converge toward the reef. It should be noted that the intervals between *G* and all the strata between *B* and *C* diverge toward the reef. These divergences may show up on well logs or in seismograph work. They constitute an important means for discovering reefs.

Relation to Subsidence. Borings and geophysical data on modern reefs suggest that in some cases at least they are thousands of feet thick. For example, according to Shepard,[1] a boring at Bikini showed that shallow-water deposits extend to a depth of 2,500 ft, and geophysical work indicates that the top of the rock on which the sediments accumulated is between 6,000 and 13,000 ft below sea level. Furthermore, soundings have shown that flat-topped mountains, known as seamounts, occur in both the Atlantic and Pacific Oceans. The flat tops of these mountains are evidently produced by erosion near sea level. Yet in some places these flat tops are thousands of feet below sea level. It seems unlikely that there has been such a large, general subsidence of the floors of both the Atlantic and Pacific Oceans since the flat tops of the seamounts were

[1] Francis P. Shepard, Evidence of World-wide Submergence, *Jour. Marine Research,* vol. **7**, p. 669 (1948).

formed, late in geologic time. A promising explanation of both the depths of the flat tops of the seamounts and the thickness of the reefs on oceanic islands is that the great mountains on which both occur gradually sink into the bed of the ocean because of their own weight.

The growth of the reefs in which oil and gas are found has in many cases also been aided by subsidence. Some of them could only be accounted for by subsidence during growth, since they are 500 to 1,000 ft thick. The subsidence in such cases is not due to the weight of the reefs, but is caused by the slow, general depression of the broad shelves, basins, or geosynclines in which the reefs occur.

Fig. 10-8, from a publication by King,[1] shows a cross section through the Permian Capitan reef. This is probably the best-known reef in the

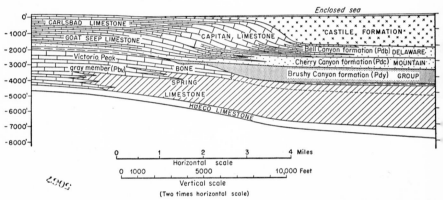

Fig. 10-8. Cross section through the Capitan reef, West Texas, showing conditions at the end of lower Ochoa (Castile) time. (*After King, U.S. Geological Survey.*)

United States. It is splendidly exposed in the Guadalupe Mountains of West Texas and New Mexico, and considerable oil production is obtained from the subsurface extension of this reef. The reef started to grow at the crest of the low arch or terrace shown in the left part of Fig. 10-8. As it grew, it advanced toward the deeper water in the direction of the fore reef. The steeply inclined beds were deposited on the side of the fore reef. The Capitan reef formed a barrier between the fore-reef clastic deposits laid down in deep water to the right and the back-reef limestones to the left. These deposits, though equivalent in age to the Capitan, are different in facies from the Capitan and from each other.

Oil and Gas Production from Reefs. Reefs are very favorable for oil and gas accumulation, presumably because a porous reef covered by an impervious sediment makes a good trap. Furthermore, the high pro-

[1] Philip B. King, Geology of the Southern Guadalupe Mountains, Texas, *U.S.G.S. Prof. Paper* 215, Fig. 7-e (1948).

portion of porous reefs which produce oil seems to indicate that suitable source rocks for generating oil are commonly deposited in association with them. Reefs are generally devoid of oil or gas production if the top is exposed at the surface. The top of a reef must be buried to a depth of at least a few hundred feet to have a suitable cover to contain the oil. One of the features that make reef production so attractive is the high percentage of reefs which are productive in the general region where conditions are favorable for reef production. Another favorable condition is the great thickness of the productive zones in many reefs. In some reefs the producing zones are over 500 ft thick. Furthermore, the rate of production per well per day is in many cases high. The Southern Field or Golden Lane of Mexico is reported to occur on a reef. A production of 260,000 bbl per day from a well in this field has been reported. This appears to be the highest rate on record. The productive areas of some reefs are considerable, and the ultimate production of many reef oil fields is estimated at well over 100,000,000 bbl.

The Discovery of Reefs. Most reefs have been found by the reflection seismograph. However, subsurface studies, gravimeter surveys, and surface geology have also been used successfully in finding them. Subsurface reefs may be located by surface geology only where the anticlines formed over the reefs by compaction can be recognized at the surface. Few reef oil fields appear to have been found by this method. Nevertheless, the recognition of this anticline in subsurface studies and seismograph surveys has resulted in the discovery of many reef oil fields. The convergence and divergence associated with reefs may aid in finding them in cross sections based on well logs and on seismograph surveys. The abnormal character of the sediments around a reef may also aid in finding it. The occurrence of these deposits in well samples shows that a reef is in the vicinity. If samples from a number of wells are available, it may be possible to determine the general direction of the reef from the drilled wells. However, this information generally does not indicate the position of the reef with sufficient exactness to warrant drilling for it without securing further data. Before drilling, it would usually be advisable to make a very detailed reflection seismograph survey of the area in which the reef is expected to occur.

Although the reflection seismograph is the most successful means of finding reefs, it is far from easy to find them by this method. Detailed reflection-seismograph surveys may fail to find reefs even if they are present in the area covered. In some cases the presence of the reef is recognized by the reflections from the surface of the reef itself. Usually, however, the top of the reef is too rough and irregular to give good reflections. The anticline formed over the reefs by differential compaction may show up on the reflection-seismograph surveys. The steeply dipping beds on the flanks of reefs may be recognizable on seismograph surveys by their abnormally steep dip. The greater velocity of the seismic vibrations through the reef core may cause the reflections from horizons beneath the reef to indicate a nonexistent anticline in the formations beneath the reef. This false anticline, though it appears to lie in the beds beneath the reef, is of course caused by the reef itself. In some cases the presence of a reef may be indicated or suggested by the absence of reflections.

The use of a very detailed gravimeter survey for finding reefs has been described by Pohly.[1] According to Pohly, gravity anomalies associated with reefs are caused chiefly by two zones, the reef core and the deposits on the flanks of the reef. The reef core may be either more or less dense

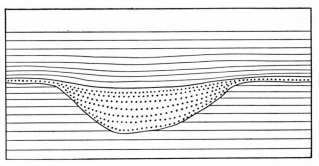

Fig. 10-9. Cross section showing a possible arrangement of the bedding in a channel deposit.

than the normal rock of the region, and may produce either a positive or a negative gravity anomaly at the surface. The deposits on the reef flanks are generally less dense than the core, and tend to produce a negative gravity anomaly. In some cases the reef is expressed on residual-gravity maps by a positive anomaly over the reef core and a negative anomaly over the reef flanks.

Channel Deposits. Deposits filling channels and narrow river valleys have some characteristic features which aid in recognizing them. These deposits are sinuous and winding in horizontal plan. In cross sections they are convex on the bottom and flat on top. Of course it is only where there is a marked contrast between the sediments in the channel and the rocks above and below it that the channel deposits show up plainly. If a channel is cut in sand and filled by sand, the channel deposit may be indistinguishable.

The stratification in the channel may be arranged as in Fig. 10-9. The strata at the base of the channel tend to be parallel to the inclined

[1] Richard A. Pohly, New Gravity Approach Aids Reef Interpretation, *World Oil,* vol. 136, no. 6, pp. 116–124 (May, 1953).

surfaces on which they are deposited. As the channel is filled, the inclination of the bedding decreases, and the last strata filling the channel may be practically horizontal. However, other arrangements of the bedding in channels also commonly occur.

Channel deposits are of interest to the petroleum geologist chiefly because they make suitable traps for oil and gas accumulation. The sediments filling channels are usually clastics. Channels form suitable traps for oil and gas accumulation only when porous and permeable sandstones or conglomerates in the channels are surrounded by impervious rocks. The reservoir rock in many oil fields in channels is sandstone, and the surrounding rock shale. The sands or gravels deposited in the channels are in many cases of fresh-water origin. The oil and gas may be derived from the adjacent shales, which may be marine deposits formed near the shore or brackish-water sediments which accumulated in bays and marshes.

Oil fields which are long and narrow are frequently called shoestring oil fields. The reservoir rocks of most shoestring oil fields are either channel deposits or offshore bars.

Offshore Bars. Offshore bars form in shallow water parallel to the coast line. Where the shore is straight, the offshore bars are also straight. Some extend for a hundred miles or so, but most offshore bars vary in length from a fraction of a mile to a few tens of miles. Along coasts that are straight for great distances the offshore bars are likely to be interrupted by the openings of bays and inlets. In some cases there is a slight offset to the general trend of the bars at the inlets. Offshore bars may show low ridges, known as growth ridges, which are parallel to the general trend of the bar. Many offshore bars eventually emerge from the sea as long, low, narrow islands composed of sand. The published information about offshore bars appears to be obtained chiefly from studying maps of these islands, rather than from investigations of the still submerged bars.

Shoestring oil fields on offshore bars are common in certain areas, particularly in southeastern Kansas and adjacent parts of Oklahoma. Shoestring fields of this type tend to be straight, and this feature distinguishes them from the winding oil pools in channel deposits. In cross section, offshore bars tend to be convex upward, with flat bases. In some cases the sands of the bar interfinger with shales on the landward side. Some typical expressions of offshore bars on maps and cross sections are shown in Figs. 10-10 and 10-11.

False Anticlines over Sand Lenses. Structure maps of oil fields commonly show the attitude of the top of the producing reservoir. In areas of very gentle dip, a lenticular sand body with a convex upper surface shows up as an anticline in a map made in this manner. This anticline is of stratigraphic and not structural origin, and is not found in the beds below or far above.   However, the strata just above the sand lens, since they are deposited nearly parallel to its upper surface, also show an anticlinal structure.   If the sand compacts less than the adjacent shales, as commonly happens, a slight anticline caused by differential compaction may extend for some distance above the sand lens.

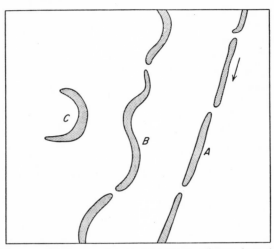

Fig. 10-10. Sketch map showing sandstone deposits in offshore bars (*A*) and channels (*B* and *C*).

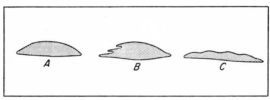

Fig. 10-11. Cross sections showing the outlines of some typical offshore bars. *A* shows common shape, *B* the tendency to interfinger with marsh deposits on the left or landward side, and *C* the growth ridges.

Deltas.   Deltas may range in dimensions from a few inches to hundreds of miles.   They could therefore be classed as minor, local, or regional sedimentary structures.   Fig. 10-2 shows the type of structure that is considered typical of deltas.   It is commonly well developed in deltas which range from a few inches to a few miles across.   It may also be found in deltas of great size if they are formed on the edge of a body of water in which the waves and shore currents are weak.   Great deltas formed on the open ocean and on bodies of water with strong waves and shore currents are likely to be so modified that the top-set, bottom-set and fore-set beds are deposited out of place or are unrecognizable.   If the longshore currents are strong, they may distribute the deposits in one direction along the coast or on the continental shelf instead of near the mouth of the river. The muddy, fresh river water may float on the salt water before mixing with it. As a result the final deposition of the suspended mud may be a great distance along the shore from the mouth of the river. In deltas formed in the open ocean or along coasts where waves and currents are strong, much of the sediment may be carried over the edge of the continental shelf before being finally deposited. A great delta formed on the ocean where shore currents are active may consist of a series of deltas one beneath another. The river may build a delta in one direction, and after a few hundred years change its course and build one in another direction. After the older deltas have been carried below sea level by subsidence, they may be covered by later deltas at a slightly higher level. The subaerial part of each delta commonly consists of channel deposits bordered by natural levees, with marsh or flood-plain deposits between the channels. On the continental shelf the marine deposits of the delta are spread out by the longshore currents. All deposits may have a very low dip, with nothing resembling fore-set beds. The deposits of the continental slopes and ocean bottoms have some resemblance to fore-set and bottom-set beds, but confusion is likely to result if these names are applied to them.

Subsidence is general in areas of great deltas. It appears that in deltas 100 miles or more across, the weight of the sediments is sufficient to press the earth's crust down slowly. If the earth's crust was in isostatic balance before the deposition of the delta began, the extra mass will presumably cause a slow flow outward from the delta in the plastic substratum at great depths below the more rigid crust. Because of this slow subsidence, great thicknesses of sediments may accumulate in water which is always shallow. Merely by chance, deltas may form in areas of subsidence. Hence the subsidence in the vicinity of large deltas may not be always caused by the weight of the sediments.

REGIONAL SEDIMENTARY STRUCTURES

A regional sedimentary structure is of regional extent and has some definite or characteristic shape or arrangement of its parts. Features which might be classified as regional sedimentary structures are continental shelves, deltas, alluvial plains, and the moraines of the continental glaciers. The continental shelves are discussed in Chap. 14; the other features do not seem to require further description in this book.

ADDITIONAL REFERENCES

Adams, J. E., and others: Starved Pennsylvanian Midland Basin, *A.A.P.G. Bull.*, vol. 35, pp. 2600–2607 (1951).

Baldwin, T. A.: San Ardo—A Stratigraphic Analysis of a California Oil Field, *A.A.P.G. Bull*, vol. 34, pp. 1981–1989 (1950).

Barrell, J.: Criteria for the Recognition of Ancient Delta Deposits, *G.S.A. Bull.*, vol. 23, pp. 377–446 (1912).

———: The Upper Devonian Delta of the Appalachian Geosyncline, Part I, The Delta and Its Relations to the Interior Sea, *Am. Jour. Sci.*, 4th ser., vol. 36, pp. 429–472 (1913).

Bass, N. W.: Origin of the Shoestring Sands of Greenwood and Butler Counties, Kansas, *Kansas State Geol. Survey Bull.* 23 (1936).

———, Letherock, C., Dillard, W. R., and Kennedy, L. E.: Origin and Distribution of Bartlesville and Burbank Shoestring Sands in Parts of Oklahoma and Kansas, *A.A.P.G. Bull.*, vol. 21, pp. 30–66 (1937).

Bates, F. W., and Copeland, R. R., Jr.: Glenmora Field, Rapides Parish, Louisiana, *A.A.P.G. Bull.*, vol. 36, pp. 146–159 (1952).

Best, J. B.: Lopez Oil Field, Webb and Duval Counties, Texas, "Stratigraphic Type Oil Fields," American Association of Petroleum Geologists, Tulsa, pp. 680–697 (1941).

Blixt, J. E.: Cut Bank Oil and Gas Field, Glacier County, Montana, "Stratigraphic Type Oil Fields," American Association of Petroleum Geologists, Tulsa, pp. 327–381 (1941).

Borger, H. D.: Case History of the Quiriquire Field, Venezuela, *A.A.P.G. Bull.*, vol. 36, pp. 2291–2330 (1952).

Bornhauser, M.: Oil and Gas Accumulation Controlled by Sedimentary Facies in Eocene Wilcox to Cockfield Formations, Louisiana Gulf Coast, *A.A.P.G. Bull.*, vol. 34, pp. 1887–1896 (1950).

Brace, O. L.: Factors Governing the Accumulation of Oil in the Mirando and Pettus Districts, Gulf Coastal Texas, and Their Application to Other Areas, *A.A.P.G. Bull.*, vol. 15, pp. 755–768 (1931).

Bridge, J., and Dake, C. L.: Initial Dips Peripheral to Resurrected Hills, *Missouri Bur. Geology and Mines, Biennial Rept. State Geologist* (1927–1928), pp. 93–99 (1929).

Bucher, W. H.: On Ripples and Related Sedimentary Surface Forms and Their Paleogeographic Interpretation, *Am. Jour. Sci.*, 4th ser., vol. 47, pp. 149–210, 241–269 (1919).

Charles, H. H.: Bush City Field, Anderson County, Kansas, in "Stratigraphic Type Oil Fields," American Association of Petroleum Geologists, Tulsa, pp. 43–56 (1941).

Corbett, C. S.: Cross-bedding and Formation Thickness Determinations, *Jour. Geology*, vol. 45, pp. 89–94 (1937).

Daly, R. A.: Coral Reefs, a Review, *Am. Jour. Sci.*, vol. 246, pp. 193–207 (1948).

Dapples, E. C., and Rominger, C. F.: Orientation Analysis of Fine-grained Clastic Sediments, a Report of Progress, *Jour. Geology*, vol. 53, pp. 246–261 (1945).

Dobrin, M. B., Perkins, B., and Snavely, B. L.: Subsurface Constitution of Bikini Atoll as Indicated by a Seismic-refraction Survey, *G.S.A. Bull.*, vol. 60, pp. 807–828 (1949).

Evans, O. F.: Origin of Spits, Bars, and Related Structures, *Jour. Geology*, vol. 50, pp. 846–865 (1942).

Fisher, B.: La Rosa Field, Refugio County, Texas, *A.A.P.G. Bull.*, vol. 25, pp. 300–307 (1941).

Freeman, J. C.: Strand-line Accumulation of Petroleum, Jim Hogg County, Texas, *A.A.P.G. Bull.*, vol. 33, pp. 1260–1270 (1949).

Freeman, L. B.: Big Sinking Field, Lee County, Kentucky, "Stratigraphic Type Oil Fields," American Association of Petroleum Geologists, Tulsa, pp. 166–207 (1941).

Garlough, J. L., and Taylor, G. L.: Hugoton Gas Field, Grant, Haskell, Morton, Stevens and Seward Counties, Kansas, and Texas County, Oklahoma, "Stratigraphic Type Oil Fields," American Association of Petroleum Geologists, Tulsa, pp. 78–104 (1941).

Goldman, M. I.: Stylolites, *Jour. Sedimentary Petrology*, vol. 10, pp. 146–147 (1940).

Grabau, A. W.: Early Paleozoic Delta Deposits of North America, *G.S.A. Bull.*, vol. 24, pp. 399–528 (1913).

Henson, F. R. S.: Cretaceous and Tertiary Reef Formations and Associated Sediments in Middle East, *A.A.P.G. Bull.*, vol. 34, pp. 215–238 (1950).

Hoffmeister, J. E., and Ladd, H. S.: The Antecedent-platform Theory, *Jour. Geology*, vol. 52, pp. 388–402 (1944).

Illing, V. C.: Role of Stratigraphy in Oil Discovery, *A.A.P.G. Bull.*, vol. 29, pp. 872–884 (1945).

Imbt, R. F., and McCollum, S. V.: Todd Deep Field, Crockett County, Texas, *A.A.P.G. Bull.*, vol. 34, pp. 239–262 (1950).

Kiersch, G. A.: Small-scale Structures and Other Features of Navajo Sandstone, Northern Part of San Rafael Swell, Utah, *A.A.P.G. Bull.*, vol. 34, pp. 923–942 (1950).

Kindle, E. M.: Recent and Fossil Ripple-mark, *Canada, Dept. of Mines and Resources, Nat. Mus. Canada Bull. 25*, 56 pp. (1917).

————: Some Factors Affecting the Development of Mud-cracks, *Jour. Geology*, vol. 5, pp. 135–144 (1917).

Ladd, H. S.: Recent Reefs, *A.A.P.G. Bull.*, vol. 34, pp. 203–214 (1950).

Lahee, F. H.: "Field Geology," McGraw-Hill Book Company, Inc., New York, 5th ed., pp. 52–103 (1952).

Layer, D. B., and others: Leduc Oil Field, Alberta, a Devonian Coral-reef Discovery, *A.A.P.G. Bull.*, vol. 33, pp. 572–602 (1949).

Lees, G. M.: Some Depositional and Deformational Problems, *Jour. Inst. Petroleum (London)*, vol. 17, pp. 259–280 (1931).

Link, T. A.: Leduc Field, Canada, *G.S.A. Bull.*, vol. 60, pp. 381–402 (1949).

————: Theory of Transgressive and Regressive Reef (Bioherm) Development and Origin of Oil, *A.A.P.G. Bull.*, vol. 34, pp. 263–294 (1950).

Lockwood, R. P., and Erdman, O. A.: Stettler Oil Field, Alberta, Canada, *A.A.P.G. Bull.*, vol. 35, pp. 865–884 (1951).

McClain, A. H.: Stratigraphic Accumulation in the Jackson-Kanawha Counties Area of West Virginia, *A.A.P.G. Bull.*, vol. 33, pp. 336–345 (1949).

McCoy, A. W. III, and others: Types of Oil and Gas Traps in Rocky Mountain Region, *A.A.P.G. Bull.*, vol. 35, pp. 1000–1037 (1951).

Malkin, D. S., and Echols, D. J.: Marine Sedimentation and Oil Accumulation: II, Regressive Marine Offlap and Overlap-Offlap, *A.A.P.G. Bull.*, vol. 32, pp. 252–261 (1948).

Mallory, W. W.: Pennsylvanian Stratigraphy and Structure, Velma Pool, Stephens County, Oklahoma, *A.A.P.G. Bull.*, vol. 32, pp. 1948–1979 (1948).

Minor, H. E., and Hanna, M. A.: East Texas Oil Field, Rusk, Cherokee, Smith, Gregg and Upshur Counties, Texas, "Stratigraphic Type Oil Fields," American Association of Petroleum Geologists, Tulsa, pp. 600–640 (1941).

Moore, E. L., and Shields, J. A.: Chimire Field, Anzoategui, Venezuela, *A.A.P.G. Bull.*, vol. 36, pp. 857–877 (1952).

Nichols, R. L.: Squeeze-ups, *Jour. Geology*, vol. 47, pp. 421–425 (1939).

North, F. J.: "Limestones, Their Origins, Distributions and Uses," Thomas Murby and Company, London, 467 pp. (1930).

Powers, S.: Reflected Buried Hills in Oilfields of Persia, Egypt and Mexico, *A.A.P.G. Bull.*, vol. 10, pp. 422–442 (1926).

Sears, J. D., Hunt, C. B., and Hendricks, T. A.: Transgressive and Regressive Cretaceous Deposits in Southern San Juan Basin, New Mexico, *U.S.G.S. Prof. Paper* 193(f) (1941).

Sebring, L., Jr.: Slick-Wilcox Field, DeWitt and Goliad Counties, Texas, *A.A.P.G. Bull.*, vol. 32, pp. 228–250 (1948).

Shepard, F. P.: Revised Nomenclature for Depositional Coastal Features, *A.A.P.G. Bull.*, vol. 36, pp. 1902–1912 (1952).

Sherrill, R. E., Dickey, P. A., and Matteson, L. S.: Types of Stratigraphic Oil Pools in Venango Sands of Northwestern Pennsylvania, "Stratigraphic Type Oil Fields," American Association of Petroleum Geologists, Tulsa, pp. 507–538 (1941).

Stearns, H. T.: An Integration of the Coral-reef Hypotheses, *Am. Jour. Sci.*, vol. 244, pp. 245–262 (1946).

Stratigraphic Type Oil Fields, American Association of Petroleum Geologists, Tulsa (1941).

Summerford, H. E., Schieck, E. E., and Hiestand, T. C.: Oil and Gas Accumulation Controlled by Sedimentary Facies in Upper Cretaceous Newcastle Sandstone, Wyoming, *A.A.P.G. Bull.*, vol. 34, pp. 1850–1865 (1950).

Swain, J. F.: Geology and Occurrence of Oil in Medina Sand of Blue Rock–Salt Creek Pool, Ohio, *A.A.P.G. Bull.*, vol. 34, pp. 1874–1886 (1950).

Swann, D. H.: Waltersburg Sandstone Oil Pools of Lower Wabash Area, Illinois and Indiana, *A.A.P.G. Bull.*, vol. 35, pp. 2561–2581 (1951).

Swesnik, R. M.: Golden Trend of South-central Oklahoma, *A.A.P.G. Bull.*, vol. 34, pp. 386–422 (1950).

Thompson, W. O.: Original Structures of Beaches, Bars and Dunes, *G.S.A. Bull.*, vol. 48, pp. 723–751 (1937).

Trefethen, J. M.: Some Features of Cherts in the Vicinity of Columbia, Missouri, *Am. Jour. Sci.*, vol. 245, pp. 56–58 (1947).

Twenhofel, W. H.: Coral and Other Organic Reefs in Geologic Column, *A.A.P.G. Bull.*, vol. 34, pp. 182–202 (1950).

Umbgrove, J. H. F.: Coral Reefs of the East Indies, *G.S.A. Bull.*, vol. 58, pp. 729–777 (1947).

Waring, W. W., and Layer, D. B.: Devonian Dolomitized Reef, D3 Reservoir, Leduc Field, Alberta, Canada, *A.A.P.G. Bull.*, vol. 34, pp. 295–312 (1950).

Weddle, H. W.: Pleasant Valley Oil Field, Fresno County, California, *A.A.P.G. Bull.*, vol. 35, pp. 619–623 (1951).

Wengerd, S. A.: Reef Limestones of Hermosa Formation, San Juan Canyon, Utah, *A.A.P.G. Bull.*, vol. 35, pp. 1038–1051 (1951).

Wharton, J. B., Jr.: Isopachous Maps of Sand Reservoirs, *A.A.P.G. Bull.*, vol. 32, pp. 1331–1339 (1948).

Wilson, R. B.: Reef Definition, *A.A.P.G. Bull.*, vol. 34, p. 181 (1950).

CHAPTER 11

STRUCTURAL SIGNIFICANCE OF LITHOLOGY

Knowledge of the structural significance of lithology is growing steadily, and the value of this knowledge to the petroleum geologist is increasing. Nevertheless, much of this subject is still incompletely understood and needs to be clarified by future research. The general problem has several aspects. In the first place, the character of the deformed rocks affects the character of the deformation. Moreover, the facies of the sediment is influenced by the structural events that precede and accompany its deposition. This means that something may be learned about these events by studying the variations in facies. Furthermore, the lithologic character or physical properties of some sediments are affected by the various structural agencies such as deformation, stresses, and depth of burial. Hence the lithology and physical properties of a sediment indicate something about its structural history.

Terms and Definitions

A clear idea of the meaning of a number of terms is helpful for understanding the subjects discussed in this chapter. "Facies" is the original character and fossil content of sediments; it refers to the qualities acquired by a sediment at the time of deposition. "Lithology" refers to the present character of the rock, regardless of how or when it was acquired. Facies is wholly of sedimentary origin. Lithology is produced in part by the character of the original sediment, and in part by the subsequent structural events which have affected the rock. For the purposes of this chapter, structural events are considered to include not only deformation and stresses, but the effects of deep burial.

"Diagenesis" is the name given to the changes in a sediment between its deposition and the time it is lithified or consolidated. Diagenesis may involve recrystallization, cementation, compaction, elimination of water, and increase in hardness and rigidity. Some of these changes are due to solution and reprecipitation of the mineral matter. Others are due to chemical reactions between the materials in the rock originally, or between the original materials and invading solutions. In general, diagenesis takes place at shallow depths and during the early history of a sediment. Some phases of diagenesis, such as the recrystallization of limestones from lime muds, are chemical in nature and not related to structure.   These phases are not treated in this chapter.

"Metamorphism" means a complete change in the nature of a rock. New minerals are developed, old ones may be recrystallized, and the pores of the sediments are generally filled with cement.   Metamorphism usually occurs at high temperatures and under great pressures, and commonly metamorphic rocks are highly deformed.   Structural petrology is the study of the relation of the orientation of the minerals and small-scale structural features of rocks to the stresses and deformation.   It has been described by Billings.[1]   Neither metamorphism nor structural petrology is discussed in this book.

EFFECT OF LITHOLOGY ON TYPE OF DEFORMATION

The manner in which deformation affects sediments is determined to some degree by the lithology.   Hard, competent rocks tend to be faulted rather than folded.   Thick competent formations tend to form larger folds than the soft, incompetent beds.   A soft or relatively plastic formation between thick competent members may be crumpled into small folds.   Furthermore, plastic sediments are more likely to be deformed while at or near the surface than rocks which have greater rigidity when freshly deposited.   Stresses may be transmitted farther through competent rocks than through plastic formations.

STRUCTURAL CONTROL OF FACIES

Facies has a structural significance because it is in part controlled by structure.   Facies is the result of sedimentary environment, and this environment is modified by such structural agencies as uplift, depression, tilting, and faulting.   Large uplifts affect the nature of the sediments for some distance from them while they are being eroded.   Tectonic processes influence the nature of the sediments by controlling the time which the particles spend at or near the surface.   Rapid, long-continued subsidence means either that rapid sedimentation must occur or that the deposits in the bottom of the depressed area are deposited at considerable depths.   Rapid deposition over a large area in turn implies uplift to furnish a source of the sediments.   The rapid deposition of a thick series of shallow-water deposits implies rapid subsidence.   Local uplifts which take place during deposition modify the character of the sediments deposited on them.   The tilting of the surface of deposition may produce density currents or slumping and sliding of the deposits down the slope.

---

[1] Marland P. Billings, "Structural Geology," Prentice-Hall, Inc., New York, pp. 332–355 (1946).

Structural Significance of Facies

Although there is no doubt that facies has structural significance, in some cases there are wide differences of opinion among geologists as to the structural significance of a given facies. This is because geologists are not yet agreed as to the environmental significance of the various facies. For example, some geologists may interpret a deposit as having been formed in shallow water, while others may interpret the same deposit as having been laid down at great depths. However, this branch of geology has been making rapid progress, and there are indications that the subject may be better understood in the future. Certainly no interpretations of structure can be made from facies until it is known what environments of deposition are indicated by the various facies. The meaning of a facies is determined in part from the fossil content, in part from lithology and sedimentary analysis, and in part from regional studies. The investigations of the meaning of facies involve stratigraphy or sedimentation rather than structural geology, and for this reason are not described in detail in this book. However, structural geologists should know in a general way how these interpretations are made, so that they can appraise the value and accuracy of the data obtained.

This general subject has been discussed by Dapples, Krumbein and Sloss,[1] by Krumbein and Sloss,[2] by Pettijohn,[3] by Rich,[4] by Sloss,[5] by Spieker,[6] by Moore,[7] and by McKee.[8]

Effect of Rate of Deposition. The nature of sedimentary deposits is markedly influenced by the rate of deposition, and this in turn is affected by tectonic agencies. If deposition is very slow, the sediments lie at or near the surface for a long period. During this time they may be buried

[1] E. C. Dapples, W. C. Krumbein, and L. L. Sloss, Tectonic Control of Lithologic Associations, *A.A.P.G. Bull.*, vol. 32, pp. 1924–1947 (1948); Integrated Facies Analysis, *G.S.A. Mem.* 39, pp. 91–94 (1949).

[2] W. C. Krumbein and L. L. Sloss, "Stratigraphy and Sedimentation," W. H. Freeman & Co., San Francisco, pp. 129–134, 213, 317–353 (1951).

[3] F. J. Pettijohn, "Sedimentary Rocks," pp. 242–261, 436–476, Harper & Brothers, New York (1949).

[4] John L. Rich, Three Critical Environments of Deposition and Criteria for the Recognition of Rocks Deposited in Each of Them, *G.S.A. Bull.*, vol. 62, pp. 1–20 (1951).

[5] L. L. Sloss, Tectonic Control of Lithologic Associations, *A.A.P.G. Bull.*, vol. 32, pp. 1924–1947 (1948); Paleozoic Sedimentation in Montana Area, *A.A.P.G. Bull.*, vol. 34, pp. 423–451 (1950).

[6] E. M. Spieker, Sedimentary Facies and Associated Diastrophism in the Upper Cretaceous of Central and Eastern Utah, *G.S.A. Mem.* 39, pp. 55–81 (1949).

[7] Raymond C. Moore, Meaning of Facies, *G.S.A. Mem.* 39, pp. 1–34 (1949).

[8] Edwin D. McKee, Facies Changes on the Colorado Plateau, *G.S.A. Mem.* 39, pp. 35–48 (1949).

and uncovered many times, shifted about by currents for long periods, abraded, and winnowed.   As a result the sand grains become rounded, and the softer or more chemically unstable minerals are broken up or destroyed.   One of the final products of this process is a pure, well-sorted quartz sand with well-rounded grains.   Deposits of this nature are developed in the Paleozoic formations of parts of Kansas and Illinois.   The sandstones are relatively free from silt, feldspar, and ferromagnesian minerals.   The limestones and dolomites tend to be free from shale or clay.   The sandstones are likely to be cross-bedded.   The deposits are generally not very thick, and there are numerous unconformities.   The fossils indicate deposition at shallow depths in waters relatively free from mud.   Bioherms may be present.   Deposits of this type are known as shelf, platform, or miogeosynclinal deposits.   They are formed in stable areas which are very slowly subsiding.

Sediments deposited rapidly are poorly sorted.   The sandstones contain silt and clay, and arkoses and graywackes are abundant.   Considerable organic material may be incorporated in the sediments.   The deposits may reach great thickness.   Shales, dirty sandstones, graywackes, arkoses and chert beds, and graded bedding are common, but in some cases fossils are scarce.   Mixtures of shale, silt, and graywacke may occur, and some deposits may be massive or may have indistinct bedding. Because of the rapid deposition, the more unstable minerals such as feldspar, pyroxene, and amphibole may be preserved in the deposits. Cross-bedding is generally not as common as in the shelf deposits, and the larger grains of the clastics are more angular.   Sediments of this nature are termed eugeosynclinal, geosynclinal, or orogenic.   They are typically developed in long, narrow geosynclines which are subsiding rapidly.   There is a difference of opinion as to the depth at which these deposits were laid down.   Some geologists consider them of shallow-water origin; others believe that in some cases they may have been laid down at great depths.   There is, however, general agreement that such sediments were laid down rapidly and indicate rapid subsidence.   Because of the poor sorting of the sandstones, arkoses, and graywackes of these strata, the permeability may be low.   Where the permeability of most of the coarser clastics is too low to produce oil, the production may be limited to the portions that have been better sorted.

Significance of the Coarseness of Clastics.   *Relation of Coarseness to Depth.*   The degree of coarseness of clastic deposits has some structural significance, though it must be interpreted with caution.   Coarseness is related to the depth of deposition, to the closeness of the source of sediments, and to some extent to the steepness of the slope down which the material was transported.   In the quiet waters of lakes and bays, the coarser sediments accumulate near the shore, and the shales in water of greater depth. The coarseness of the clastics has some significance regarding depth of deposition, particularly where the water at depth is quiet. If strong currents sweep over the bottom, sandstones may be deposited to any depth. Furthermore, the coarseness of the deposits is in many cases related to the topography of the bottom rather than to the depth below the water surface. Sandstones may accumulate on topographic highs in the sea bottom at considerable depths, while shales are laid down in topographic lows at much shallower depths. Muds may accumulate almost at sea level in bays and marshes protected from waves and currents. Sand is found scattered over parts of the continental shelves, and in some cases these sand deposits do not have much relation to the depth of the water. Furthermore, density currents may carry sands down over the continental slopes to the ocean bottom. In spite of these exceptions, however, there is a general tendency for sands to be replaced by shales as the water becomes deeper. This tendency is well illustrated by the gradual disappearance of sands Gulfward in the Tertiary deposits of the Gulf Coastal Plain.

Significance of Conglomerates. Conglomerates may be deposited along beaches, just over unconformities, and at the foot of relatively steep slopes. From the size, degree of roundness, and resistance to erosion of conglomerates it is possible to estimate how far they have traveled from their source. Some conglomerate deposits indicate the steep slopes produced by rapid uplift.

If the average size of the clastic grains of a series of sediments increases upward, progressive uplift of a neighboring land mass may be indicated. However, the same effect might be produced by the gradual filling with sediments of lakes or lowlands intervening between the source of the sediments and the area where they are deposited.

Fanglomerates. Fanglomerates are rocks consisting in part of very large angular boulders. Usually some of the boulders are several feet in length. Longwell[1] has discussed the relation of fanglomerates to faults. Fanglomerates are likely to form at the foot of the scarp of an active fault. Continued depression of the downthrown side of the fault may carry the fanglomerates below the zone of erosion, with the result that they are preserved in the sedimentary record. The fanglomerates occur only in a narrow belt along the faults on their downthrown sides. Away from the faults the fanglomerates rapidly give place to conglomerates, and still farther away to finer clastics. If the displacement along the

---

[1] Chester R. Longwell, Sedimentation in Relation to Faulting, *G.S.A. Bull.*, vol. 48, pp. 433–442 (1937); Megabreccia Developed Downslope from Large Faults, *Am. Jour. Sci.*, vol. 249, pp. 343–355 (1951).

fault continues, a series of wedge-shaped bodies of fanglomerate may form adjacent to the fault, one above another. Fanglomerates are very useful for determining when faults were active.

Relation of Coarseness and Clastic Content to Source. The percentage of clastics in a formation, and the degree of coarseness of the clastics, may indicate the direction of the source of the sediments. Both the percentage of the clastics in the sedimentary units and the coarseness of the clastics increase toward the source. Regional maps showing facies changes may indicate that near some of the shores of the sea in which a given formation was deposited there was no change in the percentage of

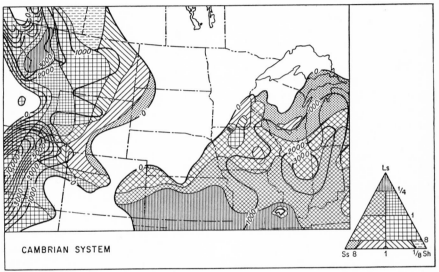

Fig. 11-1. Cambrian isopach and lithofacies map. (*After Sloss, Krumbein, and Dapples, published by permission of the Geological Society of America.*)

clastics or in their coarseness. The land back of these shores probably furnished little clastic material to the sea. This may be because the land was of low relief, because of small precipitation, or because the exposed rocks did not yield clastics on weathering. If, on the other hand, the percentage and coarseness of clastics do increase toward the shore line, the land behind it furnished clastics to the sea. This generally means structural uplift to maintain the elevation of the land. These conditions are illustrated by Figs. 11-1 and 11-2. Some clastic deposits may be produced by wave erosion at the shore line, and this should be taken into consideration in making interpretations.

One of the best ways to present the available information about changes in facies is the lithofacies map. This is a map showing the types of rock in the sedimentary units by patterns or by equal-value lines. The relative amounts of sands, shale, clastics, chemical precipitates, or evaporites may be indicated. Some lithofacies maps show the clastic ratio, which is the ratio of clastics to nonclastics. The interpretation of structural relations from lithofacies maps is likely to be an affair of some complexity. It is frequently useful to combine lithofacies and isopach maps, as in Fig. 11-1, from a paper by Sloss, Krumbein, and Dapples.[1] Areas in which the sedimentary unit contoured is very thick may be areas which were subsiding during the deposition of the unit. If the formation mapped is marine, regions where it is absent may represent either land areas or areas from which the formation was removed by subsequent erosion. The changes in facies as the zero isopach line is approached may indicate which is the case. For example, in Fig. 11-1 there is an increase in coarse clastics in the Cambrian near the zero isopach line in the vicinity of the Great Lakes and from Colorado to North Dakota. This suggests that the original termination of the Cambrian deposits was near the present position of the zero isopach. If this original termination was a shore line, the land back of this shore line was a land area which furnished coarse clastics to the sea. In case the deposits are not of marine origin, the zero isopach cannot represent the shore line. However, the increase in the coarseness of the clastics toward the margin of the deposits indicates approach to the source of the sediments, whether the deposits are marine or terrestrial. It should be noted that there is no marked increase in coarse clastics near the area of zero thickness in Idaho, though there is some increase in shale content. This may mean that the land area in Idaho during the Cambrian was of more subdued relief. In some cases the lack of increase in the coarseness of the clastics in a formation near its zero isopach may mean that the formation was once present in the area where it is now absent, and has been removed by erosion.

Structural Significance of Depth of Deposition. The determination of the depth of the water in which sediments were deposited is an aid in solving certain structural problems. For example, the question may arise as to whether a deep structural basin now containing a great thickness of sediments was first formed as a deep depression and then filled with sediments, or whether it sank as deposition continued, with the result that the sediments were all deposited in shallow water. This problem could be settled if the depth of deposition of the basal sediments of the basin could be determined.

Determination of Depth of Deposition. The depth of the water in which sediments are deposited may be determined from fossils of the bottom-dwelling organic life, from the lithology, and from the markings

[1] L. L. Sloss, W. C. Krumbein, and E. C. Dapples, Integrated Facies Analysis, *G.S.A. Mem.* 39, p. 113 (1949).

on the former surfaces preserved in the strata.   The bottom-dwelling foraminifera are especially useful for this purpose.   However, there is disagreement among geologists as to the significance of various types of lithology with regard to depth of deposition, and until this subject has been clarified it seems inadvisable to give a detailed discussion of it in a book of this nature.

Flysch and Molasse.   Flysch and molasse have been discussed by Twenhofel[1] and by Eardley and White.[2]   In the Alps flysch was deposited in a basin which was later deformed, and the sediments become coarser upward because of the rise of nearby land masses.   The molasse was laid down after the major uplift.   The sediments are comparatively undeformed, and there is a tendency to decrease in coarseness upward. Attempts have been made to apply these terms to areas in the United States and other parts of the world.   "Flysch" is used for deposits formed before a major deformation, and "molasse" for those laid down after an orogeny.   However, as Eardley and White have pointed out, the use of these terms should be avoided in discussing American geology, for their meaning is generally not clear.

Volcanics.   Lava flows, tuffs, and ashes are in many places intercalated with sediments, and extrusive rocks in sediments may be associated with deposits of chert.   Sediments may be modified not only by the content of igneous material, but by the solutions emanating from the igneous masses or derived from the weathering of tuffs and ashes. Bedded cherts have been supposed to indicate contemporaneous igneous activity, though geologic opinion on the origin of these rocks is divided. Extrusive igneous rocks have furnished sources for great volumes of sediments.   Clearly, igneous activity contemporaneous with or just preceding sedimentation should be considered in making structural interpretations from lithology.

Sudden Changes in Facies.   Some sudden changes in facies are related to structural deformation; others arise during the course of normal sedimentation and have no structural significance.   Rapid changes in facies may occur without structural cause near shore lines, at reefs, and on opposite sides of barriers of sedimentary origin, such as offshore bars which have become islands.   Sudden changes in facies may, on the other hand, be produced by local uplifts and depressions in the surface of deposition.   Where sediments of the same age but very different facies occur close together, the possibility should be considered that the deposits were

---

[1] W. H. Twenhofel, "Principles of Sedimentation," McGraw-Hill Book Company, Inc., New York, p. 23 (1939); Treatise on Sedimentation, 2d ed., The Williams & Wilkins Company, Baltimore, pp. 118–119 (1932).

[2] A. J. Eardley and Max G. White, Flysch and Molasse, *G.S.A. Bull.*, vol. 58, pp. 979–990 (1947).

originally laid down far apart and have been placed in juxtaposition by thrust faulting. However, this idea should not be accepted without corroborative evidence. If such a profound structural disturbance as a thrust fault with many miles of heave occurred in an area, some structural evidence of its existence would be expected.

Facies Changes Produced by Local Uplifts. Structural deformation occurring after deposition does not affect facies. On the other hand, the nature of the sediments may be markedly influenced by faulting or folding occurring while sedimentation is in progress. This occurs on supratenuous anticlines, in which the intervals between key horizons decrease toward the top of the structure. Two common results of uplift during deposition are the greater percentage of sandstones in the section and the deposition of better-sorted sandstones higher on the structure. These conditions have been described by Thompson and Hubbard,[1] Halbouty and Hardin,[2] Klinger,[3] Weeks and Alexander,[4] and Finn.[5] This relationship is of interest to the petroleum geologist, for it means a better prospect of finding sandstone reservoir rocks on some anticlines. Sandstones which do not occur off the supratenuous structures may be present on them, and sandstones which are present both on and off the structures may have greater permeability on the structural highs.

Rate of Deposition. The relative rates of deposition of sediments may in some cases be estimated from their facies, though facies does not give quantitative values for the rates. Shelf deposits such as clean, well-sorted sandstones and pure limestones or dolomites are deposited with relative slowness. Orogenic deposits which include graywackes are deposited much more rapidly. According to Pettijohn,[6] the time required to deposit a foot of these sediments varies from 14,000 to 8 years. Tectonic uplift is necessary for sedimentation, for if uplift did not occur the lands would ultimately be worn down and deposition would cease. Whether or not the rate of sedimentation is controlled by the rate of subsidence depends on the location of the deposit. The products of

[1] W. C. Thompson and W. E. Hubbard, Relation of Accumulation to Structure in the Oil Fields of Archer County, Texas, "Structure of Typical American Oil Fields," American Association of Petroleum Geologists, vol. 1, pp. 421–439 (1929).

[2] Michel T. Halbouty and George C. Hardin, Types of Hydrocarbon Accumulation and Geology of South Liberty Salt Dome, Liberty County, Texas, *A.A.P.G. Bull.*, vol. 35, pp. 1939–1977 (1951).

[3] Edgar D. Klinger, Cross Cut–Blake District, Brown County, Texas, "Stratigraphic Type Oil Fields," American Association of Petroleum Geologists, Tulsa, pp. 548–563 (1941).

[4] Warren B. Weeks and Clyde W. Alexander, Schuler Field, Union County, Arkansas, *A.A.P.G. Bull.*, vol. 26, pp. 1467–1516 (1942).

[5] Fenton H. Finn, Geology and Occurrence of Natural Gas in Oriskany Sandstone in Pennsylvania and New York, *A.A.P.G. Bull.*, vol. 33, pp. 303–335 (1949).

[6] *Op. cit.*, pp. 472–474.

erosion are carried by streams or other agencies until they reach a place
where the deposits are protected from erosion.   This may be the waters
of the ocean below the level of erosion, or it may be a subsiding area on
the continents.   Since the oceans have presumably been present all during geologic time, deposition of sediments in them does not require further subsidence.   On the other hand, deposits on the continents are likely

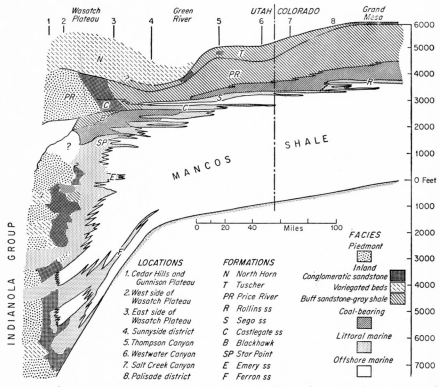

FIG. 11-2. Cross section showing distribution of facies in Upper Cretaceous between central
Utah and western Colorado.   (*After Spieker, published by permission of Geological Society
of America.*)

to be carried away again unless they are carried down below the zone of
erosion by subsidence.   Over a long period of time, therefore, the accumulation of sediments on the continents is related to subsidence, and the
rate of sedimentation in basins and geosynclines should be about the
same as the rate of subsidence.

Structural Interpretation from Facies.   Fig. 11-2, from a paper by
Spieker,[1] is a cross section showing the distribution of Upper Cretaceous
facies between central Utah and western Colorado.   The offshore marine

[1] *Op. cit.*, p. 61.

Mancos shale facies is overlain by a littoral marine facies, and this in turn by terrestrial beds carrying coals at the base. The cross section shows that the top of the Mancos is older toward the west and that the Upper Cretaceous beds of equivalent age are something like 6,000 ft thicker on the extreme western part of the cross section than on the east. Presumably this indicates that during the deposition of the sediments shown the western part of the area subsided about 6,000 ft more than the eastern part.

The source of the sediments was clearly toward the west, and the abundant conglomerates in the section on the extreme west show that the land not far to the west must have been undergoing rather rapid uplift. If the uplift had been slow, the sediments would have been finer and conglomerates would not be so much in evidence.

In some areas it is possible to determine from paleogeographic studies the thickness and extent of the sediments derived from a given source area. This gives the volume of the sediments. If the size of the source area is also known, the average amount of uplift in the source area required to produce the sediments may be calculated by dividing the volume by the area.   If, for example, the size of the source area is 16,000 square miles, and the volume of the sediments derived from it 4,000 cubic miles, the average uplift needed to produce the sediments is 4,000/16,000 or 0.25 miles. Probably this method can be used successfully only in the case of clastics. The source of marine chemical precipitates and evaporites is generally at least in part the sea water rather than the adjacent land masses.

STRUCTURAL CONTROL OF REEF LOCATION

The development of bioherms is favored by elevations in the ocean bottom. These elevations promote the growth of reef-building organisms because on them the water is shallower, the currents are greater, and the deposition of mud is less. In many cases the reef growth is initiated by conditions which have no structural control. Some reefs, however, grow on elevations in the ocean bottom produced by anticlinal uplift. Clearly only anticlines which are being uplifted during deposition can be effective in producing these elevations in the ocean bottom.

According to King,[1] the Capitan reef follows the crest of the Bone Springs arch. This arch is shown in cross section on the left side of Fig. 10-8. The Babb and Victorio flexures, north of Van Horn, Texas, are also followed by reefs of Permian age. Salas[2] states that the reef

[1] Philip B. King, The Geology of the Southern Guadalupe Mountains, Texas, *U.S.G.S. Prof. Paper* 215, pp. 19, 104 (1948).

[2] Guillermo P. Salas, Geology and Development of the Poza Rica Oil Field, Veracruz, Mexico, *A.A.P.G. Bull.*, vol. 33, pp. 1385–1409 (1949).

which produces oil in the Pozo Rico field, Mexico, formed on an anticline which was rising during reef growth. Since the anticlines on which reefs occur can in some cases be located by the reflection seismograph, this relation of anticlines to reefs may aid in reef discovery.

STRUCTURAL SIGNIFICANCE OF THE OUACHITA CHERTS

In a belt extending from southern Arkansas to the Mexican border in West Texas, there is a thick zone of bedded cherts, which are of Cambrian, Ordovician, Devonian, and Pennsylvanian age. The belt in which the cherts occur corresponds closely to a zone of intense deformation, in which the strata are strongly folded and in places cut by large thrust faults.

The close association of bedded cherts with structural deformation over such a great distance indicates a striking relation between lithology and structure. Although the association is clear, geologists disagree as to the reason for it. The environments of deposition of bedded cherts have been described by Rudemann and Wilson,[1] Hatch, Rastall, and Black,[2] Harleton,[3] and Goldstein and Hendricks.[4] Four theories have been suggested for the origin of the Ouachita cherts. One possibility is that the cherts are replacements of limestones or other rocks and that the chert was introduced by solutions from outside the series. Another possibility is that the chert is a replacement but that the silica came from the Ouachita sediments. A third theory is that the chert was deposited in beds in a geosyncline in very deep water. A fourth theory is that the cherts are sedimentary beds deposited in water at normal depth.

If the cherts are replacements, their association with the folded area is easily explained, for the heat, stresses, fracturing, and deep burial in the Ouachita geosyncline could have accounted for the metamorphism or replacement of the original rocks. If the cherts were deposited in very deep water in a geosyncline, the association of the cherts with the deformation could also be explained. The later deformation could have developed in the geosyncline, as happens in many cases. However, there is some evidence against this explanation. The very deep Ouachita geosyncline did not come into existence until the Pennsylvanian period. Furthermore, between some of the chert beds there are unconformities, and if the bedded cherts were deposited at great depths, it would be

[1] Rudolf Rudemann and T. Y. Wilson, Eastern New York Ordovician Cherts, *G.S.A. Bull.*, vol. 47, pp. 1535–1586 (1936).

[2] F. H. Hatch, R. H. Rastall, and Maurice Black, "The Petrology of the Sedimentary Rocks," George Allen & Unwin, Ltd., London, 3d ed., pp. 203–205 (1938).

[3] Bruce E. Harleton, Ouachita Chert Facies, Southeastern Oklahoma, *A.A.P.G. Bull.*, vol. 37, pp. 778–796 (1953).

[4] August Golstein, Jr., and Thomas A. Hendricks, Siliceous Sediments of Ouachita Facies in Oklahoma, *G.S.A. Bull.*, vol. 64, pp. 421–442 (1953).

necessary to assume that the surface in the Ouachita area descended many times to the great depths necessary to form the bedded cherts, and in between times rose above sea level to permit erosion. For example, according to Croneis[1] a conglomerate containing novaculite pebbles is present at the top of the Arkansas novaculite in the overlying Hot Springs sandstone and Stanley shale. The Arkansas novaculite is a bedded chert formation hundreds of feet thick.

Much evidence seems to support the idea that the Ouachita bedded cherts are sedimentary beds deposited at ordinary shallow depths. If this is the case, it is difficult to explain why they follow so closely the Ouachita geosyncline and deformation, which did not come into existence for over a hundred million years after some of the bedded cherts were laid down. The silica may have been derived from contemporaneous volcanic activity, but in this case it is also difficult to explain why the volcanic belt followed so closely the geosyncline and folding which did not come into existence until so long afterward.

A theory proposed by James[2] to account for the deposition of iron formations may also explain the formation of the Ouachita cherts. The middle Huronian sedimentary iron formations have much the same relation to the late Huronian geosynclinal deposits as the Ouachita cherts have to the upper Mississippian and Pennsylvanian geosynclinal deposits which lie above them. The middle Huronian iron formations of the Great Lakes region were deposited in the structural depression during the first stage in its development. This same depression developed into a geosyncline during the upper Huronian, and typical geosynclinal deposits accumulated in it. During the middle Huronian, iron-bearing sediments were deposited in this depression because the subsidence produced a chemical environment favorable for the deposition of sediments rich in iron. Some of the iron formations are interbedded or associated with sedimentary chert layers. This indicates that the same chemical environment which caused the deposition of the iron formations also caused the deposition of sedimentary chert. Presumably slight modifications of this chemical environment or the chemicals supplied to it could have caused the deposition of thick sedimentary cherts such as are found in the Ouachita geosyncline. The close relation of the cherts to the later geosynclinal deposits is explained by this theory, since the later deposits formed in a subsequent and more pronounced development of the same geosyncline.

In view of the great extent of the Ouachita cherts and deformation,

[1] Carey Croneis, Geology of the Arkansas Paleozoic Area, *Arkansas Geol. Survey Bull.* 3, pp. 110, 112 (1930).

[2] Harold L. James, Sedimentary Facies of Iron-formation, *Econ. Geology,* vol. 49, pp. 235–293 (1954).

this problem is of considerable importance.   Moreover, it has some bearing on the oil and gas prospects of the Ouachita facies.   For example, the solubility of silica in water is so low that if the chert was carried in from external sources by solutions, vast volumes of water must have traversed the rocks to transport it.   If the rocks of the Ouachita facies have been flushed so extensively, any oil and gas originally present would presumably have been carried away.   The fact that there is still much disagreement among geologists as to this important problem shows that there is still much to be learned about the interpretation of structure from facies and lithology.

STRUCTURAL SIGNIFICANCE OF CHANGES IN SEDIMENTS AFTER DEPOSITION

After sediments have been buried, their physical and chemical characteristics are altered by a number of agencies, some structural, others not related to structure.   In this chapter, structural agencies are considered to include not only stresses and deformation related to folding and faulting, but the temperatures and pressures associated with deep burial. Some of the results of deformation or stresses, such as fracturing, brecciation, and shearing, have already been described, and the small-scale or microscopic effects, which are the subject matter of structural petrology, are not treated in this book.

The most important result of studies of the physical and chemical changes occurring in sediments since deposition is the determination of the degree of alteration of the sediments.   This alteration is the combined effect of overburden, stresses, deformation, heat, solutions, and time.   If the alteration goes far enough, a metamorphic rock such as slate is produced.   This chapter deals only with the low-grade alteration which is not sufficiently intense to produce metamorphic rocks.   This type of alteration, if it is of regional extent, will be referred to as incipient metamorphism.   The determination of the degree of regional alteration is of importance because it may indicate depth of burial and has some bearing on the oil, gas, and ground-water prospects.   Since this subject has been treated elsewhere,[1] only a summary of the subject will be given here.

Significance of Lithologic Changes.   The compaction, lithification, and consolidation which sediments undergo when subjected to heat and pressure may be considered lithologic changes.   However, these physical changes are best studied as physical properties.   If regional alteration goes far enough, there is likely to be an increase in the coarseness of the crystals of grains of the rock.   This is illustrated in the change from

[1] William L. Russell, "Principles of Petroleum Geology," McGraw-Hill Book Company, Inc., New York, pp. 238–261 (1951).

slate to schist. Miser[1] states that the Arkansas novaculite becomes coarser-grained as it becomes more metamorphosed. There appears to be a gradual transition with increasing alteration from opal through amorphous or cryptocrystalline chert to microcrystalline chert and finally to a crystalline rock resembling a quartzite.

As sandstones are affected by regional alteration, there is a tendency for the larger quartz veins to grow still larger, and for the finer material to disappear. There may be chemical changes in the feldspars and other unstable minerals. This process has been described by Goldstein,[2] Waldschmidt,[3] Miser,[4] Harker,[5] Hatch, Rastall, and Black,[6] Gilbert,[7] Heald,[8] Taylor,[9] and Pettijohn.[10] The silica which cements the rock is probably derived from the smaller grains and particles in the vicinity, and possibly in part from the solution of the larger grains where they are at greatest stress at their points of contact. However, there is a difference of opinion as to this last point. Since this process results in the reduction of the pore space, some idea of how far it has gone may be obtained from porosity measurements.

Structural Significance of Mass Physical Properties. *Sandstones.* The mass physical properties of rocks are those which are characteristic of whole blocks or large masses of the material. Some well-known mass physical properties of sedimentary rocks are porosity, permeability, density, elasticity, resistivity, strength, thermal conductivity, magnetic susceptibility, radioactivity, and volume shrinkage on drying. Some of the mass physical properties of the clastic rocks change progressively in value as the regional alteration increases. Interest has centered on the mass physical properties of sandstones, because the variations in the porosity and permeability produced by regional alteration affect the value of the

---

[1] Hugh D. Miser, Quartz Veins in the Ouachita Mountains of Arkansas and Oklahoma, *Econ. Geology*, vol. 38, pp. 91–118 (1943).

[2] August Goldstein, Jr., Cementation of Dakota Sandstones of the Colorado Front Range, *Jour. Sedimentary Petrology*, vol. 18, pp. 108–125 (1948).

[3] W. A. Waldschmidt, Cementing Materials in Sandstones and Their Probable Influence on Migration and Accumulation of Oil and Gas, *A.A.P.G. Bull.*, vol. 25, pp. 1839–1879 (1941).

[4] *Op. cit.*, p. 105.

[5] Alfred Harker, "Metamorphism," Methuen & Co., Ltd., London, 2d ed., pp. 66–67 (1939).

[6] *Op. cit.*, pp. 104–108.

[7] Charles M. Gilbert, Cementation of Some California Tertiary Reservoir Sands, *Jour. Geology*, vol. 57, pp. 1–17 (1949).

[8] Milton T. Heald, Authigenesis of West Virginia Sandstones, *Jour. Geology*, vol. 58, pp. 624–633 (1950).

[9] Jane M. Taylor, Pore-space Reduction in Sandstones, *A.A.P.G. Bull.*, vol. 34, pp. 701–716 (1950).

[10] *Op. cit.*, pp. 481–483.

sandstones as reservoir rocks for oil, gas, and water.   The relation of the porosity of the sandstones to regional alteration has been discussed by Branner,[1] and Russell[2] has studied the relation of the porosity and crushing strength to the regional alteration of sandstones.   Although sandstones show a general decrease in porosity and increase in crushing strength as regional alteration increases, these properties are influenced by factors other than the regional alteration or depth of burial.   These factors are composition, sorting, size of grains, and the deposition of cement composed of minerals other than quartz.

The relations of the mass physical properties of shales to depth have been discussed on pages 222–225.

Shales.   Although the available information about the value of the mass physical properties of shales for determining regional alteration is too meager to be conclusive, it suggests that they are more reliable than the corresponding physical properties of sandstones.   A number of determinations have been published which give the porosities of sandstones and the porosities and densities of shales in the same wells.   These determinations indicate that the porosities and densities of shales show regular, progressive changes with depth, whereas the porosities of the sandstones have more irregular variations and show less relation to depth.   Studies of the relation between depth and physical properties of shales have been made by Athy,[3] Dickinson,[4] Hedberg,[5] and Johnson.[6]

These investigations show that in each well the porosity and density of the shales, when plotted against depth, show rather smooth curves. The rate of change decreases with depth, and at very great depths the porosity approaches zero and the bulk density approaches the grain density.   The rate of change varies from place to place, and the data, though not conclusive, suggest that the porosity at the same depth is less in the older shales.   It will be necessary to study the curves of shales of different ages and of many different regions before the subject can be clearly understood.   In selecting samples for testing, it is advisable to accept only those which consist entirely of shale or clay.   Rocks containing

[1] George C. Branner, Sandstone Porosities in Paleozoic Region in Arkansas, *A.A.P.G. Bull.*, vol. 21, pp. 67–79 (1937).

[2] William L. Russell, Porosity and Crushing Strength as Indices of Regional Alteration, *A.A.P.G. Bull.*, vol. 10, pp. 939–952 (1926).

[3] L. F. Athy, Compaction and Its Effect on Local Structure, "Problems of Petroleum Geology," American Association of Petroleum Geologists, Tulsa, pp. 811–824 (1934).

[4] George Dickinson, Geological Aspects of Abnormal Reservoir Pressures in Gulf Coast Louisiana, *A.A.P.G. Bull.*, vol. 37, pp. 410–432 (1953).

[5] Hollis D. Hedberg, The Effect of Gravitational Compaction on the Structure of Sedimentary Rocks, *A.A.P.G. Bull.*, vol. 10, pp. 1035–1072 (1926); The Gravitational Compaction of Clays and Shales, *Am. Jour. Sci.*, 5th ser., vol. 31, pp. 241–287 (1936).

[6] Frank W. Johnson, Shale Density Analysis, "Subsurface Geologic Methods," edited by L. W. LeRoy, Colorado School of Mines, Golden, Colo. pp. 329–343 (1950).

appreciable amounts of carbonates, sand, silt, or chert should be excluded, and highly organic shales should also be eliminated.

It appears that large unconformities make breaks in the curves, and that these breaks may be useful for recognizing the presence of the unconformities. Probably the unconformities show up on the curves only where great thicknesses of strata were removed by erosion during the time break represented by the unconformity. The data presented by Johnson indicate the complexity of this subject. In a well in Falcon, Venezuela, the shale densities increase by about 0.125 at the unconformity between the Eocene and Miocene, the greater densities being below. In a well in the Maracaibo Basin, on the other hand, the Eocene shales immediately below the unconformity were 0.33 less dense than the Miocene shales immediately above.

Fig. 9-1 shows estimates of the relation of the density of shales to the depth, as interpreted by several investigators.

Structural Significance of Chemical Changes in Sediments. The chemical changes in sediments produced by increasing alteration appear to consist chiefly in the escape of water and in the elimination of the volatile matter of the organic content. Nearly all shales contain appreciable quantities of organic matter, and incipient metamorphism drives off this volatile matter in the same manner as the volatile matter of coal is driven off. The final liquid and gaseous products driven off during the devolatilization of the organic matter of sediments appear to be water, nitrogen, carbon dioxide, and hydrocarbons. Possibly hydrogen and carbon monoxide are also produced. However, hydrogen and carbon monoxide are absent or extremely rare in most oil and gas pools. If they are produced in appreciable quantities during the devolatilization of the organic matter of sediments, their chemical activity probably causes their removal, leaving the more stable hydrocarbons and nitrogen to accumulate in the natural gas pools.

The devolatilization of coals during regional alteration has been studied extensively because of its bearing on oil and gas prospects. The ratio of the fixed carbon content of coals to the sum of the fixed carbon and volatile matter is called the carbon ratio, and the theory that the carbon ratios of coals can be used to determine oil and gas prospects is known as the carbon ratio theory. Russell[1] has given a detailed discussion of this subject, and it seems inadvisable to repeat it here.

ADDITIONAL REFERENCES

Adams, J. E.: Paleogeography and Petroleum Exploration, *Jour. Sedimentary Petrology*, vol. 13, pp. 108–111 (1943).

[1] William L. Russell, "Principles of Petroleum Geology," pp. 239–257 McGraw-Hill Book Company, Inc., New York (1951).

—— and others: Starved Pennsylvanian Midland Basin, *A.A.P.G. Bull.*, vol. 35, pp. 2600–2607 (1951).

Bailey, E. B.: New Light on Sedimentation and Tectonics, *Geol. Mag.*, vol. 67, pp. 77–92 (1930).

——: Sedimentation in Relation to Tectonics, *G.S.A. Bull.*, vol. 47, pp. 1715–1726 (1936).

Barnes, V. E.: Ouachita Facies in Central Texas, *Univ. of Texas, Bureau Econ. Geol., Rept. Inv.* 2, 12 pp. (1948).

Barton, D. C.: Correlation of Crude Oils with Special Reference to Crude Oil of Gulf Coast, *A.A.P.G. Bull.*, vol. 25, pp. 561–592 (1941).

——: Evolution of Gulf Coast Crude Oil, *A.A.P.G. Bull.*, vol. 21, pp. 914–946 (1937).

——: The Geological Significance and Genetic Classification of Arkose Deposits, *Jour. Geology*, vol. 24, pp. 417–449 (1916).

——: Natural History of Gulf Coast Crude Oil, "Problems of Petroleum Geology," American Association of Petroleum Geologists, Tulsa, pp. 109–155 (1934).

——: Variation and Migration of Crude Oils, Spindletop, Jefferson County, Texas, *A.A.P.G. Bull.*, vol. 19, pp. 618–643 (1935).

Barton, J. M.: Pre-Permian Axes of Maximum Deposition in West Texas, *A.A.P.G. Bull.*, vol. 29, pp. 1336–1348 (1945).

Bishop, M. S.: Isopachous Studies of Ellsworth to Traverse Limestone Section of Southwestern Michigan, *A.A.P.G. Bull.*, vol. 24, pp. 2150–2162 (1940).

Campbell, M. R.: Coal as a Recorder of Incipient Rock Metamorphism, *Econ. Geology*, vol. 25, pp. 675–696 (1930).

Cannon, G. E., and Craze, R. C.: Excessive Pressures and Pressure Variations with Depth of Petroleum Reservoirs in Gulf Coast Region of Texas and Louisiana, Petroleum Development and Technology, *A.I.M.M.E. Trans.*, vol. 127, pp. 31–38 (1938).

Chamberlin, T. C.: Diastrophism as the Ultimate Basis of Correlation, *Jour. Geology*, vol. 17, pp. 685–693 (1909).

Cooper, B. N.: Metamorphism along the Pulaski Fault in the Appalachian Valley of Virginia, *Am. Jour. Sci.*, vol. 244, pp. 95–104 (1946).

Crawford, J. G., and Larsen, R. M.: Occurrence and Types of Crude Oils in Rocky Mountain Region, *A.A.P.G. Bull.*, vol. 27, pp. 1305–1334 (1943).

Croneis, C.: Natural Gas in the Interior Highlands of Arkansas, "Geology of Natural Gas," American Association of Petroleum Geologists, Tulsa, pp. 533–573 (1935).

Crowell, J. C.: Geology of Hungry Valley Area, Southern California, *A.A.P.G. Bull.*, vol. 34, pp. 1623–1646 (1950).

——: Probable Large Lateral Displacement on San Gabriel Fault, Southern California, *A.A.P.G. Bull.*, vol. 36, pp. 2026–2035 (1952).

Dapples, E. C.: Sandstone Types and Their Associated Depositional Environments, *Jour. Sedimentary Petrology*, vol. 17, pp. 91–100 (1947).

Dobbin, C. E.: Carbon Ratios and Oil Gravities in the Rocky Mountain Region of United States, *A.A.P.G. Bull.*, vol. 13, pp. 1247–1255 (1929).

Dorsey, G. E.: Present Status of the Carbon Ratio Theory, *A.A.P.G. Bull.*, vol. 11, pp. 455–465 (1927).

Dott, R. H.: Notes on Pennsylvanian Paleogeography with Special Reference to South-central Oklahoma, *Oklahoma Geol. Survey Bull.* 40, vol. 1, pp. 51–69 (1928).

Eardley, A. J.: Paleotectonic and Paleogeologic Maps of Central and Western North America, *A.A.P.G. Bull.*, vol. 33, pp. 655–682 (1949).

Elias, M. K.: Depth of Deposition of the Big Blue (Late Paleozoic) Sediments in Kansas, *G.S.A. Bull.*, vol. 48, pp. 403–432 (1937).

Ericson, D. B., Ewing, M., and Heezen, B. C.: Deep-sea Sands and Submarine Canyons, *G.S.A. Bull.*, vol. 62, pp. 961–965 (1951).

Giles, A. W.: Boone Chert, *G.S.A. Bull.*, vol. 46, pp. 1815–1878 (1935).

Goldstein, A., Jr.: Cementation of Dakota Sandstone of the Colorado Front Range, *Jour. Sedimentary Petrology*, vol. 18, pp. 108–125 (1948).

Grabau, A. W.: "Principles of Salt Deposition," McGraw-Hill Book Company, Inc., New York, p. 435 (1920).

Haeberle, F. R.: Relationship of Hydrocarbon Gravities to Facies in Gulf Coast, *A.A.P.G. Bull.*, vol. 35, pp. 2238–2248 (1951).

Heaton, R. L.: Late Paleozoic and Mesozoic History of Colorado and Adjacent Areas, *A.A.P.G. Bull.*, vol. 34, pp. 1659–1698 (1950).

Heck, E. T.: Regional Metamorphism of Coal in Southeastern West Virginia, *A.A.P.G. Bull.*, vol. 27, pp. 1194–1227 (1943).

Hendricks, T. A.: Carbon Ratios in Part of the Arkansas-Oklahoma Coal Field, *A.A.P.G. Bull.*, vol. 19, pp. 937–947 (1935).

Hills, J. M.: Rhythm of Permian Seas, a Paleogeographic Study, *A.A.P.G. Bull.*, vol. 26, pp. 217–255 (1942).

Jones, I. W.: Carbon Ratios as an Index of Oil and Gas in Western Canada, *Econ. Geology*, vol. 23, pp. 353–380 (1928).

Jones, O. T.: Distribution of Coal Volatiles in the South Wales Coal Field and Its Probable Significance, *Geol. Soc. London Quart. Jour.*, vol. 107, pp. 51–83 (1951).

――――: Hilt's Law and the Volatile Contents of Coal Seams, *Geol. Mag.*, vol. 86, pp. 303–312, pp. 346–364 (1949).

Kay, M.: North American Geosynclines, *G.S.A. Mem.* 48, pp. 1–143 (1951).

――――: Paleogeographic and Palinspastic Maps, *A.A.P.G. Bull.*, vol. 29, pp. 426–450 (1945).

Kellum, L. B.: Geologic History of Northern Mexico and Its Bearing on Petroleum Exploration, *A.A.P.G. Bull.*, vol. 28, pp. 301–325 (1944).

King, P. B.: Permian of West Texas and Southeastern New Mexico, *A.A.P.G. Bull.*, vol. 26, pp. 535–763 (1942), facies maps treated on pp. 711–763.

Krumbein, W. C.: Lithofacies Maps and Regional Sedimentary-stratigraphic Analysis, *A.A.P.G. Bull.*, vol. 32, pp. 1909–1923 (1948).

――――: Physical and Chemical Changes in Sediments after Deposition, *Jour. Sedimentary Petrology*, vol. 12, pp. 111–117 (1942).

――――: Recent Sedimentation and the Search for Petroleum, *A.A.P.G. Bull.*, vol. 29, pp. 1233–1261 (1945).

――――: Shales and Their Environmental Significance, *Jour. Sedimentary Petrology*, vol. 17, pp. 101–108 (1947).

――――, Sloss, L. L., and Dapples, E. C.: Sedimentary Tectonics and Sedimentary Environments, *A.A.P.G. Bull.*, vol. 33, pp. 1859–1891 (1949).

Krynine, P. D.: Geomorphology and Sedimentation in the Humid Tropics, *Am. Jour. Sci.*, 5th ser., vol. 32, pp. 297–306 (1936).

Kuenen, P. H., and Migliorini, C. I.: Turbidity Currents as a Cause of Graded Bedding, *Jour. Geology*, vol. 58, pp. 91–127 (1950).

Levorsen, A. I.: Studies in Paleogeography, *A.A.P.G. Bull.*, vol. 17, pp. 1107–1132 (1933).

Lewis, J. V.: The Evolution of Mineral Coals, *Econ. Geology*, vol. 29, pp. 1–38 (1934).

Lowman, S. W.: Sedimentary Facies in Gulf Coast, *A.A.P.G. Bull.*, vol. 33, pp. 1939–1997 (1949).

Lyons, J. B.: Metamorphism of Sediments of the Deep Well near Wasco, California, and of the Deeply Buried Eocene Sediments near Ventura, California, *Jour. Geology*, vol. 48, pp. 436–443 (1940).

Malkin, D. S., and Jung, D. A.: Marine Sedimentation and Oil Accumulation on Gulf Coast: I, Progressive Marine Overlap, *A.A.P.G. Bull.*, vol. 25, pp. 2010–2020 (1941).

Melcher, A. F.: Texture of Oil Sands with Relation to Production of Oil, *A.A.P.G. Bull.*, vol. 8, pp. 716–727 (1924).

Moore, R. C.: Environment of Pennsylvanian Life in North America, *A.A.P.G. Bull.*, vol. 13, pp. 459–487 (1929).

———: The Origin and Age of the Boulder-bearing Johns Valley Shale in the Ouachita Mountains of Arkansas and Oklahoma, *Am. Jour. Sci.*, 5th ser., vol. 27, pp. 432–453 (1934).

———: Pennsylvanian Cycles in the Northern Mid-Continent Region, *Illinois Geol. Survey Bull.* 60, pp. 247–257 (1931).

———: Stratigraphic Evidence Bearing on the Problems of Continental Tectonics, *G.S.A. Bull.*, vol. 47, pp. 1785–1808 (1936).

Muller, S. W.: Sedimentary Facies and Geologic Structures in the Basin and Range Province, *G.S.A. Memoir* 39, pp. 49–54 (1949).

Murray, G. E.: Sedimentary Volumes in Gulf Coastal Plain of the United States and Mexico: III, Volume of Mesozoic and Cenozoic Sediments in Central Gulf Coastal Plain of United States, *G.S.A. Bull.*, vol. 63, pp. 1177–1191 (1952).

Nichols, E. A.: Geothermal Gradients in Mid-Continent and Gulf Coast Oil Fields, in Petroleum Development and Technology, *A.I.M.E. Trans.*, vol. 170, pp. 44–50 (1947).

Payne, T. G.: Stratigraphic Analysis and Environmental Reconstruction, *A.A.P.G. Bull.*, vol. 26, pp. 1697–1770 (1942).

Postley, O. C.: Natural Gas Developments and Possibilities East of the Main Oil and Gas Fields of the Appalachian Region, *A.A.P.G. Bull.*, vol. 19, pp. 853–857 (1935).

Price, P. H., and Headlee, A. J. W.: Geochemistry of Natural Gas in the Appalachian Province, *A.A.P.G. Bull.*, vol. 26, pp. 19–33 (1942).

——— and ———: Natural Coal Gas in West Virginia, *A.A.P.G. Bull.*, vol. 27, pp. 529–537 (1943).

——— and ———: Regional Variations in the Composition of Natural Gas in the Appalachian Province, *A.A.P.G. Bull.*, vol. 22, pp. 1153–1183 (1938).

Price, W. A.: Geomorphology of Depositional Surfaces, *A.A.P.G. Bull.*, vol. 31, pp. 1784–1800 (1947).

"Problems of Petroleum Geology," American Association of Petroleum Geologists, Tulsa (1934).

Prouty, C. E.: Paleogeographic Significance of Cambro-Ordovician Sandstones of Northeast Tennessee, *G.S.A. Bull.*, vol. 59, pp. 1344–1345 (1948).

Reed, R. D., and Hollister, J. S.: "Structural Evolution of Southern California," American Association of Petroleum Geologists, Tulsa (1936).

Reeves, F.: The Carbon-ratio Theory in the Light of Hilt's Law, *A.A.P.G. Bull.*, vol. 12, pp. 795–805 (1928).

——— and Price, P. H.: Early Devonian Gas in Northern West Virginia and Pre-Devonian Oil Prospects, *A.A.P.G. Bull.*, vol. 34, pp. 2095–2132 (1950).

Rich, J. L.: Flow Markings, Groovings, and Intra-stratal Crumplings as Criteria for Recognition of Slope Deposits, with Illustrations from Silurian Rocks of Wales, *A.A.P.G. Bull.*, vol. 34, pp. 717–741 (1950).

———: Probable Fondo Origin of Marcellus–Ohio–New Albany–Chattanooga Bituminous Shales, *A.A.P.G. Bull.*, vol. 35, pp. 2017–2040 (1951).

Rogers, H. D.: Coal and Petroleum, *Harper's New Monthly Magazine*, vol. 27, pp. 259–264 (1863).

Rubey, W. W.: Origin of the Siliceous Mowry Shale of the Black Hills Region, *U.S.G.S. Prof. Paper* 154(d).

Schmitt, G. T.: Regional Stratigraphic Analysis of Middle and Upper Marine Jurassic in Northern Rocky Mountains–Great Plains, *A.A.P.G. Bull.*, vol. 37, pp. 355–393 (1953).

Shepard, F. P.: Evidence of World-wide Submergence, *Jour. Marine Research*, vol. 7, pp. 661–678 (1948).

———: Sand and Gravel in Deep-water Deposits, *World Oil*, vol. 132, no. 1, pp. 61–68 (Jan., 1951).

———: Sediments of the Continental Shelves, *G.S.A. Bull.*, vol. 43, pp. 1017–1040 (1932).

Shrock, R. R.: "Sequence in Layered Rocks," McGraw-Hill Book Company, Inc., New York (1948).

Sloss, L. L.: Environments of Limestone Deposition, *Jour. Sedimentary Petrology*, vol. 17, pp. 109–113 (1947).

Smith, A. L., and Wilson, J. H.: Abnormal Velocities in Sedimentary Beds in Eastern Utah, *Geophysics*, vol. 2, pp. 56–62 (1937).

Somers, R. E.: Petrographic Criteria of Structure in the Cromwell Oil Field, Oklahoma, *Econ. Geology*, vol. 23, pp. 317–322 (1928).

Sorby, H. C.: On the Application of Quantitative Methods to the Study of Structure and History of Rocks, *Geol. Soc. London Quart. Jour.*, vol. 64, pp. 227–231 (1908).

Stearn, N. H.: Structure from Sedimentation at Parnell Hill Quicksilver Mine, Arkansas, *Econ. Geology,*.vol. 29, pp. 146–156 (1934).

Storm, L. W.: Resume of Facts and Opinions on Sedimentation in Gulf Coast Region of Texas and Louisiana, *A.A.P.G. Bull.*, vol. 29, pp. 1304–1355 (1945).

Sugden, W.: The Influence of Water Films Adsorbed by Mineral Grains upon the Compaction of Natural Sediments and Notes on Allied Phenomena, *Geol. Mag.*, vol. 87, pp. 26–40 (1950).

Sutton, A. H.: Time and Stratigraphic Terminology, *G.S.A. Bull.*, vol. 51, pp. 1397–1412 (1940).

Tallman, S. L.: Sandstone Types: Their Abundance and Cementing Agents, *Jour. Geology*, vol. 57, pp. 582–591 (1949).

Tarr, R. S.: Oil May Exist in Southeast Oklahoma, *Oil and Gas Jour.*, vol. 24, p. 51 (Dec. 27, 1925).

Thom, W. T., Jr.: Present Status of the Carbon-ratio Theory, "Problems of Petroleum Geology," American Association of Petroleum Geologists, Tulsa, pp. 69–96 (1934).

Tomlinson, C. W.: The Origin of Red Beds, *Jour. Geology*, vol. 24, pp. 153–179, 238–253 (1916).

Trask, P. D.: Compaction of Sediments, *A.A.P.G. Bull.*, vol. 15, pp. 271–276 (1931).

———: Oceanography and Geosynclines, *Jour. Marine Research*, vol. 7, pp. 679–685 (1948).

Trotter, F. M.: Devolatization of Coal Seams in South Wales, *Geol. Soc. London Quart. Jour.*, vol. 104, pp. 387–437 (1949).

Twenhofel, W. H.: Environment in Sedimentation and Stratigraphy, *G.S.A. Bull.*, vol. 42, pp. 407–424 (1931).

Van Houten, F. B., Krumbein, W. C., and others: Diastrophism and Sedimentation, *A.A.P.G. Bull.*, vol. 34, pp. 314–318 (1950).

Waldschmidt, W. A.: Cementing Materials in Sandstones and Their Probable Influence on the Migration and Accumulation of Oil and Gas, *A.A.P.G. Bull.*, vol. 25, pp. 1839–1879 (1941).

Wanless, H. R., and Shepard, F. P.: Sea Level and Climatic Changes Related to Late Paleozoic Cycles, *G.S.A. Bull.*, vol. 47, pp. 1177–1206 (1936).

Weeks, L. G.: Factors of Sedimentary Basin Development That Control Oil Occurrence, *A.A.P.G. Bull.*, vol. 36, pp. 2071–2124 (1952).

Weller, J. M.: Cyclical Sedimentation of the Pennsylvanian Period and Its Significance, *Jour. Geology*, vol. 38, pp. 97–135 (1950).

———: Sedimentary Cycles in the Pennsylvanian Strata; a Reply, *Am. Jour. Sci.*, 5th ser., vol. 21, pp. 311–320 (1932).

Wellman, H. W.: Depth of Burial of South Wales Coals, *Geol. Mag.*, vol. 87, pp. 305–323 (1950).

———: Metamorphic Gradient, Kent Coalfield, England, *Econ. Geology*, vol. 43, pp. 499–508 (1948).

White, C. D.: Genetic Problems Affecting the Search for New Oil Regions, *A.I.M.M.E. Trans.*, vol. 65, pp. 176–198 (1921).

———: Metamorphism of Organic Sediments and Derived Oils, *A.A.P.G. Bull.*, vol. 19, pp. 589–617 (1935).

———: Some Relations in Origin between Coal and Petroleum, *Jour. Washington Acad. Sci.*, vol. 5, pp. 189–212 (1915).

Wilson, J. H.: Lithologic Character of Shale as an Index of Metamorphism, *A.A.P.G. Bull.*, vol. 10, pp. 625–633 (1926).

Woolnough, W. G.: Geological Extrapolation and Pseud-abyssal Sediments, *A.A.P.G. Bull.*, vol. 26, pp. 765–792 (1942).

———: Influence of Climate and Topography in the Formation and Distribution of the Products of Weathering, *Geol. Mag.*, vol. 67, pp. 124–132 (1930).

———: Sedimentation in Barred Basins and the Source Rocks of Oil, *A.A.P.G. Bull.*, vol. 21, pp. 1101–1157 (1937)

CHAPTER 12

REGIONAL STRUCTURES

Regional structures are clearly of great importance in determining the locations and characteristics of oil and gas fields. Some regional structures consist of great domes with very large closure. However, with a few exceptions, oil and gas fields do not occur on purely structural traps of this size. Generally oil and gas fields related to regional structures are located on local anticlines on the regional uplifts, or on stratigraphic-structural traps on their flanks. Regional structures are also important because they control the direction of the regional dip and the thickness of sediments remaining after erosion. Regional structures which were in the process of formation during the deposition of the sedimentary section have a marked effect on the character of the sediments, and this in turn may control the location of the oil and gas fields.

DEFINITION

The basis for distinguishing between regional structures and local structures is primarily size. No definite size limit has been agreed on to separate the regional and local structures. However, in general a structural feature 10 miles in length would be considered local and one 100 miles in length regional. In a number of cases regional and local structures differ in characteristics other than size. This is true, for example, of geosynclines and geanticlines as compared with synclines and anticlines.

GEOSYNCLINES

Definition and Terminology. Geologists are not in agreement as to what constitutes a geosyncline; there is, however, agreement as to some of its characteristics. In the first place, geosynclines are of great size. All are over 100 miles long, and some are several thousand miles in length. Their width is generally at least 100 miles, and may be more than 500 miles. The maximum thickness of sediments in a geosyncline is at least a mile, and is commonly 2 to 10 miles. Another characteristic of geosynclines is that they subsided during the deposition of the sediments filling them. Before geosynclines were affected by later deformation, the strata in them dipped, in general, toward the area of maximum deposition and subsidence. The structure of geosynclines was therefore originally

279

synclinal.   Toward the area of maximum subsidence in geosynclines the formations thicken and the intervals between key horizons increase.   Formations are commonly present in this area of maximum subsidence which are absent on the flanks, and unconformities which are present on the flanks are likely to disappear toward the area of greatest subsidence.   It is generally agreed that geosynclines are characterized by great size, thick deposits, and subsidence during deposition.   According to one definition of a geosyncline, these are its distinguishing features.

According to another definition, geosynclines are long and relatively narrow and are associated with orogens.   The Appalachian and Ouachita geosynclines are good examples.   The Michigan and Eastern Interior basins and the West Texas basin would be geosynclines according to the former definition, but not according to the latter.   There is one difficulty with all definitions of geosynclines which include the presence of an orogen as one of their essential characteristics.   When an orogen does occur in a geosyncline, it may develop after a period of subsidence and deposition which may take hundreds of millions of years.   There is no way of determining definitely whether or not an orogen will eventually develop in a structural depression filled with sediments of great extent and thickness.   Since this is the case, structures could according to this definition be classified as geosynclines only if an orogen has developed.   If no orogen is present, the structural depressions could not be considered geosynclines, even though they may be geosynclines in the process of formation.   Furthermore, according to this definition, a true geosyncline would be classed as another type of structure before the development of the orogen.   When the orogen formed, the structure would change its nature and become a geosyncline.

One way to determine the meaning of the term "geosyncline" is to ascertain what terms are applied to the various large negative structural features of North America.   The term "geosyncline" is generally not applied to the Michigan and Eastern Interior basins, or to the West Texas basin.   However, the Gulf Coast structural depression is generally called a geosyncline, though there is no orogen in association with it.

In this book the term "geosyncline" is used to indicate a vast structural depression, preferably long and narrow, over 100 miles in length and generally much longer, with sediments at least a mile in thickness, and usually much thicker.   Sedimentation and subsidence must have been contemporaneous.   It is recognized that orogens accompany most geosynclines whose development has been completed.   However, the presence of an orogen is not considered an essential feature of geosynclines.   The classification of sediments beneath the continental shelves is discussed in Chap. 14.

Many new terms have been proposed to describe particular types of geosynclines. Several geologists have protested against this practice and have pointed out that it is better to describe each variety of geosyncline as it is discussed rather than to tax the memory with a great number of new names. In this book, the same policy is followed regarding the terminology of geosynclines as in the case of new terms in general. If they have come into general use, their meaning is explained, but otherwise they are generally not mentioned. The only new terms describing geosynclinal types which have come into general use are "miogeosyncline" and "eugeosyncline." Their meaning has been given on pages 286 and 292–293.

Relations to Stable Areas. A typical geosyncline is likely to be bounded on one side by a shield or stable area. The sediments of the geosyncline thin out against this shield, and there is no definite boundary between them. Formations present in the deeper parts of the geosynclines may disappear toward the shield, both because of overlap and because they are cut out at unconformities. On the other hand, unconformities present near the shield may disappear toward the axis of the geosyncline. Usually the sediments of the portion of the geosyncline near the shield are not strongly folded and their regional alteration is low. Where the sediments are sufficiently thick, this portion of the geosyncline is likely to produce oil and gas. Examples are the Appalachian oil fields, the oil fields of Oklahoma and north central Texas, and the eastern oil fields of the Rocky Mountain region.

Fig. 12-1, from a paper by Thomas,[1] shows the manner in which the formations thin out and disappear against the margins of geosynclines. The base of the Pennsylvanian in this cross section is level. Consequently the structure is shown as it was at the time when the deposition of the Pennsylvanian sediments began.

Asymmetry. The areas of thickest sediments in geosynclines appear to be generally nearer one edge rather than in the middle. The zones of thickest sediments are usually much closer to the rapidly rising welts, geanticlines, or positive areas than to the shields or stable areas on the opposite sides. The convergence of the strata is also much more rapid on this side than on the side toward the shields. These statements are true whether the welts which furnished the sources of the sediments are located on one edge of the geosynclines or in their central portions.

The structure and stratigraphy of the portions of geosynclines near the rapidly rising welts or geanticlines are generally not as well known as those of the portions near the stable shields. This is partly because of the more complex structure and greater metamorphism of these areas, and partly because many of them are inaccessible to observation because

[1] Horace D. Thomas, The Geological History and Geological Structure of Wyoming, *Wyoming Geol. Survey Bull.* 42, p. 15 (1949).

they have sunk below sea level or are covered by later deposits.   Also, the areas near the shields are relatively well known because it is in these areas that oil and gas fields occur.

Fig. 12-2, from a paper by King,[1] shows a good example of the type of asymmetry which occurs in geosynclines.   The relatively stable land lay to the right.   The Wichita Mountains uplift at the left rose during the deposition of the sediments, and the Pennsylvanian and Permian deposits of the adjacent basin were evidently derived from it.   The Anadarko basin to the right of the Wichita Mountains is considered to be a basin

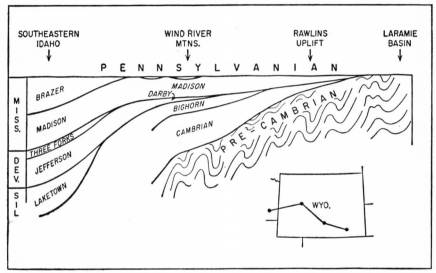

FIG. 12-1. Cross section showing the thinning of formations on the margin of geosynclines. (*After Thomas, Wyoming Geological Survey.*)

and not a geosyncline.   Nevertheless Fig. 12-2 shows the asymmetry of geosynclines better than most cross sections of genuine geosynclines. This is because in most geosynclines the sediments near the unstable borderland are so deformed or metamorphosed that the true relations are obscured.

Maximum Thickness of Sediments.   In many geosynclines the thickness of the sediments along the thickness axis cannot be measured because of metamorphism, complexity of structure, or lack of good exposures. However, enough measurements have been made to show that a great thickness is present in many geosynclines.   King[2] states that in Vermont the thickness of the sediments and interbedded volcanics is 50,000 ft.

[1] Philip B. King, "Tectonics of Middle North America," Princeton University Press, Princeton, N.J., Fig. 12-C (1951).
[2] *Ibid.*, pp. 95, 120.

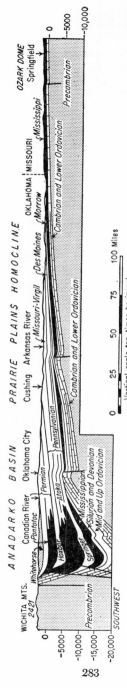

FIG. 12-2. Cross section showing asymmetry of basins and geosynclines. The Anadarko basin is on the right and the Wichita Mountain uplift on the left. Although the structural depression is known as a basin, the relations are much like those of geosynclines and geanticlines. To the right of the Wichita Mountains the black shading shows sediments derived from the Wichita Mountains and deposited in the rapidly sinking basin. (*After King, published by permission of Princeton University Press.*)

283

In the southern part of the same Appalachian geosyncline the thickness of the pre-Cambrian geosynclinal sediments is 20,000 ft, and of the Paleozoic geosynclinal sediments 30,000 to 40,000 ft. According to Hedberg[1] the thickness of the Cretaceous and Tertiary sediments in the geosyncline of eastern Venezuela is probably more than 40,000 ft. The thickness of sediments in the Ouachita geosyncline reaches 20,000 to 25,000 ft, according to Sellards and Baker.[2]

Direction of Source of Sediments. The clastic sediments of geosynclines have been derived from areas undergoing erosion on one or both sides and from uplifts within the geosynclines which rose high enough to be extensively eroded. In some cases the direction of the source of the sediments is definitely known. For example, there is no doubt that the sediments shown in cross section in Fig. 11-2 were derived from the west. On the other hand, it may be very difficult to determine the direction of source where the deformation and metamorphism are intense.

The older idea was that the sediments of geosynclines came from the uplift and erosion of unstable land masses called borderlands. Since these land masses are not now in evidence, it was supposed that they had disappeared by subsidence or been covered by later deposits. The borderlands which were supposed to have supplied sediments to the Appalachian and Ouachita geosynclines were called Appalachia and Llanoria. Appalachia was supposed to have been on or near the Atlantic coastal plain of eastern United States, and Llanoria on the Gulf coastal plain. Since these borderlands, if they ever existed, presumably shed sediments in roughly equal volumes from both sides of their crests, one would expect that another geosyncline or another vast accumulation of sediments would have formed between each of them and the ocean.

The newer concept regarding the source of sediments in geosynclines is that long narrow uplifts in the central portions of geosynclines were the source of much of the sedimentary material. Because of the small areas of these narrow uplifts or welts, they must have been greatly uplifted if they supplied any large part of the tremendous volumes of sediments in geosynclines. One difference between the borderlands and these welts should be noted. The borderlands were supposed to bound the geosynclines with which they were associated. In other words, they were located on one edge of the geosynclines. The welts, on the other hand, separate different portions of the same geosyncline. Another of the newer ideas is that the sediments of geosynclines were derived in part from volcanoes or chains of volcanic islands which sprang up near the

[1] Hollis D. Hedberg, Geology of the Eastern Venezuela Basin, *G.S.A. Bull.*, vol. 61, pp. 1175–1176 (1950).

[2] E. H. Sellards, C. L. Baker, and others, Geology of Texas, vol. 2, Structural and Economic Geology, *Univ. of Texas Bur. Econ. Geology Bull.* 3401, pp. 37, 124 (1934).

borders of the continents, on the opposite sides of the geosynclines from the stable land mass. These ideas have been expressed by King,[1] Morgan,[2] Eardley,[3] and Longwell.[4]

Sediments derived from the welts and from volcanoes seem to become more important in the later stages of the development of geosynclines. In the earlier stages, much sediment appears to be derived from the stable land masses. The erosion which furnished these earlier sediments was probably produced by broad, slow uplifts of large regions rather than by rapid uplifts of small areas. If this is the case, one would expect that sediments of the miogeosynclinal type were deposited in relatively greater abundance early in the history of geosynclines and that eugeosynclinal deposits were more in evidence in their later stages.

The discovery of undisturbed Paleozoic beds southeast of the Appalachian and Ouachita geosynclines, mentioned by King[5] and Morgan,[6] supports the idea that uplifts within the geosynclines have been the source of much of the sediments. According to the older concept, the areas where these Paleozoic sediments have been found would be in the deeply eroded portions of Appalachia and Llanoria, and Paleozoic strata would be absent. However, no uplifts which could have been important sources of sediments during development of the Ouachita geosyncline are known in the exposures of Ouachita sediments. If present, these uplifts are presumably in the region concealed by later deposits.

The chief source of the Upper Cretaceous sediments of the Rocky Mountain geosyncline appears to be definitely known. In the southern portion of this geosyncline most of them were derived from the region west of central Utah and east of the Great Valley of California. This region, which is now part of the Basin and Range province, is not commonly thought of as a geanticline or borderland. Gilluly[7] has calculated that this region must have had an average uplift of at least 3 miles during Upper Cretaceous time to supply the required volume of sediments to the geosyncline.

Character and Position of Sediments. The relation of the character of sediments to their position in geosynclines has been discussed by King.[8]

[1] *Op. cit.*

[2] Henry J. Morgan, Jr., Paleozoic Beds South and East of Ouachita Folded Belt, *A.A.P.G. Bull.*, vol. 36, pp. 2266–2274 (1952).

[3] A. J. Eardley, "Structural Geology of North America," Harper & Brothers, New York (1951).

[4] Chester R. Longwell, Tectonic Theory Viewed from the Basin Ranges, *G.S.A. Bull.*, vol. 61, pp. 413–434 (1950).

[5] *Op. cit.*, pp. 137–138.

[6] *Op. cit.*

[7] James Gilluly, The Distribution of Mountain Building in Geologic Time, *G.S.A. Bull.*, vol. 60, pp. 561–590 (1949).

[8] *Op. cit.*, pp. 72–74.

Sediments derived from the more stable land mass and laid down in the portions of the geosyncline that subside slowly are of the shelf or miogeosynclinal type. They contain well-sorted sands and clean limestones. In portions of the geosyncline which are near the rapidly rising source areas and in which subsidence and deposition are relatively rapid, the eugeosynclinal or orogenic deposits are laid down. They consist of graywackes, arkoses, shales, and in some places bedded cherts. They are poorly sorted and contain minerals that are chemically unstable. Conglomerates may be present near the sources of the sediments. In some cases the poor sorting may cause the permeability of the coarser clastics to be too low for oil production.

In the cross section shown in Fig. 12-2 the Wichita Mountains uplift plays the same role that the welts or borderlands are supposed to play in the case of the geosynclines. This long, narrow uplift was rapidly raised as the basin to the north sank, and furnished a source of the sediments of the basin. There is thus some similarity between the Wichita Mountains uplift and the Anadarko basin and the typical combination of a geanticline and geosyncline. The conditions in this area differ from those in a typical geosyncline in the intensity of the deformation and metamorphism. The sediments just north of the Wichita Mountains are cut by reverse faults and deformed into overturned folds, but the sediments thus deformed are in some places so little metamorphosed that they produce oil or gas.

Depth of Deposition. As already pointed out, there is much difference of opinion among geologists as to the depth of the water in which the eugeosynclinal facies of geosynclines were deposited. It is considered by some geologists that deposits of this type, especially if they contain bedded cherts, were laid down in water several thousand feet deep. There is general agreement that miogeosynclinal sediments are deposited at shallow depths. Where the sediments of geosynclines and basins are deposited in shallow water, it is evident that deposition keeps pace with subsidence. If subsidence were much more rapid than deposition, deep topographic troughs would be formed. Where deposition keeps pace with subsidence, the depth of deposition has no relation to the rate of subsidence. If the deposits came chiefly from one side of the geosyncline, as was frequently the case, the sediments on this side would be laid down on land or in the shallowest water. The deposits on the opposite flank of the geosyncline would accumulate in the deepest water, and the sea would be deepest near the stable land on the opposite flank from the source of sediments, where both subsidence and deposition are relatively slow. This is well illustrated by conditions in the Appalachian geosyncline in Upper Devonian time. Terrestrial and shallow-water deposits derived from the southeast formed during this time in parts of Pennsylvania. In northwestern Pennsylvania and eastern Ohio the deposits are marine and were laid down in water which, though shallow, was deeper than the water in which the sediments were deposited to the southeast. Thus the depth of the water in which the sediments were deposited was greater where subsidence was slower, and less toward the geosynclinal axis, where subsidence was greater. The same condition is found in the Upper Cretaceous Rocky Mountain geosyncline. The Upper Cretaceous sediments on the western margin of this geosyncline are terrestrial or laid down in relatively shallow water. In this part of the geosyncline both subsidence and sedimentation were most rapid. The deepest water was probably far to the east, where the sedimentation and subsidence were slower.

Relation to Source Rocks of Oil. The common association of oil fields with areas that have subsided greatly, such as geosynclines and basins, may suggest that subsidence is favorable for oil accumulation because it preserves the source rocks of oil. This in turn may suggest that the deepest parts of geosynclines, or the portions which have subsided most rapidly, are most favorable for oil accumulation. Although there is little definite information about the source rocks of oil, it does appear that the most favorable types of sediments for oil accumulation are those laid down in marine or brackish water near the shore line. Terrestrial and very deep-water deposits are much less favorable. The Paleozoic geosynclines which contain oil in North America are well enough known so that a generalization may be made about the type of sediments in which oil occurs. Many oil fields in these geosynclines are found in the miogeosynclinal or shelf deposits. These sediments were laid down in shallow water in areas where subsidence and deposition were relatively slow. The eugeosynclinal or orogenic deposits, which were laid down where deposition and subsidence were most rapid, are in a number of cases devoid of oil fields in these Paleozoic rocks. Evidently other conditions than rapidity of subsidence determine whether source rocks of oil are present.

Erratic Blocks. Enormous blocks of sedimentary rock, some over 100 ft long, are found in a number of areas in the sediments of the Appalachian and Ouachita geosynclines. They have been described by King[1] and Sellards.[2] They occur in the Cambrian and Ordovician of Quebec and Newfoundland, and in the Pennsylvanian strata in the Ouachita geosyncline of Oklahoma and the Marathon region of West Texas. Some of the limestone blocks in the Pennsylvanian shales of the Ouachita geosyncline of Oklahoma have been weathered at the surface before

[1] *Op. cit.*, pp. 84, 96, 101, 150–151.
[2] E. H. Sellards, Erratics in the Pennsylvanian of Texas, *Univ. Texas Bur. Econ. Geology Bull.* 3101, pp. 9–18 (1931).

burial. The most promising explanation of these blocks is that they broke off from the scarps of thrust faults and were carried downslope by landsliding or density currents. If this theory is correct, the slopes of the surfaces of deposition in the geosynclines must have been steep enough to permit landsliding, and thrust faulting must have been going on during deposition.

Thickness Axes. Let it be assumed that after the deposition of sediments in a geosyncline ceased, an infinite number of cross sections are made at right angles to its trend. In each cross section there will be a point at which the sediments are thickest. The line connecting these points is the thickness axis of the geosyncline. Before deformation, the strata in each geosyncline dipped toward the thickness axis from both directions. Thus before the postdepositional deformation, the regional dip in geosynclines was related to the position of these thickness axes. Since the migration and accumulation of oil and gas may have occurred before the postdepositional deformation, the original regional dips may have a bearing on the location of the oil and gas fields. If folding or tilting have occurred since deposition in the geosyncline ceased, the regional dips at present may have little relation to those occurring originally.

Variations in Positions of Trough Axes. *Definitions.* Geosynclines have both thickness and trough axes. Although the two are related, they are separate and distinct features. Structural trough axes are lines connecting the lowest points on cross sections made at present across geosynclines at right angles to their trends. If a geosyncline develops in a belt of lowlands between two regions which are topographically higher, there may also be a topographic trough axis, which is formed by a line connecting the topographically low points along the course of the geosyncline. Except by chance, the topographic trough axes do not correspond to either the structural trough axes or the thickness axes.

Relations of Thickness and Trough Axes. The thickness and trough axes of the last formation to be deposited in a geosyncline generally correspond. However, the thickness and trough axes of the older formations in the geosyncline would correspond only if there had been no tilting or folding of the formations since their deposition. This would occur only if the thickness axes of all the formations were located in a vertical plane. If the thickness axes of the later formations were not directly over the thickness axes of the older ones, the older formations would be tilted, and their trough axes would be displaced from their original positions. The thickness and trough axes differ in the effects of deformation on them. The positions of the thickness axes are not changed by later tilting or folding, but folding and tilting generally change the position of the structural trough axes.

Ideal Examples. In Fig. 12-3 the thickness axis of each formation is at or near the position of the trough axis for that particular formation. In Fig. 12-4 the thickness axes of the formations shown are all to the right of the edge of the figure.

The shifting of the trough axes with depth is illustrated in Figs. 12-3 and 12-4. Fig. 12-3 shows a geosyncline just after deposition has been completed, and before folding and thrusting. In an actual geosyncline it may be that some deformation occurs simultaneously with deposition, and that undeformed geosynclines such as shown in Fig. 12-3 do not exist. However, it is convenient for the purpose of explanation to assume that the geosyncline is still unaffected by folding and thrusting when deposition ceases.

In Fig. 12-3, *A* is a level line, and *B* is the surface of the sediments. Point *C* is where the topographic trough axis of the surface of the sedi-

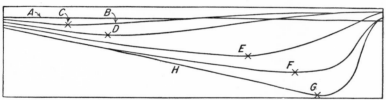

Fig. 12-3. Cross section showing shifting of the trough axes of a geosyncline with depth, as a result of lateral variations in the thickness of the formations. Aside from the differential subsidence causing the variations in the thickness of the formations, there has been very little deformation since the deposition of the sediments.

ments intersects the plane of the cross section. Similarly points *D*, *E*, *F*, and *G* mark the points where the trough axes of the various key horizons intersect the plane of the cross section. The line *H* shows the base of the sediments. The depth of the topographic depression is exaggerated relative to the thickness of the sediments, in order to make the topographic depression show up plainly on the cross section.

In Fig. 12-4 the cross section through a portion of the flank of a geosyncline is shown. Line *A* represents the land surface, *F* is a level line, and points *B*, *C*, *D*, and *E* show the points where the trough axes of the respective key horizons intersect the plane of the cross section. The line *G* marks the base of the sediments. The structure shown in Fig. 12-4 is a syncline and not a geosyncline. This is indicated by the increase in intervals between the key horizons toward the right. The trough axes of the original geosyncline before deformation were all to the right of the right edge of the figure.

Shifting of Axes Due to Divergence. In both Figs. 12-3 and 12-4 the structural trough axes are shifted in the direction of thickening of the intervals in passing downward in the sediments. Because of the great exaggeration in the vertical scales, the horizontal shifts in the trough axes appear small in the figures.   In actual geosynclines the trough axes in the older strata may be displaced 50 miles or more horizontally compared with the trough axes of the younger sediments.

The regional dip at the horizon of each stratum is toward the trough axis in that horizon.   Hence shifts in the trough axes mean shifts in the regional dip.   In the areas between the position of the trough axes in the surface and deep beds, the regional dip is in the opposite direction in the surface and deep strata.   These changes in regional dip have an important bearing on structures and traps in which oil or gas might accumulate.   The closures of anticlines are related to the direction of the regional dip.   Whether or not traps for oil and gas accumulation

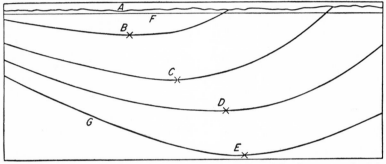

Fig. 12-4. Cross section showing the flank of a geosyncline which has been strongly deformed since the deposition of the sediments.   This figure illustrates the manner in which the trough axes at various depths are related to the deformation and thickening.

exist in an area may also be determined by the direction of the regional dip.   For example, if some porous zones which were potential oil or gas reservoirs terminated toward the east, traps would be formed where the regional dip is toward the west, but not where it is toward the east.

Applications to Appalachian Geosyncline.   The principles just discussed are well illustrated by the structural relations in the Appalachian geosyncline.   In Permian strata, the present structural trough axis of the Appalachian geosyncline lies in southeastern Ohio or northwestern West Virginia.   The trough axis in the older Paleozoic rocks is on the edge of the sharply deformed strata near the southeastern margin of the Allegheny Plateau, and roughly 75 miles southeast of the trough axis in the Permian beds.   The structure of the Allegheny Plateau is synclinal, not geosynclinal.   The intervals in the older rocks increase toward the southeast all the way across it.   It is a large syncline or synclinorium formed on the northwest flank of the Appalachian geosyncline.   A similar structure is shown in cross section in Fig. 12-4.

Relation to Orogens. An orogen is a belt of pronounced structural deformation of regional extent. The deformation may consist of folds alone, or of folds accompanied by thrust faults. The dimensions of orogens and geosynclines are very similar. Orogens are commonly 100 miles or more in width and may be thousands of miles long. Though the word orogen means "mountain-generating," and though some mountain chains correspond approximately to orogens, many of the existing mountains were not produced directly by the orogen, but were formed by later broad uplift and by erosion. For example, Reed[1] states that the Sierra Nevada, the Rocky Mountains, the Appalachian Mountains, the Andes, and the Lesser Himalayas have all been peneplained after folding and later elevated.

There is no doubt of the strong association between orogens and geosynclines. Most geosynclines are accompanied by orogens. The orogens commonly do not cover the whole of the geosyncline, and in many cases develop on the side of the geosyncline opposite to the stable land mass. The Appalachian and Ouachita geosynclines are accompanied by orogens along the whole of their known lengths.

The question arises as to whether geosynclines are always accompanied by orogens, and whether orogens occur only in geosynclines. The answer to this question may depend on how orogens and geosynclines are defined. The Gulf Coast geosyncline clearly has no orogen. Although the evidence is not clear, it appears that some orogens occur without geosynclines. For example, Weeks[2] presents maps which apparently show that the Andes mountains do not follow a geosyncline near the tropic of Capricorn. The Rocky Mountains do not follow a geosyncline all the way in their course across New Mexico.

During the formation of orogens, there is a great shortening of the earth's crust. In some places this shortening appears to amount to over 100 miles. From the analogy of the pressure-box experiment, one might suppose that this shortening resulted directly in the uplift of the mountains. However, the uplift of mountain chains appears to have a different cause. As already mentioned, the uplift of many of the mountain chains now in existence was in many cases much later than the folding.

If geosynclines and mountains always occurred together, there would be a logical basis for making a definition of "geosyncline" which would include the presence of an orogen. If, as appears at present to be the

[1] Harry Fielding Reid, The Influence of Isostasy on Geological Thought, in Figure of the Earth, "Physics of the Earth," National Research Council of the National Academy of Science, Washington, D.C., vol. 2, p. 119 (1931).

[2] L. G. Weeks, Paleogeography of South America, *G.S.A. Bull.*, vol. 59, fig. 1, p. 252, plates 2–16 (1948).

case, geosynclines occur without orogens and vice versa, the definition of a geosyncline should not imply the invariable presence of an orogen.

Deformation and Destruction.   During the development of the orogens which are commonly associated with geosynclines, the sediments are folded, overthrust, compacted, metamorphosed, and in places injected by great igneous intrusions.   Parts of geosynclines may be so uplifted and eroded that only the basement rocks remain.   The tilting and large-scale folding of geosynclines has in some cases resulted in their being separated into large synclines or synclinoria.   The rocks of geosynclines may be carried far below sea level and buried by later deposits.   Large sedimentary basins are altered and destroyed in a similar manner, except that they are not so likely as geosynclines to be associated with orogens. A paper by McKee[1] gives a good idea of the way in which geosynclines and sedimentary basins are altered by later deformation.

Alteration of Sediments.   The regional alteration of sediments in geosynclines has a very important bearing on their oil prospects.   The sediments in the central portions of many geosynclines have been altered to metamorphic rocks.   All geologists are agreed that these areas have no oil or gas prospects.   Surrounding the metamorphic zone there may be a zone in which the sedimentary rocks are somewhat altered but not metamorphosed.   The opinions of geologists are divided about how the regional alteration of this zone should be determined, and about the significance of the results.   In the outer portions of geosynclines there may be a zone of slightly deformed and slightly altered sediments near the stable land masses.   These problems are discussed in Chap. 11.

Typical History.   Some phases in the development of geosynclines seem to be of common occurrence in a number of them.   A geosyncline on the continental platforms can form only by downwarping by an amount as great as the thickness of the sediments.   The earlier sediments of the downwarped area are probably derived in large part from the land masses on one or both sides.   Ultrabasic intrusives are injected into the sediments of some sharply deformed geosynclines.   During a later stage in the development of some geosynclines long, narrow, rapidly rising welts may form in their central portions.   In other cases, chains of volcanoes may develop in the portions of geosynclines farthest from the stable land masses.   Both the welts and the volcanoes are the sources of vast volumes of sediments which accumulate in the geosynclines.   These sediments are likely to be of the eugeosynclinal type, especially if they accumulate rapidly.   The sediments derived from the stable land areas are more likely to be of the miogeosynclinal type.   However, the miogeosynclinal or shelf type of deposits may be the dominant type in a geo-

[1] Edwin D. McKee, Sedimentary Basins of Arizona and Adjoining Areas, *G.S.A. Bull.*, vol. 62, pp. 481–505 (1951).

syncline. For example, the Paleozoic sediments between the Sierra Nevada and the Front Range of the Rocky Mountains consist chiefly of carbonates, a shelf or miogeosynclinal type. They accumulated in a vast geosyncline which occupied a large part of western United States. The orogenic or eugeosynclinal sediments may form only near the welts or volcanoes which are their source, but they commonly accumulate to vast thicknesses.

Rapid uplifts of the source areas of sediments must have taken place during a large part of the development of geosynclines. Many of these areas of rapid uplift are not accessible for study, and it is not known whether this deformation was orogenic or whether it consisted of broad uplifts without sharp folds and thrusts. At a later stage in its development, the sediments of a geosyncline are likely to be affected by an orogen. This means that they are intensely folded and in some cases cut by thrust faults as well. During this time there is a great shortening of the geosyncline at right angles to its long axis. In some cases this shortening amounts to 100 miles or more. The metamorphism of the sediments of a geosyncline occurs chiefly during the orogen, and the great granite batholiths in some cases are intruded at this time. The time relations of orogens and deformation are discussed on pages 305 and 309–310.

At the close of the orogenic phase of geosynclines, they may have consisted of a series of belts or bands parallel to their axes. According to King,[1] the Appalachian geosyncline may be divided into belts or provinces in this manner. The central province of a geosyncline may consist of thoroughly metamorphosed rocks such as gneisses invaded by granite plutons. Somewhere near this central zone there are long narrow anticlines which were greatly uplifted and which may have been the source of much of the sediments. Away from this central zone the metamorphism and deformation decrease. Still farther away from the central zone the sediments are thinner and are only moderately deformed. On both sides of the central zone there may be a belt of thrust faults which dip toward the central zone. In some geosynclines no batholithic intrusions are present, and in some the sediments are not much metamorphosed.

After the orogenic stage of geosynclines there may be a prolonged interval of erosion. The final deformation may consist of normal faulting. The faults are parallel to the geosyncline and to the structures in it, and may develop 50 to 100 million years or so after the orogen.

The idea that the source of sediments in geosynclines is from welts in their central portions has been described because of its importance in geologic thought. It appears to be too early to form a final opinion as to the value of this theory. Moreover, even if it is proved that central

[1] Philip B. King, Tectonic Framework of Southeastern United States, *A.A.P.G. Bull.*, vol. 34, pp. 635–671 (1950).

welts were important sources of sediments in the Appalachian geosyncline, this would not prove that they were important sources of sediments in all geosynclines.

SHIELDS AND POSITIVE AREAS

Regions which have been persistently elevated or which have remained near sea level while adjoining regions sank below it are known as positive areas. Broad regions which have sunk at intervals are termed negative. The largest positive regions are the continental platforms. In all the continents there are great regions which have been consistently positive throughout a large part of geologic time; these are called shields. The Canadian, Baltic, and Brazilian shields are examples. Shields are composed of old, usually pre-Cambrian, rocks which were generally highly deformed and metamorphosed far back in geologic time. During the latter part of geologic time shields were generally only slightly deformed, and the deformation which did affect them generally consisted merely of broad, slow warps or normal faults. Shields may be recognized on geologic maps because the rocks which crop out on them are very old.

"Craton" also refers to a stable area, and its meaning is somewhat similar to that of "shield." However, it appears that cratons may be covered by thin sediments, while in the shields the ancient rocks are generally at the surface. Shields contain many metalliferous deposits, but they have no oil possibilities, because the sediments which produce oil elsewhere are stripped off them.

BASINS

Basins are nearly as important to petroleum geologists as geosynclines. Most of the oil and gas fields of the world occur either in geosynclines or in basins. It is well to keep in mind that there are a number of different usages of the term "basin" in geology. The term may refer to a topographic basin and have no implications with regard to structure. It may also indicate a regional structural depression of great area which does not have the characteristics of a geosyncline. The deposits of these basins may be from 1 to 10 miles in thickness, and they may be as much as 400 or 500 miles across. The shape of the basins, generally, is round or oval. If the basins were long and narrow they might be called geosynclines. In fact, as already mentioned, the distinctions between large basins and geosynclines are not agreed on, and some geologists call the large basins geosynclines. The large basins are generally free from orogens, and for this reason the sediments of basins are generally much less altered and metamorphosed than those of geosynclines. The sediments of basins are chiefly of the shelf or miogeosynclinal type. The bottoms of the basins sank as the sediments accumulated. Thus great thicknesses of sediments may have accumulated in water which was never very deep. Some basins may, however, have subsided much faster than they could be filled, with the result that some of the basin sediments were deposited at great depths. When the deposition in the regional basins was completed, the regional dip was toward the center of the basins, at an angle which was generally not over 1 or 2°. The formations and intervals generally increase in thickness toward the original center of the basin. However, it must be kept in mind that structural basins, like geosynclines, may be tilted, deformed, and partially destroyed by later deformation.

In many structural basins of great size, such as the Michigan and Eastern Interior basins and the West Texas basin, there is a general tendency for the formations to thicken down the dip. However, some structural basins or synclinal areas of great size are portions of geosynclines which have been affected by postdepositional deformation. The formations in such basins may not thicken down the dip, but may increase in thickness in a single direction clear across the basin. An example is the Allegheny Plateau area on the northwest flank of the Appalachian geosyncline. An ideal example is shown in Fig. 12-4.

The "basins" of the Rocky Mountain region have a rather special meaning. They are both structural and topographic basins. In many cases the basins are occupied by plains and are separated from each other by mountain ranges. The Paleozoic and Mesozoic strata were apparently deposited before the formation of the Rocky Mountain basins. Consequently they do not thicken toward the centers of the basins. However, the Cenozoic sediments laid down after the basins came into existence do in some cases thicken toward their centers.

Fig. 12-5, from a paper by Bartram,[1] shows the general nature of the basins in the Rocky Mountain region. The Paleozoic and Mesozoic formations increase in thickness toward the west in each basin and from one basin to the next. On the other hand, the Cenozoic sediments deposited after the formation of the basins thin out on their margins against the older rocks of the mountain ranges which bound the basins. These mountain ranges are both topographic and structural highs. The sediments deposited before and after the development of the basins are separated by pronounced unconformities. The age of these unconformities may be different in the various basins. Great quantities of oil and gas have been found in local anticlines and in stratigraphic traps in these Rocky Mountain basins.

[1] John G. Bartram, Summary of Rocky Mountain Geology, *A.A.P.G. Bull.*, vol. 23, fig. 16, p. 1149 (1939).

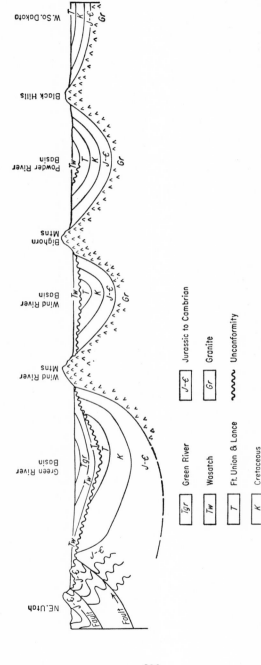

Fig. 12-5. Cross section showing the nature of the structural basins in the Rocky Mountain region. (*After Bartram, published by permission of the American Association of Petroleum Geologists.*)

REGIONAL STRUCTURES   297

The term "basin" is also used to indicate a structural low in a still larger structural depression, such as a geosyncline or a larger basin. A well-known example is the Midland basin in the West Texas basin. The term "basin" may also mean a local syncline only a mile or a few miles across.

In this book the term "basin" is used to indicate an accumulation of sediments which is of great extent and thickness, rounded or oval in shape, synclinal in structure, and devoid of orogens.

Relation of Geosynclines and Basins to Oil and Gas Fields

Most of the oil and gas fields of the world occur in geosynclines or basins. The chief reason for this is that great thicknesses of sediments, generally in part marine, are present in these structures. The chances of finding oil are greater where the sediments are thick, simply because the number of possible reservoir rocks is greater. In fact, one promising method for estimating the oil reserves of untested regions is to assume that the reserves are proportional to the number of cubic miles of sediments present. Generally some of the sediments in geosynclines and in structural basins of great area are marine. Since it is believed that the source rocks of oil were deposited in salt or brackish water, this is a very favorable feature. The slow subsidence which took place during the deposition of the miogeosynclinal facies of geosynclines and basins seems to have been sufficient to preserve the source rocks of oil. Since many good reservoir rocks and suitable source rocks are present in association with each other in basins and geosynclines, it is not surprising that oil and gas fields occur in them.

The sediments of large structural basins are much less affected by orogens than the sediments of geosynclines. In fact, the absence of orogens from the large basins is one of the characteristics which distinguish them from geosynclines. Sediments which have been affected by metamorphism or regional alteration to such an extent that the oil fields are absent are much more common in geosynclines than in basins. In the central portion of an orogen, the strata are generally so highly deformed and altered that oil and gas fields are absent. On the other hand, the margins of the orogens may be very favorable regions for oil and gas accumulation, because the sediments there are less altered and because the gentler folds on the margins make good structural traps for oil and gas accumulation.

In general, the larger the area covered by a basin, the better are its oil and gas prospects. However, even relatively small basins may contain great oil fields. For example, over 3 billion bbl of oil have been produced from an area of only about 1,500 square miles in the Los Angeles basin.

GEANTICLINES AND BORDERLANDS

One would expect from its name that a geanticline would be the opposite and counterpart of a geosyncline. According to this concept, a geanticline would have been repeatedly uplifted and would have supplied sediments to the adjacent regions that were sinking. In the sedimentary rocks on the margins of the geanticline, the intervals between key horizons would thin out toward its crest. It is to be expected that the great erosion of the crests of geanticlines would strip off the younger sediments, and in some cases expose the pre-Cambrian basement.

One idea regarding a geanticline is that it is parallel to a geosyncline on one side, and by its uplift and erosion supplied sediments to the adjacent geosyncline. This would make a geanticline the same as a borderland. The older theory was that the borderlands Appalachia, Llanoria, and Cascadia furnished sediments to the geosynclines inland from them. A later theory is that the borderlands do not exist, but that the sediments of geosynclines were derived in large part from rapidly rising narrow anticlines or welts forced up in the central parts of geosynclines. These welts could also be considered geanticlines; at least they represent one possible meaning of the term.

In the United States there are several geosynclines which all geologists admit are good examples of this type of structure. However, it is doubtful if there is any structure in the United States which all geologists would consider a good example of a geanticline. The Cincinnati anticline is sometimes called an anticline, sometimes a geanticline. In spite of its great length, it never furnished great volumes of sediments to the adjacent geosyncline and basins. For this reason it is not an ideal example of a geanticline. Possibly the Ozark uplift is the best example of a geanticline in the United States. However, it does not have the long, narrow shape which some geologists maintain is a fundamental characteristic of geanticlines. As previously mentioned, the Wichita Mountains uplift has some of the characteristics of a geanticline. However, it is flanked by basins and not by geosynclines.

MISCELLANEOUS REGIONAL STRUCTURES

Regional Arches. A regional arch is simply an anticline which is large enough to be considered regional rather than local. In the United States the dips on the flanks of regional arches are usually rather gentle, in most cases not more than a few degrees. Commonly the intervals between key horizons in the sediments decrease toward the crest of the arch, showing that the arch was in the process of growth during the deposition of the sediments on it. The axes of regional arches generally plunge in the direction of the regional dip. Domes and closures on the arches may be produced by reversals of this plunge. If the regional arches traverse an area which is in general devoid of oil and gas fields, the arches may also be devoid of them. If, however, the arches traverse areas which contain scattered oil or gas fields, they tend to cluster along the axes of the regional arches. Examples are the LaSalle anticline, the Nemaha uplift, and the Bend arch.

Domal Uplifts. If geanticlines are considered to be long, narrow structures, a separate classification is needed for rounded or oval uplifts of regional extent. These uplifts have the same general shape and in some cases the same approximate size as the structural basins. Examples are the Adirondack, Black Hills, and Bowdoin dome uplifts. If a sufficient thickness of sediments is retained on these domes, they are promising areas for oil or gas accumulation.

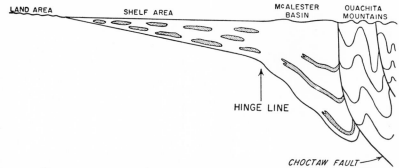

FIG. 12-6. Cross section showing the McAlester basin and shelf to the northwest of it, as they were at the end of the deposition of the early Pennsylvanian sediments. (*After Weirich, published by permission of the American Association of Petroleum Geologists.*)

Shelves. A structural shelf is very similar to a structural terrace. In fact, about the only difference between the two is that "shelf" is generally used to indicate a regional structure. A large area of relatively low dip on the flank of a basin or geosyncline would be called a shelf. Generally a shelf is somewhat more favorable for the accumulation of oil or gas than the surrounding areas of steeper dip. Figs. 12-6 and 12-7 show a structural shelf. The term "shelf" also appears to be used rather vaguely for areas which have subsided slightly or very slowly and have received only a moderate thickness of sediments. The regional dip of such areas is generally low, and they may be between or on the flanks of basins and geosynclines. In the term "shelf deposits," the word "shelf" means much the same as "miogeosynclinal." It refers to the facies of the deposits, and not to the type of structure in which they are found. Some geosynclines are largely filled with deposits of this type, and many structural basins are completely filled with them.

It has been remarked that the conditions of deposition are relatively favorable for the generation of oil in the type of deposits known as shelf, miogeosynclinal, or cratonic.   Deposits of this type may be laid down on true structural shelves, platforms, basins, or regional arches between geosynclines.   The important point is that the uplift and depression in the

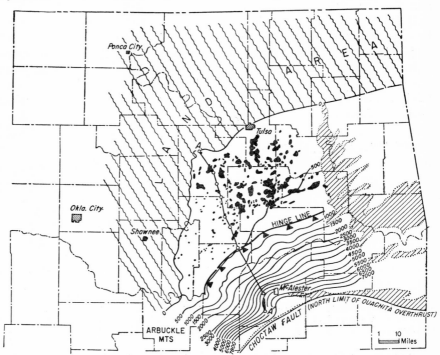

Fig. 12-7. Isopach map of Atoka unit (early Pennsylvanian) in southeastern Oklahoma. Parallel diagonal lines indicate outcrop on the south and east.   Zero isopach is shore line. Abrupt change in spacing of isopach lines at hinge line marks shelf edge.   Black indicates oil fields producing from Gilcrease and Dutcher sands in the Atoka unit.   The wavy lines to the northwest indicate land.   The limitation of the oil fields to the shelf should be noted. (*After Weirich, published by permission of the American Association of Petroleum Geologists.*)

regions where the sediments are derived and deposited are relatively slow. Figs. 12-6 and 12-7, from a paper by Weirich,[1] show how the occurrence of oil pools may be related to structural shelves and shelf-type deposits. Fig. 12-6 shows a generalized cross section of the early Pennsylvanian strata on the northwest flank of the McAlester Basin in southeastern Oklahoma.   On the structural shelf shown in Figs. 12-6 and 12-7 the early Pennsylvanian sediments contain discontinuous sandstone deposits in which oil and gas pools have accumulated.   To the southeast and

[1] Thomas Eugene Weirich, Shelf Principle of Oil Origin, Migration and Accumulation, *A.A.P.G. Bull.*, vol. 37, pp. 2030, 2032 (1953).

closer to the axis of the geosyncline, subsidence and deposition were much more rapid than on the shelf. The sediments which were deposited rapidly are devoid of oil pools, but there are a number of pools on the shelf, where deposition was much slower.

The lack of oil production in the eugeosynclinal deposits of the Ouachita geosyncline does not mean that this type of deposits is everywhere unfavorable for oil production. The relations may be quite different in the post-Paleozoic sediments. For example, Travis[1] states that the Eocene strata which produce oil in northwestern Peru are orogenic. They appear to be eugeosynclinal sediments which were deposited in rapidly subsiding areas.

Platforms. A structural platform is a broad, flat-topped anticline or uplift of regional extent. It is a favorable general location for oil accumulation on local traps. The best-known example of a structural platform is probably the Central Basin platform in the West Texas basin.

Flexures. A flexure is a regional structure much like a monocline. That is, it consists of a zone of steep dips bounded on both sides by zones of gentler dip. The flexures of the Gulf Coast are generally associated with an abnormally rapid thickening of some of the formations. This indicates that the flexure was forming during the deposition of the sediments which thicken in this manner.

Starved and Well-fed Basins

Adams[2] has described the peculiar manner of deposition of the sediments in the Midland basin. The Midland basin is the portion of the West Texas basin which lies just east of the Central Basin platform. Pennsylvanian formations which are fairly thick up the dip to the east, thin out down the dip into the Midland basin, and in the bottom of the basin they are only a small fraction of their thickness updip. Where the sediments thin out down the dip, there are abnormally steep dips of sedimentary origin into the basin. These dips resemble the fore-set dips of deltas, and are like them in that they do not affect the underlying beds.

Adams terms basins in which this condition occurs "starved," meaning starved of sediments. In starved basins the sediments are not supplied rapidly enough to fill the basin as it subsides. Hence the thickest portion of the sediments is on the margin of the basin, while thin deposits which accumulated very slowly in very deep water occur near the bottom of the structural depression. The opposite of "starved" is presumably "well-fed." In well-fed basins sediments are supplied so rapidly that the

---

[1] Russell B. Travis, La Brea–Parinas Oil Field, Northwestern Peru, *A.A.P.G. Bull.*, vol. 37, p. 2100 (1953).

[2] J. E. Adams and others, Starved Pennsylvanian Midland Basin, *A.A.P.G. Bull.*, vol. 35, pp. 2600–2607 (1951).

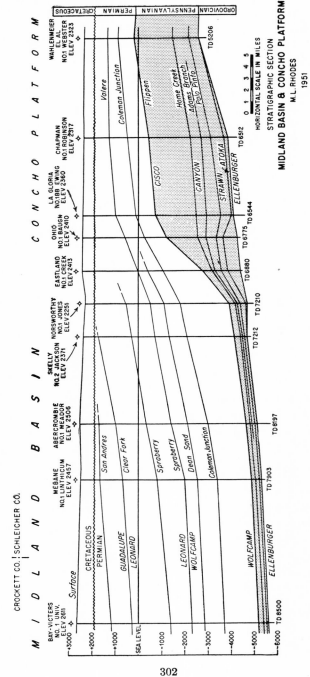

Fig. 12-8. Cross section showing starved condition of Midland basin in Pennsylvanian time. (*After Adams and others, published by permission of the American Association of Petroleum Geologists.*)

basin is kept filled with sediments as it subsides. Starved basins may be recognized by the thinning of the formations and intervals downdip. The abnormally steep dips of the fore-set beds may also aid in recognizing them. In well-fed basins the formations thicken down the dip into the basin.

Since sediments generally do thicken down the dip into geosynclines and basins, most of the great structural depressions on the continents evidently belong to the well-fed type. On the other hand, investigations may show that starved basins are more common than has been supposed. The oceans, the Mediterranean, and the Gulf of Mexico are starved according to the definitions given above. However, the term properly applies to basins on the continental platforms, where sources of sediments are present which eventually fill the basins.

The recognition of the starved condition is a great help in working out the correlation of the sediments in a basin, and in solving its structural problems. No doubt the oil prospects of sediments laid down during the formation of a basin are affected by its being starved or well fed.

Fig. 12-8, from the paper of Adams and others,[1] shows the manner in which the starved condition of the Midland basin is expressed. Up the regional dip to the east the Pennsylvanian contains a considerable thickness of limestones, including a number of reefs. Oil is produced from reservoirs in these limestones. Down the dip to the west and near the bottom of the Midland basin, the Pennsylvanian consists of dark shales, dark silts, and dark limestones. The thickness of this section decreases from about 3,000 ft up the dip to the east to about 300 ft in the bottom of the basin. The thick sediments to the right were evidently deposited in shallow water, but the thin sediments in the bottom of the basin must have been deposited in water which at times reached depths of around 2,000 to 3,000 ft. This condition has some resemblance to the top-set, fore-set, and bottom-set beds of deltas.

REGIONAL STRUCTURES OF THE UNITED STATES

Fig. 12-9 shows the regional structures of the United States that are important to the petroleum geologist. Structures that have no bearing on the occurrence of oil and gas are not shown. In the southwestern portion of the United States there is a large region classed as "basin and range" (No. 105 in Fig. 12-9). This region has been discussed on previous pages. In some parts of it, particularly in Arizona, there are large areas which have not been much affected by faults, but in general the typical fault-block structure of the basin and range occurs throughout this territory. The regional structures of the basin and range are not shown in Fig. 12-9. It has produced very little oil and no important quantities

[1] *Op. cit.*, Fig. 3.

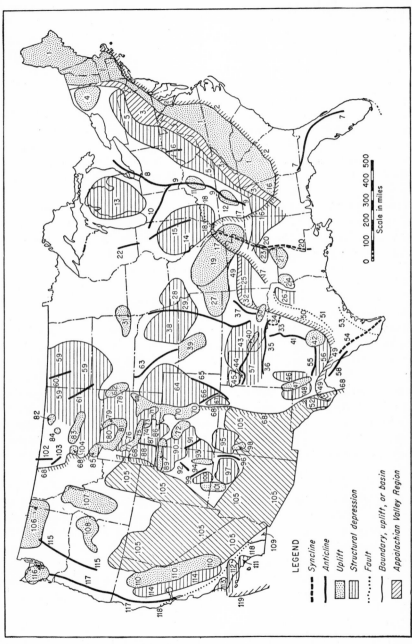

FIG. 12-9. Map showing regional structures in the United States.

of gas. The Gulf Coast geosyncline and the West Texas basin (often called Permian basin) are shown in Fig. 12-10. Table 12-1 gives the key to the numbers shown in Fig. 12-9.

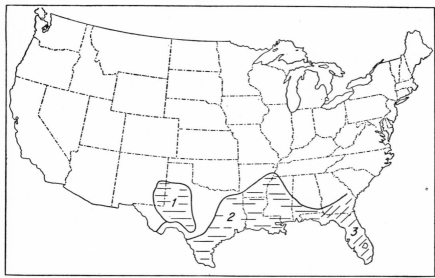

Fig. 12-10. Map showing the West Texas basin (1), the Gulf Coast geosyncline (2), and the possible eastern part of the Gulf Coast geosyncline in Florida (3).

TIME RELATIONS OF OROGENS AND DEFORMATION

The time relations of orogens and deformation constitute an important problem in structural geology. According to Gilluly,[1] the prevailing view regarding this problem is that the earth's crust is generally fairly stable, except for broad gentle warping, and that there are brief orogenic epochs of intense deformation, which are practically simultaneous all over the world. As evidence against this conception, Gilluly cites the fact that in 60 oil fields in California unconformities have developed at 42 different times in the last 26 million years. Furthermore, Gilluly has calculated that the source area for the sediments of the Rocky Mountain Cretaceous geosyncline must have been uplifted an average of ½ mile during the Lower Cretaceous and 3 to 5 miles during the Upper Cretaceous. Longwell[2] has pointed out that the orogeny during the Jurassic and Cretaceous periods apparently progressed eastward with time, and that the supposed distinction between the Nevadan and Laramide orogenies grows more

[1] James Gilluly, The Distribution of Mountain Building in Geologic Time, *G.S.A. Bull.*, vol. 60, pp. 561–590 (1949).

[2] Chester R. Longwell, Tectonic Theory Viewed from the Basin Ranges, *G.S.A. Bull.*, vol. 61, pp. 422–424 (1950).

TABLE 12-1. REGIONAL STRUCTURES SHOWN IN FIG. 12-9

No.	Region	Character	Name
1	Eastern states	Pre-Cambrian and Paleozoic igneous and metamorphic rocks at the surface. Intense deformation and strong metamorphism	Includes central Appalachians, Piedmont, and Blue Ridge
2	Eastern states	Northwest boundary of Cretaceous and Tertiary deposits of Atlantic coastal plain	"Fall line" or inland edge of coastal plain
3	Eastern states	Strongly folded sediments cut by thrust faults	Appalachian Valley region
4	N.Y.	Uplift	Adirondack Mountains
5	Eastern states	Synclinorium	Allegheny synclinorium
6	W.Va., Ohio	Anticline	Burning Springs–Volcano anticline
7	Fla.	Anticline	Florida arch
8	Ohio; Ont., Can.	Anticline	Findlay arch
9	Ala., Tenn., Ky., Ohio	Anticline	Cincinnati anticline
10	Ill., Ind., Ohio	Anticline	Kankakee arch
11	Ky.	Uplift on anticline	Lexington dome
12	Tenn.	Uplift on anticline	Nashville dome
13	Mich.	Basin	Michigan basin
14	Ill., Ky., Ind.	Basin	Eastern Interior basin, also called Illinois basin
15	Ill.	Anticline	LaSalle anticline
16	Ala., Miss.	Basin or homocline	Black Warrior basin
17	Ala., Tenn., Ky., Mo., Ark.	Contact of Paleozoic rocks with Mesozoic or Cenozoic strata	Boundary of Mississippi Embayment
18	Ky., Ill.	Fault and uplift	Rough Creek–Gold Hill fault
19	Missouri, Ark., Tenn.	Uplift	Ozark uplift
20	La., Miss., Ark.	Synclinial axis	Mississippi River syncline
21	La., Ark.	Uplift	Monroe-Sharkey uplift
22	Wis., Ill.	Anticline	Wisconsin arch
23	Ark., Miss.	Basin	Desha basin
24	La., Tex.	Uplift	Sabine uplift
25	Okla., Ark.	Synclinorium	Arkansas Valley region
26	Tex.	Syncline or basin	East Texas basin
27	Kans., Okla.	Uplift	Chautauqua arch
28	Kans., Mo., Iowa, Nebr.	Basin	Forest City basin

TABLE 12-1. REGIONAL STRUCTURES SHOWN IN FIG. 12-9 (*Continued*)

No.	Region	Character	Name
29	Okla., Kans., Nebr.	Anticline	Nemaha uplift
30	Okla.	Uplift	Arbuckle Mountains
31	S. Dak., Iowa	Uplift and buried ridge	Sioux uplift
32	Okla.	Basin	McAlester basin
33	Tex.	Syncline	Fort Worth syncline
34	Tex.	Anticline	Muenster arch
35	Tex.	Anticline	Red River arch
36	Tex.	Anticline	Matador uplift
37	Okla.	Anticline	Hunton arch
38	Kans., Nebr.	Basin	Salina basin
39	Kans.	Uplift	Central Kansas uplift
40	Okla.	Uplift	Wichita Mountains uplift
41	Tex.	Anticline	Bend arch
42	Tex.	Uplift	Llano uplift
43	Okla., Tex.	Basin	Anadarko basin
44	Tex.	Anticline and buried ridge	Amarillo or Panhandle uplift
45	Tex.	Basin	Dalhart basin
46	Tex.	Basin	Midland basin
47	Tex.	Uplift or structural platform	Central Basin platform
48	Tex.	Basin	Delaware basin
49	Tex., Okla., Ark.	Northwest limit of Ouachita deformation	
50	Tex.	Fault zone	Balcones fault zone
51	Tex.	Fault zone	Luling-Mexia-Talco fault zone
52	Tex.	Basin	Marfa basin
53	Tex.	Fault zone or flexure	Sam Fordyce–Vanderbilt fault zone or Vicksburg flexure
54	Tex.	Trough or shallow syncline	Rio Grande trough
55	Tex.	Anticline	Name not established
56	Tex.	Basin	Kerr basin
57	Tex.	Basin	Plainview basin
58	Tex., Mexico	Anticline	Chittim anticline
59	N.Dak., Mont., S.Dak.	Basin	Williston basin
60	N.Dak.	Anticline	Nesson anticline
61	Mont., N.Dak.	Anticline	Cedar Creek (Baker-Glendive) anticline
62	Wyo., S.Dak.	Uplift	Black Hills uplift
63	Nebr.	Anticline	Chadron anticline

TABLE 12-1. REGIONAL STRUCTURES SHOWN IN FIG. 12-9 (*Continued*)

No.	Region	Character	Name
64	Colo., Nebr., Wyo.	Basin	Denver basin
65	N.Mex., Colo.	Anticline	Sierra Grande–Las Animas arch
66	Colo.	Anticline	Apishapa arch
67	Colo., N. Mex.	Basin	Raton basin
68	Rocky Mountain	Eastern edge of Rocky Mountain or basin and range deformation	
69	Wyo.	Uplift	Hartville uplift
70	Colo.	Uplift	Front range
71	Wyo.	Basin	Laramie basin
72	Colo.	Uplift	White River uplift
73	Wyo.	Basin	Hanna basin
74	Wyo.	Anticline	Rawlins uplift
75	Wyo.	Uplift	Sweetwater uplift
76	Wyo.	Basin	Wind River basin
77	Wyo.	Uplift	Wind River Mountains
78	Wyo.	Basin	Powder River basin
79	Wyo.	Uplift	Big Horn Mountains
80	Wyo.	Basin	Big Horn basin
81	Wyo.	Uplift	Owl Creek uplift
82	Mont.	Uplift	Bowdoin dome
83	Mont.	Uplift	Big Snowy anticlinorium
84	Mont.	Uplift	Little Rocky Mountains uplift
85	Mont.	Uplift	Beartooth uplift
86	Wyo.	Basin	Washaki basin
87	Wyo.	Anticline	Rock Springs uplift
88	Wyo.	Basin	Green River basin (also called Bridger basin)
89	Utah, Wyo.	Uplift	Uinta Mountains
90	Utah, Colo.	Basin	Uinta basin
91	Colo.	Uplift	Uncompahgre uplift
92	Utah	Anticline	San Rafael swell
93	Utah, Colo.	Basin	Paradox salt basin
94	Utah	Uplift	Monument uplift
95	N.Mex., Colo.	Basin	San Juan basin
96	Ariz.	Anticline	Defiance uplift
97	Ariz.	Basin	Black Mesa basin
98	N. Mex.	Uplift	Zuni uplift
99	Utah	Anticline	Circle Cliffs uplift
100	Utah	Basin	Kaiparowitz basin
101	Utah, Ariz.	Anticline	Kaibab uplift

TABLE 12-1. REGIONAL STRUCTURES SHOWN IN FIG. 12-9 (*Continued*)

No.	Region	Character	Name
102	Mont.; Alberta, Can.	Arch	Sweetgrass arch
103	Mont.	Arch	South arch
104	Mont.	Uplift	Little Belt uplift
105	Western states	Large fault blocks with mountains on uplifts and late Cenozoic and Recent sediments in depressed blocks; includes some large areas without exposed faults	Basin and Range region
106	Wash.	Area of exposed batholiths	
107	Idaho, Mont.	Large batholith	Idaho batholith
108	Oreg.	Uplift of strongly folded sediments	Blue Mountains uplift
109	Calif., Mexico	Basin	Imperial Valley
110	Calif.	Uplift	Sierra Nevada
111	Calif.	Basin	Los Angeles basin
112	Calif.	Basin	Ventura basin
113	Calif.	Basin	Santa Maria basin
114	Calif.	Basin	San Joaquin–San Bernadino Valley
115	Wash., Oreg.	Mountain range of complex structure	Cascade Range
116	Wash.	Uplift of folded rocks	Olympic Mountains
117	Calif., Oreg., Wash.	Uplift of folded rocks	Coast Range
118	Calif.	Strike-slip fault	San Andreas fault
119	Pacific Ocean	West boundary of Continental Borderland off southern California.	

uncertain as more field evidence comes in. King[1] states that epochs of deformation have been found near the end of six geologic periods in the Paleozoic in the Appalachian geosyncline. As knowledge increases, these epochs seem to merge into each other.

Many of the anticlines which produce oil or gas are of the supratenuous type in which folding was contemporaneous with deposition. By comparing the intervals on and off these structures, and allowing for the possible effects of compaction, it has been found that many of these folds were deformed over a whole geologic period, or possibly during several periods. In some cases the folding is intermittent, with periods of uplift and quiescence alternating. If the folds of orogens develop in the same manner, the orogens must be of much greater duration than has been generally supposed.

[1] Philip B. King, "Tectonics of Middle North America," Princeton University Press, Princeton, N.J., pp. 78–79 (1951).

During the latter part of the development of a geosyncline, orogenic or eugeosynclinal deposits are generally laid down, either continuously or at intervals. These deposits indicate very rapid uplifts of adjacent land masses. Presumably these uplifts are something different from the broad, slow warping which is supposed to occur between orogens. If these uplifts are considered to be part of orogens, then orogens must commonly extend over large parts of geologic periods and in some cases several periods.

The evidence given above shows that the older ideas of the duration of orogenies should be questioned. A theory formerly widely accepted was that eras were separated by profound structural deformations known as revolutions, and that periods were separated by lesser structural deformations known as disturbances. It was also assumed that revolutions and disturbances were of short duration, geologically speaking. In view of the new evidence, the truth of this theory seems doubtful. However, the data are at present by no means conclusive. Problems of this nature, which have world-wide implications, can presumably be settled only by evidence from all over the world.

ADDITIONAL REFERENCES

Alcock, F. J.: Appalachian Region, "Geology and Economic Minerals of Canada," *Canada Geol. Survey, Bull.*, Econ. Geology Series No. 1, pp. 98–155 (1947).

Alvarez, M., Jr.: Tectonics of Mexico, *A.A.P.G. Bull.*, vol. 33, pp. 1319–1335 (1949).

Anderson, J. L.: Petroleum Geology of Colombia, South America, *A.A.P.G. Bull.*, vol. 29, pp. 1065–1142 (1945).

Applin, P. L., and Applin, E. R.: Regional Subsurface Stratigraphy and Structure of Florida and Southern Georgia, *A.A.P.G. Bull.*, vol. 28, pp. 1673–1753 (1944).

Bailey, E. B.: "Tectonic Essays, Mainly Alpine," Oxford University Press, New York (1935).

Bailey, T. L.: Late Pleistocene Coast Range Orogenesis in Southern California, *G.S.A. Bull.*, vol. 54, pp. 1549–1568 (1943).

Baker, A. A.: Geologic Structure of Southeastern Utah, *A.A.P.G. Bull.*, vol. 19, pp. 1472–1507 (1935).

Baker, N. E., and Henson, F. R. S.: Geological Conditions of Oil Occurrence in Middle East Oil Fields, *A.A.P.G. Bull.*, vol. 36, pp. 1885–1901 (1952).

Ballard, N.: Stratigraphy and Structural History of East-central United States, *A.A.P.G. Bull.*, vol. 22, pp. 1519–1555 (1938).

Barton, D. C.: Foreword, "Gulf Coast Oil Fields, a Symposium on the Gulf Coast Cenozoic," American Association of Petroleum Geologists, Tulsa (1936).

———, Ritz, C. H., and Hickey, M.: Gulf Coast Geosyncline, *A.A.P.G. Bull.*, vol. 17, pp. 1446–1458 (1933).

Bartram, J. G., Imbt, W. C., and Shea, E. F.: Oil and Gas in Arbuckle and Ellenburger Formations, Mid-Continent Region, *A.A.P.G. Bull.*, vol. 34, pp. 682–700 (1950).

Beltz, E. W.: Principal Sedimentary Basins in East Indies, *A.A.P.G. Bull.*, vol. 28, pp. 1440–1454 (1944).

Bucher, W. H.: "The Deformation of the Earth's Crust: An Inductive Approach to the Problems of Diastrophism," Princeton University Press, Princeton, N.J. (1933).

————: Geologic Structure and Orogenic History of Venezuela, *G.S.A. Mem.* 49, pp. 1–113 (1952).

Bybee, H. P.: Some Major Structural Features of West Texas, *University of Texas Pub.* 3103, pp. 19–26 (1931).

Carsey, J. B.: Geology of Gulf Coast Area and Continental Shelf, *A.A.P.G. Bull.*, vol. 34, pp. 361–385 (1950).

Cheney, M. G., and Goss, L. F.: Tectonics of Central Texas, *A.A.P.G. Bull.*, vol. 36, pp. 2237–2265 (1952).

Clapp, F. G.: Geology of Eastern Iran, *G.S.A. Bull.*, vol. 51, pp. 1–101 (1940).

Cohee, G. V.: Cambrian and Ordovician Rocks in Michigan Basin and Adjoining Areas, *A.A.P.G. Bull.*, vol. 32, pp. 1417–1448 (1948).

Collet, L. W.: "The Structure of the Alps," Edward Arnold & Co., London, 2d ed. (1935).

Croneis, C.: Geology of the Arkansas Paleozoic Area with Especial Reference to Oil and Gas Possibilities, *Ark. Geol. Survey Bull.* 3 (1930).

DeSitter, L. U.: Pliocene Uplift of Tertiary Mountain Chains, *Am. Jour. Sci.*, vol. 250, pp. 297–307 (1952).

Driver, H. L.: Genesis and Evolution of Los Angeles Basin, California, *A.A.P.G. Bull.*, vol. 32, pp. 109–125 (1948).

Eardley, A. J.: Ancient Arctica, *Jour. Geology*, vol. 56, pp. 409–436 (1948); vol. 57, pp. 319–320 (1949).

————: Petroleum Geology of Aquitaine Basin, France, *A.A.P.G. Bull.*, vol. 30, pp. 1517–1545 (1946).

————: Tectonic Divisions of North America, *A.A.P.G. Bull.*, vol. 35, pp. 2229–2237 (1951).

Ekblaw, G. E.: Kankakee Arch in Illinois, *G.S.A. Bull.*, vol. 49, pp. 1425–1430 (1938).

Engeln, O. D. von: "Geomorphology, Systematic and Regional," The Macmillan Company, New York (1942).

Estorff, F. E. von: Tectonic Framework of Northwestern South America, *A.A.P.G. Bull.*, vol. 30, pp. 581–590 (1946).

Fenneman, N. M.: "Physiography of Eastern United States," McGraw-Hill Book Company, Inc., New York (1938).

————: "Physiography of Western United States," McGraw-Hill Book Company, Inc., New York (1931).

Fettke, C. R.: Subsurface Trenton and Sub-Trenton Rocks in Ohio, New York, Pennsylvania and West Virginia, *A.A.P.G. Bull.*, vol. 32, pp. 1457–1493 (1948).

Finn, F. H.: Geology and Occurrence of Natural Gas in Oriskany Sandstone in Pennsylvania and New York, *A.A.P.G. Bull.*, vol. 33, pp. 303–335 (1949).

Fisk, H. N.: "Geological Investigation of the Alluvial Valley of the Lower Mississippi River," conducted for the Mississippi River Commission (War Department, Corps of Engineers, U.S. Army) (1944).

Freeman, L. B.: Regional Aspects of Silurian and Devonian Subsurface Stratigraphy in Kentucky, *A.A.P.G. Bull.*, vol. 35, pp. 1–61 (1951).

"Geology of California," American Association of Petroleum Geologists, Tulsa (1933).

Glaessner, M. F.: Geotectonic Position of New Guinea, *A.A.P.G. Bull.*, vol. 34, pp. 856–881 (1950).

———— and Teichert, C.: Geosynclines: A Fundamental Concept in Geology, *Am. Jour. Sci.*, vol. 245, pp. 465–482, 571–591 (1947).

Goldstein, A., Jr., and Reno, D. H.: Petrography and Metamorphism of Sediments of Ouachita Facies, *A.A.P.G. Bull.*, vol. 36, pp. 2275–2290 (1952).

Gonzales de Juana, C.: Elements of Diastrophic History of Northeastern Venezuela, *G.S.A. Bull.*, vol. 58, pp. 689–702 (1947).

Gregory, J. W., ed.: "The Structure of Asia," Methuen & Co., Ltd., London, (1929).

Griggs, D. T.: A Theory of Mountain-building, *Am. Jour. Sci.*, vol. 237, pp. 611–650 (1939); abstract, *G.S.A. Bull.*, vol. 49, p. 1884 (1938).

Gutenberg, B.: Earthquakes and Structure in Southern California, *G.S.A. Bull.*, vol. 54, pp. 499–626 (1943).

Hager, D.: Tectonics of North-central States, *A.A.P.G. Bull.*, vol. 33, pp. 1198–1205 (1949).

Heck, E. T.: New York Subsurface Geology, *A.A.P.G. Bull.*, vol. 32, pp. 1449–1456 (1948).

Horberg, C. L., Nelson, V. E., and Church, H. V., Jr.: Structural Trends in Central Western Wyoming, *G.S.A. Bull.*, vol. 60, pp. 183–215 (1949).

Houston Geological Society: Western Gulf Coast, *A.A.P.G. Bull.*, vol. 35, pp. 385–392 (1951).

Hunter, C. D.: Kentucky Subsurface, *A.A.P.G. Bull.*, vol. 32, pp. 1647–1657 (1948).

Jones, O. T.: On the Evolution of the Geosyncline, *Geol. Soc. London Quart. Jour.*, vol. 94, pt. 2, pp. lx–cx (1938).

Kay, G. M.: Development of the Northern Allegheny Synclinorium and Adjoining Regions, *G.S.A. Bull.*, vol. 53, pp. 1601–1657 (1942).

———: Geosynclinal Nomenclature and the Craton, *A.A.P.G. Bull.*, vol. 31, pp. 1289–1293 (1947).

———: Geosynclines in Continental Development, *Science*, vol. 99, No. 2580, pp. 461–462 (1944).

———: North American Geosynclines, *G.S.A. Mem.* 48, pp. 1–143 (1951).

Keith, A.: Outlines of Appalachian Structure, *G.S.A. Bull.*, vol. 34, pp. 309–380 (1925).

Kellum, L. B.: Geologic History of Northern Mexico and Its Bearing on Petroleum Exploration, *A.A.P.G. Bull.*, vol. 28, pp. 301–326 (1944).

———, Imlay, R. W., and Kane, W. G.: Evolution of the Coahuila Peninsula, Mexico: I, Relation of Structure, Stratigraphy and Igneous Activity to an Early Continental Margin, *G.S.A. Bull.*, vol. 47, pp. 969–1008 (1936).

King, P. B.: Permian of West Texas and Southeastern New Mexico, *A.A.P.G. Bull.*, vol. 26, pp. 535–763 (1942).

Knopf, A.: The Geosynclinal Theory, *G.S.A. Bull.*, vol. 59, pp. 649–669 (1948).

Lafferty, R. C.: Central Basin of Appalachian Geosyncline, *A.A.P.G. Bull.*, vol. 25, pp. 781–825 (1941).

Lawson, A. C.: Insular Arcs, Foredeeps and Geosynclinal Seas of the Asiatic Coast, *G.S.A. Bull.*, vol. 43, pp. 353–382 (1932).

Lee, W., and others: Structural Development of the Forest City Basin of Missouri, Kansas, Iowa and Nebraska, *U.S.G.S. F7 Oil and Gas Inv. Preliminary Map* 48 (1946).

Lees, G. M.: Foreland Folding, *Geol. Soc. London Quart. Jour.*, vol. 108, pp. 1–34 (1952).

Leith, A.: Application of Mechanical Structural Principles in the Western Alps, *Jour. Geology*, vol. 39, pp. 625–640 (1931).

Locke, A., Billingsley, P. R., and Mayo, E. B.: Sierra Nevada Tectonic Pattern, *G.S.A. Bull.*, vol. 51, pp. 513–539 (1940).

Lockett, J. R.: Development of Structures in Basin Areas of Northeastern United States, *A.A.P.G. Bull.*, vol. 31, pp. 429–446 (1947).

Lombard, A. E.: Appalachian and Alpine Structures—A Comparative Study, *A.A.P.G. Bull.*, vol. 32, pp. 709–744 (1948).

Loveley, H. R.: Geological Occurrence of Oil in United Kingdom, with Reference to Present Exploratory Operations, *A.A.P.G. Bull.*, vol. 30, pp. 1444–1516 (1946).

Lowman, S. W.: Sedimentary Facies in the Gulf Coast, *A.A.P.G. Bull.*, vol. 33, pp. 1939–1997 (1949).

Maher, J. C.: Structural Development of Las Animas Arch, Lincoln, Cheyenne and Kiowa Counties, Colorado, *A.A.P.G. Bull.*, vol. 29, pp. 1663–1665 (1945).

Maync, W.: Ancient Arctica: Remarks and Supplement, *Jour. Geology*, vol. 59, pp. 314–319 (1949).

Mellen, F. F.: Black Warrior Basin, Alabama and Mississippi, *A.A.P.G. Bull.*, vol. 31, pp. 1801–1816 (1947).

Mertie, J. B., Jr.: Mountain Building in Alaska, *Am. Jour. Sci.*, 5th ser., vol. 20, pp. 101–124 (1930).

Miser, H. D.: Structure of the Ouachita Mountains of Oklahoma and Arkansas, *Oklahoma Geol. Survey Bull.* 50, 30 pp. (1929).

——— and Sellards, E. H.: Pre-Cretaceous Rocks Found in Wells in Gulf Coastal Plain South of Ouachita Mountains, *A.A.P.G. Bull.*, vol. 15, pp. 801–818 (1931).

Moore, R. C.: Stratigraphic Evidence Bearing on Problems of Continental Tectonics, *G.S.A. Bull.*, vol. 47, pp. 1785–1808 (1936).

Murray, G. E.: Cenozoic Deposits of Central Gulf Coastal Plain, *A.A.P.G. Bull.*, vol. 31, pp. 1825–1850 (1947).

———: Sedimentary Volumes in Gulf Coastal Plain of the United States and Mexico: III, Volume of Mesozoic and Cenozoic Sediments in Central Gulf Coastal Plain of United States, *G.S.A. Bull.*, vol. 63, pp. 1177–1191 (1952).

Nettleton, L. L.: Relation of Gravity to Structure in the Northern Appalachian Area, *Geophysics*, vol. 6, pp. 270–286 (1941).

Oppenheim, V.: Geological Reconnaissance in Southeastern Peru, *A.A.P.G. Bull.*, vol. 30, pp. 254–264 (1946).

———: The Structure of Colombia, *Am. Geophys. Union Trans.*, vol. 33, pp. 739–749 (1952).

Paschal, E. A.: Major Tectonic Provinces of Oklahoma and Their Relation to Oil and Gas Fields, *A.A.P.G. Bull.*, vol. 25, pp. 1–22 (1941).

Pirtle, G. W.: Michigan Structural Basin and Its Relationship to Surrounding Areas, *A.A.P.G. Bull.*, vol. 16, pp. 145–152 (1932).

"Possible Future Oil Provinces in the United States and Canada," American Association of Petroleum Geologists, Tulsa (1941).

Possible Future Petroleum Provinces of North America, *A.A.P.G. Bull.*, vol. 35, pp. 141–498 (1951), a symposium conducted by the American Association of Petroleum Geologists.

Powers, S.: Age of Folding of the Oklahoma Mountains, the Ouachita, Arbuckle and Wichita Mountains of Oklahoma and the Llano-Burnet and Marathon Uplifts of Texas, *G.S.A. Bull.*, vol. 39, pp. 1031–1072 (1928).

"Problems of Petroleum Geology," American Association of Petroleum Geologists, Tulsa (1934).

Reed, R. D., and Hollister, J. S.: "Structural Evolution of Southern California," American Association of Petroleum Geologists, Tulsa; Thomas Murby & Co., London (1936). Also issued as *A.A.P.G. Bull.*, vol. 20, no. 12, December, 1936.

Reeves, F.: Australian Oil Possibilities, *A.A.P.G. Bull.*, vol. 35, pp. 2479–2525 (1951).

———: Status of German Oil Fields, *A.A.P.G. Bull.*, vol. 30, pp. 1546–1584 (1946).

Rich, J. L.: Oil Possibilities in South America in the Light of Regional Geology, *A.A.P.G. Bull.*, vol. 29, pp. 495–563 (1945).

Rodgers, J.: Evolution of Thought on Structure of Middle and Southern Appalachians, *A.A.P.G. Bull.*, vol. 33, pp. 1643–1654 (1949).

Roliff, W. A.: Salina-Guelph Fields of Southwestern Ontario, *A.A.P.G. Bull.*, vol. 33, pp. 153–188 (1949).

Russell, L. S.: Land and Sea Movements in the Late Cretaceous of Western Canada, *Royal Soc. Canada Proc. and Trans.*, 3rd ser., vol. 33, pp. 81–99 (1939).

Schuchert, C.: "Historical Geology of the Antillean-Caribbean Region or the Lands Bordering the Gulf of Mexico and the Caribbean Sea," John Wiley & Sons, Inc., New York (1935).

———: Orogenic Times of the Northern Appalachians, *G.S.A. Bull.*, vol. 41, pp. 701–724 (1930).

———: Sites and Nature of the North American Geosynclines, *G.S.A. Bull.*, vol. 34, pp. 151–230 (1923).

——— and Longwell, C. R.: Paleozoic Deformations of the Hudson Valley Region, New York, *Am. Jour. Sci.*, 5th ser., vol. 23, pp. 305–326 (1932).

Scott, J. C.: Folded Faults in Rocky Mountain Foothills of Alberta, Canada, *A.A.P.G. Bull.*, vol. 35, pp. 2316–2347 (1951).

Shanazarov, D. A.: Petroleum Problem of Siberia, *A.A.P.G. Bull.*, vol. 32, pp. 153–197 (1948).

Sherrill, R. E.: Some Problems of Appalachian Structure, *A.A.P.G. Bull.*, vol. 25, pp. 416–423 (1941).

Siever, R.: The Mississippian-Pennsylvania Unconformity in Southern Illinois, *A.A.P.G. Bull.*, vol. 35, pp. 542–581 (1951).

Skeels, D. C.: Gravity in Sedimentary Basins, *Am. Geophys. Union Trans.*, vol. 21, pp. 187–202 (1940).

Spangler, W. B.: Subsurface Geology of Atlantic Coastal Plain of North Carolina, *A.A.P.G. Bull.*, vol. 34, pp. 100–132 (1950).

——— and Peterson, J. J.: Geology of Atlantic Coastal Plain in New Jersey, Delaware, Maryland, and Virginia, *A.A.P.G. Bull.*, vol. 34, pp. 1–99 (1950).

Spieker, E. M.: Late Mesozoic and Early Cenozoic History of Central Utah, *U.S.G.S. Prof. Paper* 205–(d) (1946).

Stephenson, L. W.: Major Marine Transgressions and Regressions and Structural Features of the Gulf Coastal Plain, *Am. Jour. Sci.*, 5th ser., vol. 16, pp. 281–298 (1928).

Stoces, B., and White, C. H.: Structural Geology with Special Reference to Economic Deposits, The Macmillan Company, New York (1935).

Storm, L. W.: Resume of Facts and Opinions on Sedimentation in Gulf Coast Region of Texas and Louisiana, *A.A.P.G. Bull.*, vol. 29, pp. 1304–1335 (1945).

Stoyanow, A.: Paleozoic Paleogeography of Arizona, *G.S.A. Bull.*, vol. 53, pp. 1255–1282 (1942).

Suess, E.: "The Face of the Earth," Oxford University Press, New York, 5 vols. (1904–1924).

Sutton, F. A.: Geology of Maracaibo Basin, Venezuela, *A.A.P.G. Bull.*, vol. 30, pp. 1621–1741 (1946).

Tainsh, H. R.: Tertiary Geology and Principal Oil Fields of Burma, *A.A.P.G. Bull.*, vol. 34, pp. 823–855 (1950).

Taylor, E. F.: Geology and Oil Fields of Brazil, *A.A.P.G. Bull.*, vol. 36, pp. 1613–1626 (1952).

Thom, W. T., Jr.: Position, Extent and Structural Makeup of Appalachia, *G.S.A. Bull.*, vol. 48, pp. 315–321 (1937).

Thomas, C. R.: Geology and Petroleum Exploration in Magallanes Province, Chile, *A.A.P.G. Bull.*, vol. 33, pp. 1553–1578 (1949).

Ver Steeg, K.: Some Structural Features of Ohio, *Jour. Geology*, vol. 52, pp. 131–138 (1944).

Ver Wiebe, W. A.: Ancestral Rocky Mountains, *A.A.P.G. Bull.*, vol. 14, pp. 765–788 (1930).

Walters, R. P.: Oil Fields of Carpathian Region, *A.A.P.G. Bull.*, vol. 30, pp. 319–336 (1946).

Walton, P. T.: Geology of the Cretaceous of the Uinta Basin, Utah, *G.S.A. Bull.*, vol. 55, pp. 91–130 (1944).

Waterschoot van der Gracht, W. A. J. M. van: Permo-carboniferous Orogeny in South Central United States, *A.A.P.G. Bull.*, vol. 15, pp. 991–1057 (1931).

Weeks, L. G.: Factors of Sedimentary Basin Development That Control Oil Occurrence, *A.A.P.G. Bull.*, vol. 36, pp. 2071–2124 (1952).

Wheeler, R. R., and Jacobsen, L.: Moore Formation of Anadarko Basin, Oklahoma, a Discussion, *A.A.P.G. Bull.*, vol. 34, pp. 139–146 (1950).

Willard, B.: Origin of the Lackawanna Basin, Pennsylvania, *Jour. Geology*, vol. 54, pp. 246–251 (1946).

Willis, B., and Willis, R.: "Geologic Structures," New York, McGraw-Hill Book Company, Inc., 3d ed. (1934).

Wilson, C. W., Jr.: Probable Connection of the Nashville and Ozark Domes by a Complementary Arch, *Jour. Geology*, vol. 47, pp. 583–597 (1939).

——— and Born, K. E.: Structure of Central Tennessee, *A.A.P.G. Bull.*, vol. 27, pp. 1039–1059 (1943).

CHAPTER 13

SUPERFICIAL STRUCTURES

Though superficial structures are of no value as an indication of oil and gas pools, nevertheless petroleum geologists should be familiar with them. Unless a geologist understands the nature of superficial structures, he is likely to confuse them with the larger structural features which determine the location of oil and gas fields. The distinction between superficial and deep-seated structures is in some cases easy, in others very difficult.

In common geologic usage, any exposed structural feature which does not extend more than a few hundred feet below the surface would be considered a superficial structure. To the petroleum geologist, the important point is whether or not a structure extends downward to the formations which may produce oil or gas. If the formation which produces oil is at a depth of 2 miles and the surface structure terminates downward at a depth of 1 mile, the effect on the oil prospects is the same as if the structure terminated a few hundred feet below the surface. Structures which do not extend to the base of the sediments are treated in this chapter, but their inclusion does not mean that all such structures should be classed as superficial.

Primary Sedimentary Structures

There is no need for repeating here the description of primary sedimentary structures given in Chap. 10. The abnormally steep dips which occur in some primary sedimentary structures constitute superficial structures in the sense in which the term is used in this chapter. These dips may occur on a small scale as a result of cross-bedding or channeling and in general because of deposition on sloping surfaces. Ordinarily these dips can easily be distinguished from the dips produced by structural deformation. Where the dips do not continue over a large stratigraphic section, the flat-lying strata above and below the steep dips indicate their nature. The distinction between dips of stratigraphic and sedimentary origin may, however, become difficult where the dips are at the same angle over vertical intervals of 25 to 50 ft. In such cases neither the base nor the top of the dipping beds may be exposed. Some idea of the nature of these dips may be obtained if they are plotted on

316

maps. Dips on the flanks of folds have a rather regular pattern determined by the character of the folding. Dips produced by sedimentary causes would be likely to be either highly irregular and variable, or in the same general direction over a large area. Another criterion is whether the steep dips which continue for some distance bring up deeper formations.

Some idea of the reliability of dips can be obtained from the nature of the rocks in which they occur. Cross-bedding and initial dips are common in conglomerates, sandstones, and some medium- to coarse-grained limestones. Dips of this nature are absent or much less common in bedded cherts, coals, limestones of lithographic or extremely fine texture, and bituminous shales. In many cases it is known that steep dips of sedimentary origin are especially likely to occur in certain geologic formations and that the dips in other formations are generally due to tectonic disturbances. For example, the dips in the Chattanooga and Woodford formations are nearly always reliable. Some beds betray the fact that they were deposited on a sloping surface by thickening rather rapidly down the slope.

Sedimentary dips of great vertical and horizontal extent may occur in association with deltas, reefs, and starved basins. It may be only as a result of regional studies that the true nature of such structures is determined.

STRUCTURES DUE TO SOLUTION

Processes Involved. Superficial structures may be produced by the solution of any soluble rock, but only where the solution of the soluble rock takes place beneath the surface and the overlying beds subside unequally to take the place of the material removed by solution. If the rock surrounding the zone dissolved out is strong enough to support the weight of the overlying material, a cave is produced, and no superficial structure is formed. However, the condition in which the roof supports this weight is a temporary one, geologically speaking. With the lapse of geologic time, caverns generally become so extensive that the roofs cave in. If the overlying material is weak, or if the soluble material is dissolved over a large area, the overlying strata settle down as fast as solution takes place, and no void is formed. If the overlying beds settle by the same amount over a large area, no steep dips and consequently no superficial structures are produced. In the solution of a thick formation, even though all of it may eventually be removed, the rate of solution may vary from place to place. As a result dips and irregularities in the overlying beds may be produced, even though the total amount of subsidence is eventually everywhere the same.

Structures Produced by Solution of Limestones and Dolomites. Superficial dips produced by such solutions are very common. In arid regions, where limestones and dolomites act as resistant rocks, superficial structures caused by their solution are comparatively rare. In more humid climates, where the solubility of limestones renders them less resistant to erosion than the associated sandstones and shales, superficial structures produced by solution are common. Where the solution of limestones or dolomites is extensive, a peculiar topography known as karst may develop. It is characterized by sinkholes, disappearing streams, internal drainage, caves, and valleys without outlets at the surface. The solution of limestones and dolomites leaves as residue a reddish or reddish-brown clay which usually contains chert or other insoluble contents of the original carbonates.

The steep dips formed by the solution of limestones and dolomites may occur in these rocks themselves, or in the overlying relatively insoluble strata. The tilted beds are likely to be broken up, and cracks in them may be filled with red clay, but not with the vein materials. Superficial structures formed by the solution of limestones and dolomites are generally easily recognized by their association with karst topography, characteristic residual clays, and outcrops of limestones and dolomites.

Structures Produced by Solution of Salt and Gypsum. Caves and karst topography may be produced by the solution of gypsum. Superficial dips may also be produced by the slumping over zones where solution of gypsum takes place, but their nature is generally easily recognized by the characteristic topography and by the outcrops of gypsum.

Difficult problems of structural interpretation are produced by the solution of salt. In arid areas such as Iran, salt may crop out. However, in most humid and semiarid regions, the salt is dissolved by ground water a considerable distance below the surface, in some cases as much as 1,000 ft underground. A variety of superficial structures may be produced by the settling of the strata which overlay the salt before its solution. The result of this settling may be a jumble of steep local dips and normal faults of small horizontal extent. These dips vary rapidly horizontally and probably also vertically. If there are isolated areas in which the salt is not dissolved, the strata may remain at higher levels over these remnants. As a result, elevations taken on key horizons above the salt layer may show closed anticlines which do not extend downward below the horizon of the salt layer, and which therefore have no value as prospective traps for oil and gas.

Misinterpretations of gravity and seismic data may also be made unless the conditions near the termination of the salt layer are understood. For example, an isolated area of thick salt might be misinterpreted from seismic data as a closed anticline in the formations below the salt.

Clearly geologists should be skeptical of the value of surface structures which occur in or near the zone where thick salt beds are dissolved at depth. The distinction between superficial and deep-seated structures may be so uncertain in this zone that promising tectonic anticlines may be passed up on the supposition that they are superficial. In the United States the superficial structures produced by salt solution in western Kansas and West Texas are well known. In these areas the interpretation of the superficial structures is greatly aided by the subsurface data provided by deep wells. In a region where no wells had been drilled the interpretation of the superficial structures produced by salt solution might be very difficult.

Fig. 13-1 is a cross section indicating the nature of the superficial structures which may develop near the updip termination of a thick salt layer.

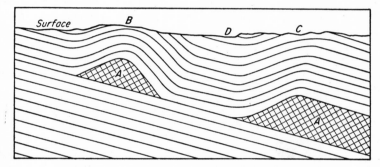

FIG. 13-1. Ideal cross section showing the types of superficial structures that may be produced by the solution of a thick salt layer, *A*, at depth.

Structural features caused by the removal of dissolved salt are produced on a grand scale in the region of the Great Lakes, particularly in the vicinity of the Mackinac Straits area. According to Landes,[1] a breccia produced by the collapse of the sediments over the zones where the Silurian salt has been dissolved is widely distributed in this region. A large part of the brecciation occurred before middle Devonian time, and in some places the brecciation extends over a vertical interval of 1,500 feet. This solution of the salt with resultant slumping may be a factor in causing the depressions now occupied by lakes Michigan, Huron, Erie, and Ontario.

STRUCTURES DUE TO ABSORPTION OF WATER AND TO WEATHERING

Near the surface certain rocks swell. This swelling is probably chiefly due to the absorption of water, though other chemical reactions may possibly play a part. The swelling may produce small, sharp folds which

[1] Kenneth K. Landes, Geology of the Mackinac Straits Region, *Michigan Geol. and Biol. Survey Pub.* 44, ser. 37 (1945).

die out rapidly downward. Anhydrite, bentonite, and shales are known to produce structures of this type by swelling on absorbing water. If the strata which swell contain thin, hard beds of limestone or sandstone, the hard strata may buckle up into long, narrow anticlines like the pressure ridges of ice floes. These anticlines may be 5 to 50 ft across and 1 to 15 ft high. It is possible that such folds may also be caused by relief near the surface of stresses retained from the time when the rocks were deeply buried.

The change from anhydrite to gypsum may produce superficial folds. Calcium sulfate several thousand feet below the earth's surface occurs as anhydrite. As the anhydrite beds are brought closer to the surface by the erosion of the overburden, the anhydrite generally absorbs water and changes to gypsum while still covered by a considerable thickness of strata. This change may possibly take place at depths of 100 to 1,000 ft. According to Twenhofel,[1] the change from anhydrite to gypsum involves an increase in volume of over 60 per cent. However, Muir[2] states that the anhydrite bed in the Blaine formation has changed to gypsum without change in volume. On the other hand, superficial folds occur in association with some gypsum beds, and pressure ridges and blisters due to swelling have been noted on the outcrops of beds of calcium sulfate in which the absorption of water was not complete when they became exposed. These characteristics show that considerable expansion may be involved in this change. The possibilities are that there is an equal volume change, that there is an increase in volume with an equivalent increase in the thickness of the calcium sulfate bed without folding, and that there is an increase of volume with the production of folds to relieve the lateral pressure. Sharp folds of small extent near gypsum beds may have originated in this manner. If so, they would die out rapidly away from the gypsum bed. In the United States superficial structures of this type do not appear to be of much importance. However, according to Woolnough,[3] structures of this general type are developed on a grand scale in Queensland. Osmond[4] has described a superficial structure which was formed during a period of two days in June, 1949. Limestone strata in the bed of a creek were buckled up into a hollow anticline about 10 ft high and 1,000 ft long. Swelling due to absorption of water and sliding

[1] W. T. Twenhofel, "Principles of Sedimentation," McGraw-Hill Book Company, Inc., New York, p. 536 (1939).

[2] J. Lawrence Muir, Anhydrite-Gypsum Problem of the Blaine Formation, Oklahoma, *A.A.P.G. Bull.*, vol. 18, pp. 1309–1310 (1934).

[3] W. G. Woolnough, Pseudo-tectonic Structures, *A.A.P.G. Bull.*, vol. 17, pp. 1098–1106 (1933).

[4] John C. Osmond, Jr., Recent Small-scale Deformation of Limestone Strata, Concho County, Texas, *A.A.P.G. Bull.*, vol. 34, pp. 1743–1747 (1950).

of the strata down the slopes under the influence of gravity are possible causes of this structure.

STRUCTURES DUE TO SLUMPING

Structures due to slumping are so common that geologists should be familiar with them. The importance of these structures lies in the danger of their being confused with deep-seated structures, and in the errors which they may cause in structure mapping.

Relation to Present Surface. Slumping may occur where a plastic formation is at or near the surface in an area of moderate to large relief. Common locations for slumps are along mesas, escarpments, and steep channels and banks of streams and rivers. Landslides differ from slumps

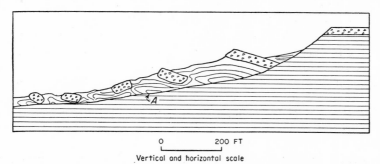

0   200 FT

Vertical and horizontal scale

FIG. 13-2. Ideal cross section showing typical relations of slumped blocks. *A* is the gliding surface.

in their greater rapidity of movement. Slumping is greatly favored by the presence of a plastic rock, and if a plastic formation is present, the slumps may traverse gentle to moderate slopes. Since rocks near the surface become plastic only when moist, slumping is greatly favored by conditions which allow moisture to be collected and retained in contact with a rock which becomes plastic on absorbing water. This condition commonly occurs where a sandstone, limestone, or glacial deposit is underlain by a shale.

As they descend the slopes large slump blocks tend to "toe in" or dip in the direction from which they came. This condition is illustrated by Fig. 13-2. In humid regions the soil and weathered rock tend to creep slowly down the slope. This may cause the superficial dips in the weathered rock to be directed downslope. Under these conditions any fragments of key horizons on or in the soil are carried below the level of the outcrops, and it may be necessary to make allowances for this in mapping structure. Under extreme conditions the strata on the sides of the hills settle slowly into the valleys, and superficial anticlines may form along the valleys.   Slumping has been described by Hollingworth, Taylor and Kellaway,[1] by Brown,[2] and by Sharpe.[3]

Gliding Surfaces.   Slumped blocks are commonly divided from the stationary rocks on which they rest by a break along which the slippage occurred.   According to the common definitions of faults, these surfaces are faults.   However, even if the surfaces on which ordinary slump blocks glide are faults, it would be confusing to make no distinction between these surfaces and the common types of faults.   Regardless of definitions, most geologists think of faults as having a cause which is more deep-seated than the superficial gliding of small slumps.   The gliding surfaces of slumps a few hundred feet across are generally not mapped as faults and are apparently not considered faults.   If, on the other hand, the blocks involved in the slumping are miles in extent, their gliding surfaces would be considered faults.   In the discussions of the origin of large, nearly horizontal faults, sliding downslope under the influences of gravity is cited as a possible cause, and there is generally no suggestion that these surfaces would not be classed as faults if they are produced in this manner. The gliding surfaces of all slump blocks may show slickensides, and veins of gypsum are occasionally seen along them.   Aside from this, these surfaces in the case of the smaller blocks are generally devoid of the veins and cementation which are common along the faults formed at greater depths.

Relation to Buried Topography.   Hills and valleys which were formed during the geologic past and have been preserved by being buried in sediments are fairly common.   It is to be expected that some slump blocks related to these former surfaces would also be preserved.   However, it appears from a study of the literature that slumps of this nature are quite rare and are not of much importance in making structural interpretations.

Relation to Surfaces of Deposition.   Many sediments are deposited on gently sloping surfaces.   These surfaces may be alluvial plains, flood plains, the bottoms of lakes, bays, gulfs, and inland seas, continental shelves, top-set and fore-set slopes of deltas, and terraces and slopes of sedimentary origin.   The angles of slope of the surfaces of deposition may vary from practically zero to the angle of rest of the material.   Some

---

[1] S. E. Hollingworth, J. H. Taylor, and G. A. Kellaway, Large-scale Superficial Structures in the Northampton Ironstone Field, *Geol. Soc. London Quart. Jour.*, vol. 100, pp. 1–44 (1944).

[2] Charles Barrington Brown, On a Theory of Gravitational Sliding Applied to the Tertiary of Ancon, Ecuador, *Geol. Soc. London Quart. Jour.*, vol. 94, pp. 359–370 (1938).

[3] C. F. S. Sharpe, "Landslides and Related Phenomena," Columbia Geomorphic Studies, Columbia University Press, New York (1938).

sediments are highly plastic when freshly deposited. One would expect, therefore, that superficial structures produced by slumping down the surfaces of deposition would be fairly common. These structures have been described by Kuenen,[1] Dorreen,[2] Bailey, Collet, and Field,[3] and Jones.[4]

In the sediments of many regions there are structures which have probably formed in this manner and which have some characteristics that aid in recognizing them. They are in general developed on a very small scale. The folds are usually only a few feet or a few tens of feet across, and the normal or reverse faults which may be associated with these folds generally do not extend for more than a few tens of feet. The structure and the bedding or stratification in the deformed beds in some cases have an indistinct appearance, as though the strata were blurred by mixing or kneading. The axial planes of the folds, and the reverse faults, if there are any, tend to dip in the opposite direction to the slope of the surface at the time of deposition. Sandstone beds may be bent at high angles or contorted without fracturing. Angular unconformities of very small extent are common, and the erosion of the deformed beds may produce intraformational conglomerates. Large lumps of sandstone may become embedded in shale, and large blocks of shale in sandstone. The most important distinguishing characteristic of these structures is that they are confined to single beds or formations. If the undeformed strata beneath can be observed, the superficial nature of the folding is established. If only the undeformed overlying strata are in evidence, it is necessary to take into consideration the possibility that an angular unconformity is present.

Fig. 13-3 is an ideal cross section through a zone which has slumped shortly after deposition. The thickening and thinning of the sandstone bed, the isolated blocks of sandstone and shale, and the truncation of the superficial structures at the top of the disturbed zone are features which have been observed in the field. The present dip of the formations may be quite different from the dip at the time when the slumping took place.

Sharp folds involving 100 ft or more of sediments are present in a number of areas—for example, in the Pennsylvanian strata of Ohio and

[1] P. H. Kuenen, "Marine Geology," John Wiley & Sons, Inc., New York, pp. 238–248 (1950).

[2] J. M. Dorreen, Rubble Bedding and Graded Bedding in Talara Formation of Northwestern Peru, *A.A.P.G. Bull.*, vol. 35, pp. 1829–1849 (1951).

[3] E. B. Bailey, L. W. Collett, and R. M. Field, Paleozoic Submarine Landslips near Quebec City, *Jour. Geology*, vol. 36, pp. 577–614 (1928).

[4] Owen Thomas Jones, On the Sliding or Slumping of Submarine Sediments in Denbighshire, North Wales, during the Ludlow Period, *Geol. Soc. London Quart. Jour.*, vol. 93, pp. 241–283 (1937).

Oklahoma. It is not certain whether these are due to large-scale slumping, or whether they are ameboid structures of tectonic origin. Deepseated folds which were forming during the deposition of a thick series of plastic sediments might produce effects in the shallow strata which would be quite similar to the effects of slumping down the slopes of the surfaces of sedimentation. However, if the folding had a deep-seated tectonic origin, the disturbed zone might not terminate abruptly at any sedimentary horizon, but might continue indefinitely downward. In other words, the folds might change their shapes or characteristics gradually with depth, as in Fig. 13-4. If sediments which differed greatly in their physical character were folded, there might be an abrupt change in the

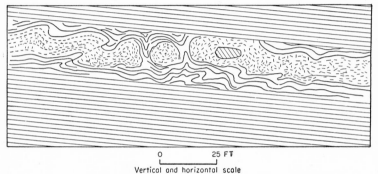

O   25 FT

Vertical and horizontal scale

FIG. 13-3. Cross section showing effect of slumping soon after deposition.

character of the deformation at the contact of competent and incompetent formations, but this is quite different from the complete termination of the deformation at the base of zones of slumping.

Distinction between Large Slump Blocks and Thrusts. In some cases it is difficult to distinguish large slumps from thrust blocks. Certainly there are marked differences in the opinions of geologists as to the interpretation of these structures. According to Taff[1] and Stevens,[2] slumped masses of shale have moved from the Temblor Mountains eastward for two or three miles to their present position over the McKittrick oil field, and the covering of the upturned edges of the oil sands by this shale has produced the trap in which the oil accumulated. However, in the discussion of Taff's paper, Condit maintains that the movement of the

[1] J. A. Taff, Geology of McKittrick Oil Field and Vicinity, Kern County, California, *A.A.P.G. Bull.*, vol. 17, pp. 1–15 (1933).

[2] John B. Stevens, McKittrick Area of the McKittrick Oil Field, in Geologic Formations and Economic Development of the Oil and Gas Fields of California, *California Div. of Mines Bull.* 118, pp. 510–511 (1943).

shale is due to thrusting. Harrison and Falcon[1] have described the modification of the surface structure of the anticlinal mountains of Iran by the slumping of beds down the slopes. A structure apparently formed in this manner is shown in the syncline at the extreme right of the lowest cross section in Fig. 13-5. Reeves[2] states there has been extensive gliding due to gravity along low-angle faults in the vicinity of the Bearpaw Mountains, Montana. The gliding was directed away from the uplift.

TECTONIC STRUCTURES WHICH DIE OUT RAPIDLY DOWNWARD

All folds and faults eventually disappear downward, some at depths of only a few hundred feet, some at considerable depths but within the sediments, and some within the basement rocks. For the sake of completeness, a number of structural types which terminate downward above the base of the sediments are discussed or mentioned in this chapter. The inclusion of these types in this chapter does not mean that they should be classed as superficial. This term is generally reserved for structures which do not persist over a vertical stratigraphic section of more than a few hundred feet.

Folds of tectonic origin which die out or change their shapes within a few hundred or a few thousand feet of depth are called disharmonic. Fig. 13-4, from a paper by Darton,[3] is a cross section through some typical folds of this nature. The lowest coal bed in the cross section lies nearly flat beneath the sharp folds in the upper coals. Folds of this general type are probably of fairly common occurrence in sedimentary rocks, particularly where thick shales are deformed. In some cases it would clearly be difficult to distinguish these folds from those produced by slumping, solution, or absorption of water.

The folds shown in Fig. 13-4 are so small that they would not be expected to continue to great depths. However, a number of cases are known in which folds a mile to several miles in width disappear downward at depths of about a mile or less. If the anticline on which a wildcat well is drilled disappears downward above the prospective producing horizons, the well is generally dry. Unless other wells in the vicinity are available for comparison, it may not be known that the structure disappears with depth. There are two indications which show that an anticline is decreasing in vertical relief with depth. If a wildcat well is in a

---

[1] J. V. Harrison and N. L. Falcon, Gravity Collapse Structures and Mountain Ranges, as Exemplified in Southwestern Iran, *Geol. Soc. London Quart. Jour.*, vol. 92, pp. 91–102 (1936).

[2] Frank Reeves, Shallow Folding and Faulting around the Bearpaw Mountains, *Am. Jour. Sci.*, 5th ser., vol. 10, pp. 187–200 (1925).

[3] N. H. Darton, Some Structural Features of the Northern Anthracite Coal Basin, Pennsylvania, *U.S.G.S. Prof. Paper* 193(d), fig. 14-E (1940).

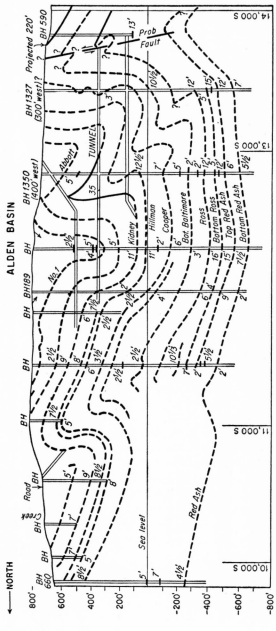

Fig. 13-4. Cross section showing disharmonic folds in the Pennsylvanian strata of Pennsylvania. (*After N. H. Darton, U.S. Geological Survey.*)

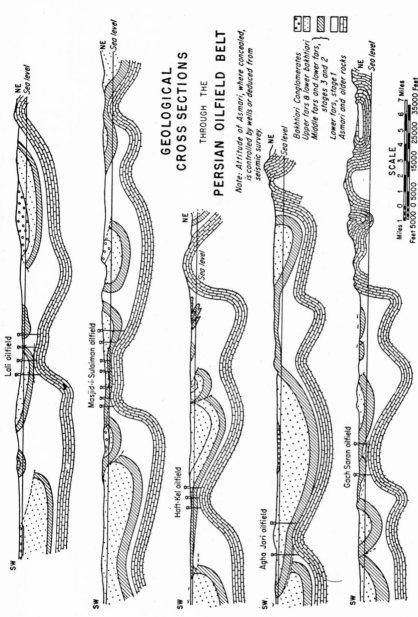

GEOLOGICAL
CROSS SECTIONS

THROUGH THE

PERSIAN OILFIELD BELT

Note: Attitude of Asmari, where concealed,
is controlled by wells or deduced from
seismic survey.

Bakhtiari Conglomerates
Upper fars & lower bakhtiari
Middle fars and lower fars,
stages 3 and 2
Lower fars, stage 1
Asmari and older rocks

SCALE

Miles 1 0 1 2 3 4 5 6 7 Miles
Feet 5000 0 5000 15000 25000 35000 Feet

Lali oilfield

Masjid-i-Sulaiman oilfield

Haft-Kel oilfield

Agha Jari oilfield

Gach Saran oilfield

Fɪɢ. 13-5. (After Lees, Quarterly Journal of the Geological Society of London.)

327

region in which there has been some scattered drilling, comparison with other wells indicates how much higher or lower than normal the various key horizons are running.   If the anticline on which the well is drilled disappears downward, the well runs less and less high as deeper beds are penetrated, and encounters the key beds below the base of the anticline at about normal elevation.   If a well runs 200 ft higher than normal, at the horizon of a shallow key bed, and normal in a deeper key bed, the interval between the two beds must be 200 ft greater than normal. Accordingly, the intervals are abnormally thick in an anticline which dies out downward.   The loss of closure or height of the anticline is equal to the total increase in the intervals.   The percentage of surface anticlines over a mile in width which disappear downward at depths of about a mile or less is unknown but probably small.

It appears that discordance in the shallow and deep folds is especially likely during the deformation of a thick series of relatively rigid or competent rocks which is overlain by a thick series of plastic beds.   This condition is well illustrated in the oil fields of Iran.   According to Lees[1] there is a marked discordance between the surface and subsurface structure in this region.   Fig. 13-5, from another paper by Lees,[2] illustrates this condition.   The lower formations are thick, competent limestones ranging in age from Eocene to lower Miocene.   Great quantities of oil are produced from the upper part of this zone.   Above these competent limestones there is a thick series of plastic strata containing much salt. Fig. 13-5 shows that there is such a marked discordance in structure that some surface synclines overlie the pronounced anticlines from which oil is produced.   Furthermore, the thrust fault which springs from the Agha Jari anticline crops out about four miles to the southwest of it.   Clearly surface structure would be an unreliable guide to the structure of the deeper beds in such areas as this.

STRUCTURES OF IGNEOUS ORIGIN

Diapir structures, salt domes, and structures produced by the intrusion of igneous rocks into the sediments all die out above the base of the sediments.   Diapir structures and salt domes have been discussed in Chap. 8. Structures caused by igneous intrusion have not produced much oil or gas as yet.   However, some oil production has been found in or associated with igneous rocks in Mexico, and in Texas southeast of Austin. Oil or gas production has also been obtained from uplifts probably or possibly produced by igneous intrusion in the Tow Creek structure,

---

[1] G. M. Lees, The Geology of the Oilfield Belt of Iran and Iraq, "Science of Petroleum," Oxford University Press, New York, vol. 1, p. 147 (1938).

[2] G. M. Lees, Foreland Folding, *Geol. Soc. London Quart. Jour.*, vol. 108, part 1, fig. 21, p. 31 (1952).

Colorado, described by Heaton,[1] in the Whitlash dome of northern Montana, described by Bartram and Erdmann,[2] and in association with the igneous intrusion of the Marysville Buttes, California, described by Johnson.[3]

Some of the oil and gas production on traps related to igneous intrusions is on laccoliths. A laccolith is a structural dome of sediments over a lens-shaped or hemispherical igneous intrusion. The dome is produced by the intrusion and not by tectonic forces.

An anticline or dome produced during the formation of a laccolith would generally be considered much less promising for oil and gas production than an anticline of similar size produced by uplift without igneous intrusion. It is therefore important in some cases to determine whether an anticline is a laccolith. The structure is more likely to be a laccolith if it is isolated, of rounded form, and not part of a regular system of folds, if igneous intrusions are present on or near it, and if other laccoliths occur in the region.

Probably many laccoliths are unproductive because the fracturing resulting from the intrusion allows the oil and gas to escape. Near large intrusions the porosity and permeability of the prospective producing horizons may be greatly reduced by induration and cementation. It appears that a dome produced by igneous intrusion would be more likely to produce oil or gas if the strata over the intrusion were young geologically, chiefly composed of shale, only moderately deformed, and devoid of igneous outcrops at the surface. It seems probable that as untested structures of other types become scarce, geologists will give more attention to the oil and gas prospects of uplifts of igneous origin.

CRYPTOVOLCANIC AND METEORIC STRUCTURES

A number of peculiar structures called "cryptovolcanic" are known in various parts of the world. The greatest known concentration occurs in the Paleozoic rocks of central and east central United States west of the Appalachian geosyncline. These structures have clearly been produced by vast explosions, but the geologists who have studied them differ as to whether the explosions were produced by volcanic action or meteoric impact. These structures or related features have been dis-

[1] Ross L. Heaton, Relation of Accumulation to Structure in Northwestern Colorado, "Structure of Typical American Oil Fields," American Association of Petroleum Geologists, Tulsa, vol. 2, pp. 107–108 (1929).

[2] John G. Bartram and Charles E. Erdmann, Natural Gas in Montana, "Geology of Natural Gas," American Association of Petroleum Geologists, Tulsa, pp. 245–276 (1935).

[3] Harry R. Johnson, Marysville Buttes (Sutter Buttes) Gas Field, in Geologic Formations and Economic Development of the Oil and Gas Fields of California, *California Div. of Mines Bull.* 118, pp. 610–615 (1943).

cussed by Baldwin,[1] Boon and Albritton,[2] Bucher,[3] Wilson,[4] and Wilson and Born.[5]

Cryptovolcanic structures are roughly circular in outline and vary from less than a mile to several miles in diameter. In the central portions of these structures the sedimentary rocks are shattered or brecciated, and in some the breccia has been injected as dikes. In many of these structures the normal sedimentary formations of the region can be recognized in spite of their shattered condition. In the central portion the shattered formations have in a number of cases been uplifted above the normal elevation of the same formations outside the disturbed area. Outside this uplifted region, there is generally a depressed area, forming a rim-shaped syncline or portions of such a syncline. Faults having a radial or peripheral arrangement may be present. There are many dips at high angles.

The cryptovolcanic structures of central and eastern United States have been formed at a number of different times during the geologic past. Neither igneous rocks nor meteoric material have been found in association with these structures. However, it appears that meteoric craters formed in the geologic past would probably be devoid of recognizable meteorites. Most of the original meteor would probably be vaporized by the heat generated by the impact, and the remainder would presumably soon be destroyed by weathering. Meteoric material is absent or very rare in and around some of the recent or Pleistocene craters of meteoric origin.

In recent years some evidence has become available which supports the idea that these structures are of meteoric origin. Studies of the moon suggest that from 50,000 to 500,000 craters have been formed on it by meteoric impact. Three large craters, located in Arizona, on the Ungava Peninsula east of Hudson Bay, and in Australia, were formed

[1] Ralph B. Baldwin, "The Face of the Moon," University of Chicago Press, Chicago (1949).

[2] John D. Boon and Claude C. Albritton, Jr., Meteorite Craters and Their Possible Relationship to "Cryptovolcanic Structures," *Field and Lab.*, vol. 5, pp. 1–9 (1936); Meteorite Scars in Ancient Rocks, *Field and Lab.*, vol. 5, pp. 53–64 (1937); Established and Supposed Examples of Meteoric Craters and Structures, *Field and Lab.*, vol. 6, pp. 44–56 (1938); The Impact of Large Meteorites, *Field and Lab.*, vol. 6, pp. 57–64 (1938).

[3] Walter H. Bucher, "Cryptovolcanic Structures in the United States," *Sixteenth Internat. Geol. Cong.*, pp. 1055–1083 (1933); Volcanic Explosion and Overthrusts, *Am. Geophys. Union Trans.*, vol. 14, pp. 238–242 (1933).

[4] Charles W. Wilson, Jr., Wilcox Deposits in Explosion Craters, Stewart County, Tennessee, and Their Relations to the Origin and Age of the Wells Creek Basin Structure, *G.S.A. Bull.*, vol. 64, pp. 753–768 (1953).

[5] Charles W. Wilson, Jr., and K. E. Born, The Flynn Creek Disturbance, Jackson County, Tennessee, *Jour. Geology*, vol. 44, pp. 815–835 (1936).

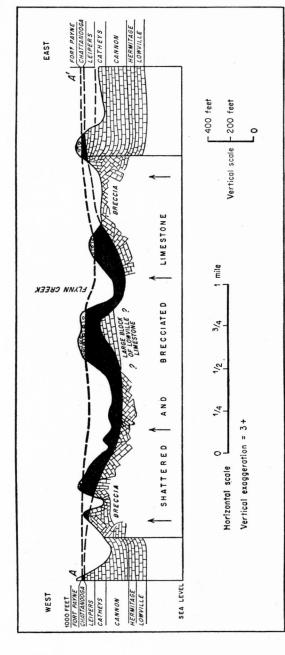

FIG. 13·6. Cross section through the Flynn Creek disturbance, Jackson County, Tenn., a cryptovolcanic or meteoric structure. Note the central peak of limestone and the thickening of the Chattanooga shale which fills the crater. (*After Wilson and Born, published by permission of the Journal of Geology.*)

during the past 100,000 years or so.   A much larger number would be expected to have formed on the earth during geologic time.   Furthermore, the central uplifts found in some of the cryptovolcanic structures seem to be more easily explained by the meteoric hypothesis.   These central uplifts occur, for example, in the Wells Creek Basin, Flynn Creek, and Steinheim structures.   If these structures are due to meteoric impact, the central uplifts may consist of masses of rock which have been driven downward and intensely compressed by the impact, and which have sprung up again because of the compressive stresses and elastic rebound. Furthermore, according to Wilson, the nature of the 2,000-ft core taken in the Wells Creek Basin structure supports the meteoric hypothesis. If the meteoric origin of these structures becomes established, they should be referred to as "meteoric" rather than "cryptovolcanic."   Fig. 13-6, from a paper by Wilson and Born,[1] is a cross section through a typical example of a cryptovolcanic structure.   The central uplift of shattered Lowville limestone is clearly shown.   The abrupt thickening of the Chattanooga shale indicates that the crater was formed such a short time before the deposition of this shale that erosion had not had time to obliterate the crater before the deposition of the Chattanooga shale began.

Cryptovolcanic or meteoric structures might become traps for oil and gas where they are buried under an impervious cover.   Production might be derived from open fractures, from porous breccias, or from stratigraphic or compaction structures developed over the craters.   The observed fractures and breccias in these structures are generally tightly cemented, but this cementation may not have affected all parts of structures of this type.   The best prospects for production are in the cryptovolcanic structures which are buried deeply.   Since such structures would be extremely difficult to find, it is not surprising that no oil or gas production is definitely known to come from a cryptovolcanic or meteoric structure.   Because of their rarity, the total reserves of oil on these structures are probably not large.   However, they are common enough so that petroleum geologists should have some knowledge of them.

ADDITIONAL REFERENCES

Baldry, R. A.: Slip-planes and Breccia Zones in the Tertiary Rocks of Peru, *Geol. Soc. London Quart. Jour.*, vol. 94, pp. 347–358 (1938).

Becker, G. F.: Mechanics of the Panama Canal Slides, *U.S.G.S. Prof. Paper* 98(n), pp. 253–261 (1917).

Beets, C.: Miocene Submarine Disturbances of Strata in Northern Italy, *Jour. Geology*, vol. 54, pp. 229–245 (1946).

Born, K. E., and Wilson, C. W., Jr.: The Howell Structure, Lincoln County, Tennessee, *Jour. Geology*, vol. 47, pp. 371–388 (1939).

Brown, H. J. W.: Minor Structures in the Lower Greensand of East Kent and West Surrey, *Geol. Mag.*, vol. 62, pp. 439–450 (1925).

[1] *Op. cit.*, p. 824.

Capps, S. R.: Observations of the Rate of Creep in Idaho, *Am. Jour. Sci.*, vol. 239, pp. 25–32 (1941).

Collingwood, D. M., and Rettger, R. E.: Lytton Springs Oil Field, Caldwell County, Texas, *A.A.P.G. Bull.*, vol. 10, pp. 953–975 (1926).

Cooper, J. R.: Flow Structures in the Berea Sandstone and Bedford Shale of Central Ohio, *Jour. Geology*, vol. 51, pp. 190–203 (1943).

Dane, C. H., and Pierce, W. G.: Fossil Sink Holes in Cretaceous Beds of Prowers County, Colorado, *A.A.P.G. Bull.*, vol. 18, pp. 1493–1505 (1934).

Dobbin, C. E.: Structural Conditions of Oil and Gas Accumulation in Rocky Mountain Region, United States, *A.A.P.G. Bull.*, vol. 27, pp. 417–478 (1943).

Fairbridge, R. W.: Submarine Slumping and Location of Oil Bodies, *A.A.P.G. Bull.*, vol. 30, pp. 84–92 (1946).

Gardner, J. H.: Rock Distortion on Local Structures in Oil Fields of Oklahoma, *A.A.P.G. Bull.*, vol. 6, pp. 228–243 (1922).

Guppy, D. J., and Matheson, R. S.: Wolf Creek Meteorite Crater, Western Australia, *Jour. Geology*, vol. 58, pp. 30–36 (1950).

Harrison, J. V., and Falcon, N. L.: Collapse Structures, *Geol. Mag.*, vol. 71, pp. 529–539 (1934).

Hughes, U. B.: Shallow Salt-type Structure in Permian of North-central Texas, *A.A.P.G. Bull.*, vol. 16, pp. 577–583 (1932).

Hunt, C. B.: New Interpretation of Some Laccolithic Mountains and Its Possible Bearing on Structural Traps for Oil and Gas, *A.A.P.G. Bull.*, vol. 26, pp. 197–203 (1942).

Judson, S.: Large-scale Superficial Structures—A Discussion, *Jour. Geology*, vol. 55, pp. 168–175 (1947).

Kiersch, G. A.: Small-scale Structures and Other Features of Navajo Sandstone, Northern Part of San Rafael Swell, Utah, *A.A.P.G. Bull.*, vol. 34, pp. 923–942 (1950).

King, P. B.: The Geology of the Southern Guadalupe Mountains, Texas, *U.S.G.S. Prof. Paper* 215, pp. 15–16 (1948).

Kuenen, P. H.: Significant Features of Graded Bedding, *A.A.P.G. Bull.*, vol. 37, pp. 1044–1066 (1953).

Landes, K. K., and Ockerman, J. W.: Origin of Domes in Lincoln and Mitchell Counties, Kansas, *G.S.A. Bull.*, vol. 44, pp. 529–540 (1933).

MacDonald, D. F.: The Geology of the Panama Canal with Special Reference to the Slides, *Mem. Nat. Acad. Sci.*, vol. 18, pp. 45–67 (1924).

Melton, F. A.: Carolina Bays, *Jour. Geology*, vol. 58, pp. 128–134 (1950).

Nichols, R. L.: Squeeze-ups, *Jour. Geology*, vol. 47, pp. 421–425 (1937).

Price, W. A.: Caliche and Pseudo-anticlines, *A.A.P.G. Bull.*, vol. 9, pp. 1009–1017 (1925).

Rettger, R. E.: Experiments on Soft-rock Deformation, *A.A.P.G. Bull.*, vol. 19, pp. 271–292 (1935).

Russell, W. L.: The Possibilities of Oil in Western Ziebach County, *South Dakota Geol. and Nat. History Survey Circ.* 20, pp. 16–18 (1925).

———: Local Subsidence in Western Kansas, *A.A.P.G. Bull.*, vol. 13, pp. 605–609 (1929).

———: Stratigraphy and Structure of the Smoky Hill Chalk in Western Kansas, *A.A.P.G. Bull.*, vol. 13, pp. 595–609 (1929).

———: Structures in Western Haakon and Eastern Pennington Counties, *South Dakota Geol. and Nat. History Survey Bull.* 28, pp. 13–21 (1926).

Sellards, E. H.: Oil Accumulation in Igneous Rocks, "Science of Petroleum," Oxford University Press, New York, vol. 1, pp. 261–265 (1938).

Simonson, R. R., and Krueger, M. L.: Crocker Flat Landslide Area, Temblor Range, California, *A.A.P.G. Bull.*, vol. 26, pp. 1608–1631 (1942).

Teas, L. P.: Differential Compacting Cause of Certain Claiborne Dips, *A.A.P.G. Bull.*, vol. 7, pp. 370–378 (1923).

Tomlinson, C. W.: Odd Geologic Structures of Southern Oklahoma, *A.A.P.G. Bull.*, vol. 36, pp. 1820–1840 (1952).

Townsend, R. C.: Deformation of Fort Union Formation near Lignite, North Dakota, *A.A.P.G. Bull.*, vol. 34, pp. 1552–1564 (1950).

Twenhofel, W. H.: Significance of Some of the Surface Structures of Central and Western Kansas, *A.A.P.G. Bull.*, vol. 9, pp. 1061–1070 (1925).

Williams, H.: The Geology of Crater Lake National Park, Oregon, with a Reconnaissance of the Cascade Range Southward to Mount Shasta, *Carnegie Inst. Washington Pub.* 540, pp. 1–162 (1942).

CHAPTER 14

STRUCTURE OF CONTINENTAL SHELVES

The interest of oilmen and petroleum geologists in the continental shelves is occasioned primarily by the realization that they contain great reserves of oil. However, entirely aside from the commercial developments, the continental shelves are of considerable interest because of their bearing on the general structural problems of geosynclines, continents, and oceans. In their search for oil fields on the continental shelves, geologists and geophysicists look for local structures. A knowledge of the general or regional structure of the continental shelves would doubtless be an aid in prospecting for these local structures.

GEOGRAPHY

Near the shores of the continents the sea bottom slopes very gently toward the oceans for some distance. At a depth of roughly 450 ft the angle of slope increases abruptly. This change marks the seaward boundary of the continental shelf and the landward edge of the continental slope. The depth of the water at the edge of the continental shelf varies from 400 to 600 ft, and is therefore fairly constant all over the world. The width of the continental shelf varies from a few miles to over 300 miles, and the angle of slope of the shelf varies in a corresponding manner. In the United States the continental shelves are narrow off southern California and wide off Louisiana, western Florida, and eastern New England. The continental shelves are about 250 miles wide off eastern Maine, and even wider in the region of the Grand Banks off southeastern Canada. Wide continental shelves are also found in the region of the East Indies, east of China, between New Guinea and Australia, in the North Sea, near Bering Strait, and off the shores of the Arctic Ocean.

The height of the continental slope may average around 12,000 ft, its width 10 to 75 miles, and its angle of slope generally 2 to 15 per cent. According to Shepard,[1] the average angle of slope of the continental slopes is 4° 17' for the first 1,000 fathoms of descent. In some areas, for example off the western coast of Florida, there are definite cliffs on the continental slopes which must be fault scarps. Between the steep continental slopes

[1] Francis P. Shepard, "Submarine Geology," Harper & Brothers, New York, p. 187 (1948).

and the nearly level ocean bottoms there is a zone of gentle slopes known as the continental rise.

Sources of Information

Information regarding the structure of the continental shelves is derived from many sources.   One of the most important is the study of the surface and subsurface geology of the adjacent lands.   The changes in the structure and stratigraphy as the coast line is approached indicate the probable nature of the structural and stratigraphic conditions on the inner margins of the continental shelves.   However, where the shelves are wide, this method does not give much information about the structure of the outer portions of the shelves.   Samples taken on the continental shelves and slopes indicate the nature of the sediments and conditions of sedimentation.   From this information something may be inferred about the nature of the deposits at various depths in the geologic past.   Many samples of bedrock have been obtained from the continental slopes and from the submarine canyons on them.   These samples yield valuable information regarding the structure and stratigraphy of the outer portions of the continental shelves.   Drilling has not revealed much about the general structure of the continental shelves because it has generally been confined to their inner margins.   The accurate maps of the topography of the continental shelves and slopes obtained from sonic soundings have been a great help in making structural interpretations.   The delta of the Mississippi River has extended nearly all the way across the continental shelf.   Consequently drilling on land on the delta has yielded much valuable information about the structure of the continental shelves at this point.   However, the most important information about the structure of this region has come from geophysics, and this promises to be true for some time to come.   The local structures on which oil or gas production occurs on the continental shelf are found by geophysical means, and geophysical surveys of the outer portions of some of the continental shelves have given important information about their general structure.

Submarine Canyons

For many years the origin of the canyons which extend down the continental slopes has been a perplexing problem.   In attempting to solve this problem, geologists, geophysicists, and oceanographers have brought to light information which has a bearing on the origin and structure of the continental shelves and slopes as well as on the origin of the canyons.   Most of the canyons head near the upper portion of the continental slope or in the outer edge of the continental shelf.   A few, such as the Hudson canyon, are the continuations of shallow depressions which cross the continental shelves. Many of these canyons extend clear down to the bottom of the continental shelves at depths of around 12,000 ft. Furthermore, some valleys extend across the gently sloping ocean bottoms; the Hudson canyon has such an extension.

During the maximum extent of the Pleistocene glaciation the level of the oceans was considerably lower than it is now. Although the exact amount of lowering is difficult to determine, the general opinion seems to be that the maximum was around 300 to 500 ft. Some valleys which traverse the continental shelves may have formed during this depression of sea level. However, since submarine canyons extend to depths of over 10,000 ft, and since valleys apparently formed in the same manner as the canyons traverse the ocean bottoms, it seems clear that submarine canyons have in general not been formed by subaerial erosion. This problem has been discussed by Bucher,[1] Crowell,[2] Ericson, Ewing, and Heezen,[3] Shepard,[4] Shepard and Emery,[5] Stetson,[6] Tolstoy,[7] and von Engeln.[8]

Submarine canyons appear to have been excavated chiefly by density currents, possibly aided by landslides. Near some coasts there appear to be former land areas which are now submerged beneath the ocean. Valleys excavated by subaerial erosion may be found in such areas, but it does not seem reasonable to suppose that the continental slopes all over the world have been depressed many thousands of feet in late Cenozoic time.

DEPOSITIONAL RELATIONS

The rather uniform depth of the outer edges of the continental shelves all over the world indicates that this depth is controlled by some factor that is related to sea level. It appears that this factor is the depth at which the sediments can remain permanently in place without being moved again by waves or currents. If sea level were permanently

---

[1] Walter H. Bucher, Submarine Valleys and Related Geologic Problems of the North Atlantic, *G.S.A. Bull.*, vol. 51, pp. 489–511 (1940).

[2] John C. Crowell, Submarine Canyons Bordering Southern California, *Jour. Geology*, vol. 60, pp. 58–83 (1952).

[3] D. B. Ericson, Maurice Ewing, and Bruce C. Heezen, Deep Sea Sands and Submarine Canyons, *G.S.A. Bull.*, vol. 62, pp. 961–966 (1951).

[4] Francis P. Shepard, Mass Movements in Canyon Heads, *Am. Geophys. Union Trans.*, vol. 32, pp. 405–418 (1951).

[5] Francis P. Shepard and K. O. Emery, Submarine Topography off the California Coast, *G.S.A. Special Paper* 31, pp. 1–171 (1941).

[6] Henry C. Stetson, Geology and Paleontology of the Georges Bank Canyons: I, Geology, *G.S.A. Bull.*, vol. 47, pp. 339–366 (1936).

[7] Ivan Tolstoy, Submarine Topography in the North Atlantic, *G.S.A. Bull.*, vol. 62, pp. 441–450 (1951).

[8] O. D. von Engeln, Submarine Canyons and the Ice Age, *Jour. Geology*, vol. 58, pp. 161–163 (1950).

lowered 300 ft, with conditions otherwise the same, it is to be expected that eventually the upper part of the deposits of the continental shelf would be eroded and redeposited with the edge of the shelf at the same depth as it is at present. During the maximum extent of Pleistocene glaciation, when the sea level was depressed around 300 or 500 ft, the sediments of the continental shelves were presumably eroded and deposited in deeper water. However, the duration of this lowering was probably too short to permit marked changes in the general configuration of the continental shelves.

Under normal conditions sediments are continually being washed across the continental shelves and dropped over the edge of the continental slope. If there were no faulting or other deformation, it seems that the steepness of slope of the continental shelves would depend on the angle of rest of the material. In other words, the angle of slope is limited by slumping, sliding, and density currents. Density currents are produced by differences in density of fluids. Sea water mixed with considerable proportions of mud is so much denser than pure sea water that it will flow rapidly down steep slopes, and may accomplish considerable erosion during its descent. Material carried down the continental slopes by slumping or density currents is spread over the ocean bottoms near the lower edge of the continental shelves. This may account for the continental rise.

Well-developed continental shelves require many millions of years to accumulate. During this time faulting, folding, or warping may modify the shape of the deposits. Furthermore, as the continental shelf is built up seaward from the coast line, sediments generally accumulate landward from the shore to form an alluvial coastal plain. The combined weight of the sediments of the coastal plains and continental shelves constitutes such a large load on the crust of the earth that some sagging would be expected where these deposits are thick and widespread. If this sagging went far enough, a long, narrow basin or geosyncline would be produced, and the older deposits under the continental slopes and outer portions of the continental shelves would dip toward the land. The more recent deposits, however, might continue to dip toward the ocean all the way across the continental shelves and slopes.

IMPORTANT STRUCTURES

Regional Structure. At present there is little reliable information as to the structure of the continental slopes and the outer portions of the continental shelves. Sampling has shown that Upper Cretaceous and Tertiary formations crop out on the continental slopes or in the submarine canyons which extend down them. For example, Stetson[1] states

---

[1] *Op. cit.*, p. 365.

that the contact between the Upper Cretaceous and younger sediments intersects the continental slope or the submarine canyons on Georges Bank (off southeastern Canada) at a depth of about 480 to 600 m. In the continental shelf off eastern United States these Upper Cretaceous and Tertiary formations are nearly level or dip very gently seaward almost out to the continental slopes. The fact that they crop out in the continental slopes and submarine canyons may indicate that they are cut off abruptly at the slope. This abrupt termination suggests faulting. However, the relations might possibly be explained by postulating steep

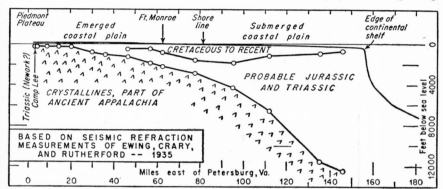

FIG. 14-1. Cross section through the continental shelf off the Atlantic coast east of Petersburg, Va. (*After Miller, published by permission of the Geological Society of America.*)

seaward dips on the continental slopes, or by assuming that sediments formerly present have been removed by slumping.

The best evidence as to the structure of the continental shelves is obtained from seismograph surveys across them. According to Miller[1] and to Ewing and others,[2] the continental shelf off the Atlantic coast of the United States is in places a submarine terrace of sedimentary origin, with the strata dipping toward the sea from the shore to the continental slope. This type of structure is illustrated in Fig. 14-1, from Miller's[3] paper. In other places the older sediments dip toward the land near the outer margin of the continental shelf, as illustrated by Fig. 14-2,

[1] B. L. Miller, Geophysical Investigations in the Emerged and Submerged Atlantic Coastal Plain: II, Geological Significance of Geophysical Data, *G.S.A. Bull.*, vol. 48, pp. 803–812 (1937).

[2] Maurice Ewing, A. P. Crary, and H. M. Rutherford, Geophysical Investigations in the Emerged and Submerged Atlantic Coastal Plain: I, Methods and Results, *G.S.A. Bull.*, vol. 48, pp. 753–802 (1937); Maurice Ewing, George P. Woollard, and A. C. Vine, III, Barnegat Bay, New Jersey, Section, *G.S.A. Bull.*, vol. 50, pp. 257–296 (1939); IV, Cape May, New Jersey, Section, *G.S.A. Bull.*, vol. 51, pp. 1821–1840 (1940); Maurice Ewing and others, V, Woods Hole, New York, and Cape May Sections, *G.S.A. Bull.*, vol. 61, pp. 877–892 (1950).

[3] *Op. cit.*, fig. 1.

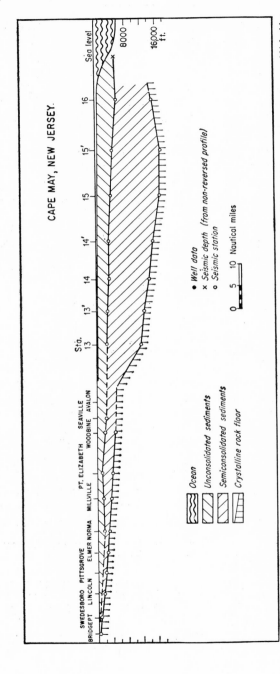

Fig. 14-2. Cross section through the continental shelf off the Atlantic coast near Cape May, N.J. (*After Ewing and others, published by permission of the Geological Society of America.*)

340

which is taken from one of the papers of Ewing and others.[1] The maximum thickness of the sediments found in these surveys is about 16,000 ft.

Faulting Parallel to Coasts. In some regions there is good evidence of faulting along the borders of the continents. A fault is suggested where the coast lines are straight, where deep water is present close offshore, and where continental shelves are absent or poorly developed. Other evidence of faulting might consist of the truncation near the coast of relatively young sediments, structures, or erosion surfaces. Soundings have shown what appear to be fault scarps paralleling the coast at various depths. However, such faults do not appear to be particularly related to the continental shelves, and their occurrence in the continental-shelf deposits may be more or less accidental. The continental shelves appear to be poorly developed or absent along faulted coasts.

Faulting on Continental Slopes. Two possible explanations for the continental slope are that it is the steeply dipping seaward side of a huge sedimentary terrace, and that it is a fault scarp. As the pile of sediments advances seaward, the inclination of the strata in the sediments accumulating on the continental slope would have approximately the same inclination as the slope, and would resemble the fore-set beds of a delta in that they would be underlain and overlain by gently dipping beds. There are two means of discovering faults on the continental slopes. The scarps may be detected by sounding, or the breaks in the slope of the underlying formations may be detected by seismic surveys. Jordan[2] has described what appears to be a fault scarp on the continental slope west of Florida. Possibly the fault scarp owes its preservation to being composed of limestone. Where the sediments consist of soft clastics, fault scarps on the continental slopes may soon be obliterated by slumping.

If the gently dipping formations of the continental shelf terminate abruptly against the continental slopes, a fault is suggested. However, no fault may be present if the strata bend down abruptly at the continental slopes and dip parallel to them, as is suggested by Fig. 14-3. In Fig. 14-2 the top of the semiconsolidated sediments is shown passing horizontally under most of the continental slope. If any horizon can be traced beneath the continental slopes without displacement, only faults of very low dip can be present. A fault with a dip nearly as low as the angle of dip of the continental slopes would presumably be a slump which would not cut the sediments below a certain depth. Of course it is possible that the major fault would occur near the base of the continental

[1] Ewing, Woollard, and Vine, *op. cit.*, IV, fig. 1.
[2] G. F. Jordan, Continental Slope off Appalachicola River, Florida, *A.A.P.G. Bull.*, vol. 35, pp. 1978–1993 (1951).

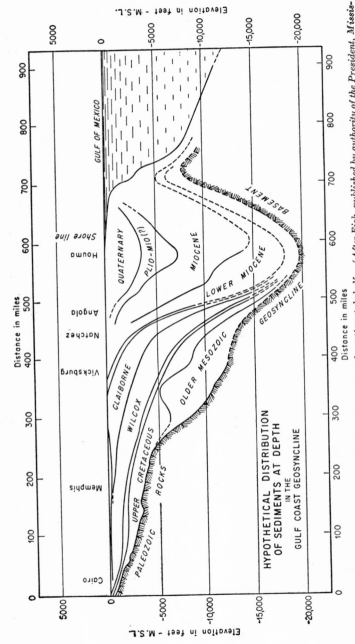

Fig. 14-3. Cross section through Mississippi embayment and continental shelf. (*After Fisk, published by authority of the President, Mississippi River Commission, Corps of Engineers, U.S. Army, Vicksburg, Miss.*)

slopes, and that the slumping would extend back toward land a considerable distance from the main fault. Nevertheless, the relations shown in Fig. 14-2 suggest that there is no fault on the continental slope in this locality. Much more information is needed to determine how important faulting is on the continental slopes.

Possible Types of Structure. The structure of the continental shelves may be of four possible types. One is a terrace of sediments dipping toward the ocean, as is illustrated by Fig. 14-1. Another is a terrace of sediments modified by the subsidence of the central portion of the wedge. This produces a basin or synclinal feature in the older sediments, as is shown in Fig. 14-2. The third is a well-developed geosyncline, as is illustrated by Fig. 14-3 from a paper by Fisk.[1] A fourth type is a wedge of sediments cut off by faults on the continental slope. The second and third types may be modified by faulting, particularly on the continental slopes. Furthermore, where the continental shelves have a geosynclinal structure of the type shown in Fig. 14-3, the continental slopes have clearly migrated a considerable distance seaward during the course of the formation of the geosyncline. If faulting occurred on the continental slopes all during the development of the geosyncline, the earlier faults which formed on former positions of the continental slopes would be far inland from the present position of the continental slopes.

Seaward Displacement of the Thickness Axes. A discussion of the thickness axes of continental shelves may throw light on their origin and structure. The thickness axes of continental shelves may be defined in the same manner as the thickness axes of geosynclines. The thickness axis of each formation is a line connecting points of its maximum thickness in a series of transverse cross sections through the continental shelves. These thickness axes are generally roughly parallel to the coast. They tend to be displaced seaward with the passage of geologic time. This is because the zones where the conditions of sedimentation are similar shift gradually seaward, if there is no structural deformation. These zones trend parallel to the shore line; in each of them there is a similar sedimentary facies, and the thicknesses of the formations deposited during a given interval tend to be more or less similar. These zones are the terrestrial alluvial coastal plain, the littoral zone, the continental shelf, the continental slope, and the continental rise. These zones would shift slowly seaward together as the continental slopes move seaward during deposition. This shift may be compared to the forward movement of the front of a delta. During each time interval the thickest deposits would presumably be laid down on the continental slope or the conti-

---

[1] H. N. Fisk, "Geological Investigation of the Alluvial Valley of the Lower Mississippi River," conducted for the Mississippi River Commission, (War Dept. Corps of Engineers, U.S. Army) (1944).

nental rise, and thus the thickness axes would migrate seaward with these features.

In many areas the crust of the earth subsides as it is loaded with a great thickness of sediments. This permits the deposition of more sediments, and these in turn produce further subsidence. Eventually no more subsidence takes place, but by the time this equilibrium is attained on the inner portion of the continental shelves, subsidence is proceeding in a belt closer to the ocean. Thus the seaward migration of the zone of maximum subsidence also tends to cause the thickness axes to migrate seaward. This conclusion that the thickness axes migrate seaward is based on the assumption that there is no deformation except that produced by the weight of the sediments. If there is warping or tilting of the crust due to other causes, quite different results may be produced. These thickness axes are closely related to the regional dips at different levels, as was explained in the discussion of geosynclines.

CHANGE IN ANGLE OF DIP WITH DEPTH

It is characteristic of the deposits of coastal plains and continental shelves that the seaward dip increases with depth. This is the result of the progressive tilting toward the ocean which took place during the deposition of the sediments. The intervals between the key horizons also increase seaward. The seaward tilting may be due to the load on the crust produced by the sediments of the continental shelves, or it may be caused in part by warping of the crust which is independent of the load. Whatever the cause is, the downward increase in dip toward the ocean occurs only in the landward portion of the belt of sediments. Seaward from a certain line, the seaward dip of the older sediments must be less than the seaward dip of the younger sediments. This would be true whether the older strata dip toward the land in the outer portion of the continental shelves, or whether they dip toward the ocean all the way across the shelf.

The landward dips in the older deposits under the outer portions of the continental shelves have not been proved by drilling on the continental shelves. They are, however, shown by the seismograph cross sections of the continental shelf off the Atlantic coast of the United States, one of which is shown in Fig. 14-2. Landward dips in the older deposits are shown in Fig. 14-3 and in other cross sections of the Gulf Coast geosyncline. However, these landward dips in the Gulf Coast geosyncline are postulated on theoretical grounds, and there is as yet no direct evidence of them from geophysics or from drilling.

CONTINENTAL BORDERLANDS

Off the coast of southern California there is a belt about 160 miles in maximum width which is known as the Continental Borderland. The topography of this area is irregular, with many topographic basins separated by ridges. The depth of the water is generally 1,000 to 5,000 ft. At the western edge of this region there is an abrupt drop to the normal depth of the bottom of the Pacific Ocean. The western boundary of the Continental Borderland off southern California is shown in Fig. 12-9.

The Continental Borderland has been described by Shepard and Emery[1] and by Clark.[2] It seems to consist of structural basins filled with sediments and intervening topographic and structural highs. Apparently its general structure is like that of the adjacent portions of California. If the submerged basins are like the similar basins on the adjacent mainland, some of them would contain rich oil fields. However, as explained below, this does not mean that this oil could be profitably produced.

TOPOGRAPHIC HIGHS ON OUTER EDGE OF CONTINENTAL SHELF

Near the seaward edge of the continental shelf or upper portion of the continental slope off Texas and Louisiana there are a large number of submerged hills, some of which are several hundred feet in height. These features have been described by Shepard[3] and Weaver.[4] Hills on the nearly level plains near the coast of Louisiana and Texas commonly overlie salt domes. It is therefore a natural supposition that the hills on the continental shelf may also lie over salt domes. However, it is also possible that they are reefs. Reef growth at depths of 400 to 600 ft may have been promoted by the lowering of sea level during the Pleistocene glaciations. Moreover, even if these hills do overlie salt domes, reefs or reef-type deposits may form on them. At the present time it does not seem possible to establish definitely the mode of origin of these topographic features. However, even if they are salt domes, they lie in water far too deep for economic drilling at the present time. Some of the hills and valleys near the outer edge of the continental shelf may have been produced by large-scale slumping.

TIME RELATIONS

Perhaps the most remarkable feature of the known continental shelves is that they have accumulated since the beginning of the Mesozoic era. The continental shelves which must have formed before the beginning of the Mesozoic are either missing entirely or have become modified or

[1] Francis P. Shepard and K. O. Emery, *op. cit.;* Lithology of the Sea Floor off Southern California, *G.S.A. Bull.*, vol. 56, pp. 431–478 (1945).

[2] Bruce L. Clark, Tectonics of the Coast Ranges of Middle California, *G.S.A. Bull.*, vol. 41, p. 808 (1930).

[3] Francis P. Shepard, Salt Domes Related to the Mississippi Submarine Trough, *G.S.A. Bull.*, vol. 48, pp. 1349–1361 (1937).

[4] Paul Weaver, Variations in History of Continental Shelves, *A.A P.G. Bull.*, vol. 34, pp. 351–360 (1950).

disguised so that they are no longer recognizable. It seems certain that deposits must have accumulated on the edge of the continents continuously since the continents and oceans were formed. The Paleozoic era is longer than the combined Mesozoic and Cenozoic eras, and the whole of geologic time is about ten or more times as long as the combined Mesozoic and Cenozoic. Accordingly, one would expect that the continental shelves formed during the Paleozoic would be at least as large as those formed since the beginning of the Mesozoic, and that the continental shelves formed during the whole of geologic time before the beginning of the Mesozoic would be roughly ten times the volume of the continental shelves formed since. Furthermore, some geologists have postulated the existence of the borderlands Appalachia, Llanoria, and Cascadia on the edges of the North American continent during the Paleozoic era. It has been supposed that a large part of the vast volumes of sediments which fill the adjacent synclines inland from these borderlands were derived from them. It seems reasonable to suppose that on the seaward side of the divides of these uplifts a more or less equal amount of erosion and deposition took place. Since these sediments must have been deposited in the adjacent oceans, one would expect continental shelves underlain by a great volume of sediments on the seaward side of the borderlands. No indications of such deposits have been found.

This absence of Paleozoic continental shelves appears to be related to some other peculiarities of Paleozoic paleogeography. Some of the orogens of this era appear to plunge into the ocean at the continental borders. Some of the Paleozoic formations, such as those of the Cape and Karroo series of South Africa, give the impression that when deposited they extended a considerable distance out into what is now the ocean. The continental glaciers of the Permian in some areas moved from what is now ocean toward the land. The theory of continental drift has been proposed to explain these and other features. Whatever the true explanation may be, there is no doubt that this is one of the most important unsolved problems of geology.

OIL AND GAS PROSPECTS

The distribution of oil and gas fields on land adjacent to the continental shelves has long made it a practical certainty that a considerable number of oil or gas fields would underlie the continental shelves. The shore line has advanced and retreated many times without affecting the oil reservoirs at depth, and its present position is more or less a matter of chance. However, in considering the oil and gas prospects of the continental shelves the economics of oil and gas production must be carefully considered. Although it is likely that many scores of billions of barrels of oil underlie the continental shelves, it may be that only a small percentage of this oil can be recovered at a profit. Oil which cannot be profitably recovered from the continental shelves would presumably be left there, and if so its effect on the economy of the world would be the same as if it had never existed.

Another very important factor in oil and gas developments on the continental shelves is the difficulty of drilling in deep water. Carsey[1] places the extreme limit of the depth of water with the present methods of drilling at 100 ft. Practically all the wells on the continental shelf have been drilled in water less than 60 ft deep, though in protected areas free from severe storms, such as Lake Maracaibo, wells have been drilled in deeper water. Presumably the oil and gas fields on the continental shelf in water deeper than 100 ft will never be developed unless the relative price of oil rises greatly, or unless an economical method for drilling in deep water is devised. Estimates of the oil and gas reserves of the continental shelves are likely to be misleading unless the effect of the depth of water and other economic factors is carefully considered and stated along with the estimates.

Oil fields and oil prospects on the continental shelves have been discussed by Pratt,[2] *World Oil*,[3] Carsey,[4] and Lintz.[5] Carsey states that the distribution of the leases taken in the Gulf of Mexico indicates that about 120 structures have been found by geophysical work. Descriptions of most of these structures have not been published. However, it is likely that the structures found consist of salt domes and fault traps like those which produce oil on the adjacent lands. Although the continental shelf off the coast of southern California is narrow, some of the highly prolific producing oil fields of the mainland extend under this continental shelf. The drilling on the continental shelf of California has been mainly on extensions of fields which produce on land. In the Gulf of Mexico, on the other hand, most of the wildcat drilling has been on previously untested structures.

Unless a satisfactory and economical method for drilling wells in water over 100 ft deep is developed, drilling for oil on the continental shelves will be in the shallow areas near the adjacent land. The continental shelf adjacent to the land is likely to have the same oil-producing charac-

[1] J. Ben Carsey, Geology of Gulf Coastal Area and Continental Shelf, *A.A.P.G. Bull.*, vol. 35, p. 385 (1951).

[2] Wallace E. Pratt, Petroleum on the Continental Shelves, *A.A.P.G. Bull.*, vol. 31, pp. 657–672 (1947).

[3] Anonymous, The Search for Oil on the Continental Shelf, *World Oil*, vol. 129, pp. 50–58 (Dec., 1949).

[4] J. Ben Carsey, Geology of Gulf Coastal Area and Continental Shelf, *A.A.P.G. Bull.*, vol. 34, pp. 361–385 (1950).

[5] Bernard B. Lintz, Tidelands Outlook: Tempered Optimism, *Oil and Gas Jour.*, vol. 52, no. 5, pp. 62–64 (June 8, 1953).

teristics as the nearby land.   Thus wildcatting for oil on the continental shelf will probably be limited for some time to areas where the adjacent land produces oil.   Hence there is no immediate likelihood of drilling on the continental shelves off the Atlantic coast of the United States.   There is no oil or gas production from the Atlantic coastal plain, and accordingly none would be expected on the inner portion of the continental shelf.   In the outer portion of the Atlantic continental shelf conditions may be different, but the water in this portion is generally too deep for drilling at present.

Even on the inner margins of the continental shelves the expenses of discovering and producing oil and gas are said to be several times as great as on the adjacent mainland.   However, the oil companies operating on the continental shelves have undoubtedly considered carefully the prospects for obtaining a profit, and the fact they continue to carry on wildcatting shows that they consider that some oil production from the continental shelves will ultimately be profitable.

It is probably the prospect of finding great oil fields which induces oil companies to seek oil on the continental shelves in spite of the uncertainties of titles and the greater expense of finding and producing oil.   In many portions of the adjacent lands the area has been so thoroughly prospected that the discovery of vast oil fields is impossible or extremely difficult.   On the other hand, there is little doubt that such fields occur on the continental shelves.   This conclusion is indicated by the fact that they occur on the adjacent lands, where conditions are similar.

ADDITIONAL REFERENCES

Anderson, J. L.: Northeastern United States, Possible Future Petroleum Provinces of North America, *A.A.P.G. Bull.*, vol. 35, pp. 421–437 (1951).

Benioff, H.: Seismic Evidence for the Fault Origin of Oceanic Deeps, *G.S.A. Bull.*, vol. 60, pp. 1837–1856 (1949).

Bornhauser, M.: Possible Ancient Submarine Canyon in Southwestern Louisiana, *A.A.P.G. Bull.*, vol. 32, pp. 2287–2290 (1948).

Buffington, E. C.: Submarine Natural Levees, *Jour. Geology*, vol. 60, pp. 473–479 (1952).

Carsola, A. J., and Dietz, R. S.: Submarine Geology of the Two Flat-topped Northeast Pacific Seamounts, *Am. Jour. Sci.*, vol. 250, pp. 481–497 (1952).

Dietz, R. S.: Geomorphic Evolution of Continental Terrace (Continental Shelf and Slope), *A.A.P.G. Bull.*, vol. 36, pp. 1802–1819 (1952).

——— and Menard, H. W.: Origin of Abrupt Change in Slope at Continental Shelf Margin, *A.A.P.G. Bull.*, vol. 35, pp. 1994–2016 (1951).

Emery, K. O.: Continental Shelf Sediments of Southern California, *G.S.A. Bull.*, vol. 63, pp. 1105–1108 (1952).

Ericson, D. B., Ewing, M., and Heezen, B. C.: Turbidity Currents and Sediments in North Atlantic, *A.A.P.G. Bull.*, vol. 36, pp. 489–511 (1952).

Ewing, M.: The Atlantic Ocean Basin, in The Problem of Land Connections across the South Atlantic, with Special Reference to the Mesozoic, edited by Ernst Mayr, *Am. Mus. Nat. History Bull.*, vol. 39, pp. 87–91 (1952).

———— and Press, F.: Crustal Structure and Surface-wave Dispersion, *Seismolog. Soc. America Bull.*, vol. 40, pp. 271–280 (1950).

Fairbridge, R. W.: Coarse Sediments at the Edge of the Continental Shelf, *Am. Jour. Sci.*, vol. 245, pp. 146–153 (1947).

————: Submarine Slumping and Location of Oil Bodies, *A.A.P.G. Bull.*, vol. 30, pp. 84–92 (1946).

Gunn, R.: A Quantitative Study of the Lithosphere and Gravity Anomalies along the Atlantic Coast, *Franklin Inst. Jour.*, vol. 237, pp. 139–154 (1944).

Gutenberg, B.: Crustal Layers of the Continents and Oceans, *G.S.A. Bull.*, vol. 62, pp. 427–440 (1951).

Heezen, B. C., and Ewing, M.: Turbidity Currents and Submarine Slumps and the 1929 Grand Banks Earthquake, *Am. Jour. Sci.*, vol. 250, pp. 849–873 (1952).

Holtedahl, O.: Supposed Marginal Fault Lines in the Shelf Area off Some High Northern Lands, *G.S.A. Bull.*, vol. 61, pp. 493–500 (1950).

Houston Geological Society: Western Gulf Coast, Possible Future Petroleum Provinces of North America, *A.A.P.G. Bull.*, vol. 35, pp. 385–392 (1951).

Johnson, D. W.: "The Origin of Submarine Canyons, a Critical Review of Hypotheses," Columbia University Press, New York (1939).

Kindle, E. M.: Sea-bottom Samples from the Cabot Strait Earthquake Zone, *G.S.A. Bull.*, vol. 42, pp. 557–574 (1945).

Kuenen, P. H.: Density Currents in Connection with the Problem of Submarine Canyons, *Geol. Mag.*, vol. 75, pp. 241–249 (1938).

————: The Formation of the Continental Terrace, *Advancement of Sci.*, vol. 7, no. 25, pp. 76–80 (1950).

————: "Marine Geology," John Wiley & Sons, Inc., New York (1950).

———— and Migliorini, C. I.: Turbidity Currents as a Cause of Graded Bedding, *Jour. Geology*, vol. 58, pp. 91–127 (1950).

Lawson, A. C.: Sea Bottom off the Coast of California, *G.S.A. Bull.*, vol. 61, pp. 1225–1242 (1950).

Leet, L. D.: Status of Geological and Geophysical Investigations on Atlantic and Gulf Coastal Plain, *G.S.A. Bull.*, vol. 51, pp. 873–886 (1940).

Lowman, S. W.: Sedimentary Facies in Gulf Coast, *A.A.P.G. Bull.*, vol. 33, pp. 1939–1997 (1949).

Menard, H. W., and Dietz, R. S.: Mendocino Submarine Escarpment, *Jour. Geology*, vol. 60, pp. 266–278 (1952).

———— and ————: Submarine Geology of the Gulf of Alaska, *G.S.A. Bull.*, vol. 62, pp. 1263–1285 (1951).

Murray, H. W.: Submarine Mountains in the Gulf of Alaska, *G.S.A. Bull.*, vol. 52, pp. 333–362 (1941).

Oliver, J. E., and Drake, C. L.: Geophysical Investigations in the Emerged and Submerged Atlantic Coastal Plain: VI, The Long Island Area, *G.S.A. Bull.*, vol. 62, pp. 1287–1296 (1951).

Price, W. A.: Building of the Gulf of Mexico, *First Ann. Meeting Gulf Coast Assoc. Geol. Societies*, pp. 7–39 (1951).

Shepard, F. P.: Composite Origin of Submarine Canyons, *Jour. Geology*, vol. 60, pp. 84–96 (1952).

————: Evidence of World-wide Submergence, *Jour. Marine Research*, vol. 7, pp. 661–678 (1948).

————: Sand and Gravel in Deep-water Deposits, *World Oil*, vol. 132, no. 1, pp. 61–68 (January, 1951).

————: Sediments of the Continental Shelves, *G.S.A. Bull.*, vol. 43, pp. 1017–1039 (1932).

————: Submarine Erosion, a Discussion of Recent Papers, *G.S.A. Bull.*, vol. 62, pp. 1413–1418 (1951).

————, and Cohee, G. V.: Continental Shelf Sediments off Mid-Atlantic Coast, *G.S.A. Bull.*, vol. 47, pp. 441–458 (1936).

Sverdrup, H. U., Johnson, M. W., and Fleming, R. H.: "The Oceans," Prentice-Hall, Inc., New York (1942).

Treadwell, T. K., Jr.: Submarine Topography of the Continental Slope of the North-west of Mexico, *Scripps Inst. Oceanography, Submarine Geology Report* 7, pp. 1–7 (1949).

Umbgrove, J. H. F.: Origin of Continental Shelves, *A.A.P.G. Bull.*, vol. 30, pp. 249–253 (1946).

Veatch, A. C., and Smith, P. A.: Atlantic Submarine Valleys of the United States and the Congo Submarine Valley, *G.S.A. Special Paper* 7, 101 pp. (1939).

Weaver, P.: Continental Shelf of Gulf of Mexico, *A.A.P.G. Bull.*, vol. 35, pp. 393–398 (1951).

Woodford, A. O.: Stream Gradients and Monterey Sea Valley, *G.S.A. Bull.*, vol. 62, pp. 799–852 (1951).

CHAPTER 15

DATING STRUCTURAL EVENTS

A knowledge of the time of formation of the structural features of a region is needed to build up a clear conception of its geologic history. The geologic history of an area would include information about the paleogeography and its changes, regional and local uplifts and depressions, erosion, deposition, faulting, tilting, and the development of climate and types of life. The portion of geologic history which is most important to petroleum geologists deals with the order of development of the structural features, the deposition of the formations, and the accumulation of oil and gas. In the discussions of the various subjects which have preceded this chapter there have been brief descriptions of the methods of dating various features. The importance of the subject justifies gathering information on this subject together in one short chapter.

ABSOLUTE DATING

When a geologist speaks of dating a structural event, he generally has in mind determining its age relative to the associated stratigraphic units or structural features. The age and duration of the various world-wide time units since the beginning of the Cambrian can be given fairly accurately in millions of years, but the petroleum geologist is generally more interested in the order of occurrence of the events. It is this order of occurrence which is related to the oil and gas prospects, and if the order of events were unchanged, the oil and gas prospects would probably not be much affected if the age in millions of years were considerably increased or decreased.

METHODS AND AIDS TO RELATIVE DATING

Topographic Methods. The age of structural features formed late in geologic time may in some cases be approximated by studying the topography. The degree of dissection of a fault scarp is a rough measure of its age. Very young anticlines are likely to conform rather closely to the topography. In some cases topographic relief is produced by structural deformation, and this topography is buried by sediments before it can be destroyed by erosion. The nature of this buried topography gives a rough indication of the length of time between the formation of the structural feature and its burial by sediments.   In estimating the age of structural features by the degree of erosion of the topography produced directly by the structural deformation, due allowance must be made for variations in the size of the topographic features, the resistance of the rocks to erosion, the climate, and the effects of vegetation.   Generally folds which have been so little eroded that structure and topography conform closely are Pleistocene or Recent.   The topographic features produced by direct deformation in pre-Cenozoic time have generally been planed off by erosion since their formation.   If after this planation they are again uplifted and eroded, topographic features closely related to the structure may again appear.   However, these topographic features are produced by the varying resistance of the rocks to erosion, and cannot be used to determine the time of formation of the structural features by which they are indirectly produced.   In the United States east of the Rocky Mountain region, most of the structural features are so old that the original topography produced directly by deformation has been destroyed by erosion. Consequently the degree of dissection of the present topography related to these structural features cannot be used to date them.

Truncation.   Folds and faults must be younger than the strata where they occur and older than the oldest overlying bed unaffected by the deformation.   Since there is erosion and truncation of the older beds at the angular unconformity separating the deformed and undeformed strata, this method may be considered to use truncation in dating the structures. There are causes of uncertainty which sometimes complicate the problem of determining the age of deformation in this manner.   For example, there may be a considerable difference in the age of the youngest deformed and oldest undeformed beds, with resultant uncertainty in the exact time of deformation.   Furthermore, where the deformation extends over a great area, as in an orogeny, the proper conditions for dating may occur in only one or two places.   Thus it may not be possible to determine whether the deformation occurred everywhere at the same time.

Changes in Throw of Faults.   Where a fault develops during the deposition of the strata it cuts, it is possible to learn how long it was active and how much of the vertical movement occurred during the deposition of the various displaced formations.   One way of doing this is to study the changes in throw at the fault plane.   The difference in the throw at the top and base of a formation or interval is considered to be a measure of the amount of vertical movement which took place during the deposition of the formation or interval.   This method is accurate only where dip-slip movement predominates, and where the change in throw is not much influenced by mechanical causes.   The movement of strike-slip faults cannot be dated in this manner.   However, in the oil-producing regions outside of California dip-slip faults appear to be generally much more numerous and important than strike-slip faults. In areas such as the Gulf Coast, where it is known that strike-slip faults are absent or very rare, the assumption that the faults are dip-slip is justified.

It is difficult to estimate the influence of mechanical effects in causing the throw of faults to change with depth. Faults with short horizontal extent are seen in many surface exposures, and it is generally supposed that these faults also have a short vertical extent. The vertical and horizontal extension of faults appears to be more or less equal. Thus a fault which extends for only ½ mile along its outcrop would be expected to have extended vertically for about ½ mile when first formed. If a fault has a maximum throw of 30 ft and extends for a total distance of only ½ mile vertically, the throw must decrease from 30 ft to zero in approximately ¼ mile above and below the point of maximum throw. If a small stock or laccolith were intruded into the strata at great depths, the faults formed by its intrusion would presumably die out a moderate distance from the intrusion. This decrease in the throw of faults away from the exciting cause may also occur in the faults which form over salt domes.

Let it be supposed that the movement along the fault plane continues during the deposition of the sediments displaced. The rate of deposition is determined in part by the topography of the surface of deposition. The rate is greater in depressions in this surface and less on its elevations. In general it appears that this difference in the rate of deposition on the upthrown and downthrown sides of faults is sufficient to maintain a fairly level surface of deposition across the upthrown and downthrown sides of the active faults. If this is the case, the thickness of the formations varies by an amount equal to the vertical movement during their deposition. Thus the difference in the throw of a fault in the top and bottom of a formation is the vertical displacement along the fault which took place during the deposition of the formation.

As an example of this principle, let it be assumed that there is a series of formations, A, B, C, D, E, and F, A being the oldest and F the youngest. The throw of a fault in the basal strata of these formations is as follows: A, 200 ft; B, 200 ft; C, 160 ft; D, 40 ft; E, 30 ft; and F, 30 ft. The vertical movement in feet along the fault plane during the time of deposition of these formations is therefore as follows: A, 0; B, 40; C, 120; D, 10; and E, 0. At some time after the deposition of the basal beds of formation F, 30 ft of additional throw developed along the fault, but the time when this throw occurred cannot be determined from the data given.

Isopach Maps for Dating Faults. The time of movement of faults which were active during the deposition of formations they cut may be determined from isopach maps of these formations. A marked change in the thickness of a formation at a fault indicates that the fault was active during the deposition of the formation. The displacement of the fault during the deposition of the formation is equal to the difference in its thickness on opposite sides of the fault. Table 15-1, taken from a paper by Wendlandt and Shelby,[1] shows the thicknesses of some of the formations in the Talco field, Texas. The trap which has caused the accumulation of the oil in this field is produced by a large fault. On the downthrown side of this fault there is a graben. The right-hand column of Table 15-1 gives the difference between the thicknesses on the upthrown side and the thicknesses on the downthrown side in the graben. This difference is the vertical movement of the fault during the time of deposition of the formation.

TABLE 15-1. THICKNESSES OF FORMATIONS ON UPTHROWN AND DOWNTHROWN
SIDES OF FAULT IN THE TALCO FIELD, TEXAS

Formation	On downthrown side	On upthrown side	Difference
Upper Cretaceous			
Brownstown	215	200	15
Austin	595	545	50
Eagleford	540	435	105
Woodbine	610	510	100
Lower Cretaceous			
Washita	675	535	140
Fredericksburg	300	228	72
Paluxy	562	312	250
Upper Glen Rose	1,230	1,025	205
Lower Glen Rose	400	400	0

The throw of this fault on the base of the Glen Rose is about 1,400 ft. Table 15-1 shows that the movement began with the Upper Glen Rose. The differences between the thicknesses above the Upper Glen Rose on the upthrown and downthrown sides of the fault vary irregularly, indicating that the rate of movement along the fault plane also varied from time to time. The five Upper Cretaceous formations above the Brownstown and the basal formation of the Eocene are either of the same thickness on the upthrown and downthrown sides of the fault, or are only slightly thicker on the downthrown side. This indicates that there was no movement or only a slight amount of movement along the fault plane

[1] E. A. Wendlandt and T. H. Shelby, Jr., Talco Oil Field, Franklin and Titus Counties, Texas, "Structure of Typical American Oil Fields," American Association of Petroleum Geologists, vol. 3, pp. 432–451 (1948).

during the deposition of these formations. On the other hand, the displacement of the fault in the Eocene beds at the surface is about 360 ft. Evidently the movement along the fault plane was discontinuous.

Isopach Maps for Dating Folds. Folds which developed during the deposition of the folded sediments may be dated accurately by means of isopach maps, provided that sufficient data as to the variations in thickness are available. Folding which ceased entirely before the deposition of a series of formations does not directly affect the thickness of these formations. However, if the folding has produced buried topographic relief, compaction over these buried hills may produce slight changes in thickness in the overlying formations. Intense folding which takes place after deposition commonly causes thinning of the plastic formations on the flanks of the folds and thickening near their axes. This statement applies to the true stratigraphic thickness measured at right angles to the strata. The variations in thickness due to folding occurring before or after the deposition of a series of sediments are not used to measure the time of occurrence of the folding; these variations are mentioned merely in order that they may not be confused with variations in thickness due to folding which is contemporaneous with deposition.

The amount of thickening or thinning of a formation or interval of strata indicates the amount of depression or uplift which occurred during the deposition of the formation. This thickening in the synclines and thinning near the crest of the anticlines is an indication that the folding took place during deposition. Anticlines in which this thinning takes place are called supratenuous. Supratenuous folds are shown in Figs. 4-5 and 15-1. The amount of uplift of an anticline during the deposition of a series of beds may be determined by comparing the actual thickness on the anticline with the normal thickness. The normal thickness may be determined in an area which is not folded, but a correction for the regional thinning or thickening must be applied to ascertain the normal thickness in the area of a given fold. For example, if a formation thins northward at a rate of 40 ft per mile, and normal thickness in an undeformed area 5 miles north of an anticline is 600 ft, normal thickness at the anticline is 800 ft. If a region is all folded, normal thickness may be difficult to estimate.

The determinations of the time and amount of deformation by isopach maps are based on the assumption that the surface of deposition is maintained nearly level during the accumulation of sediments by variations in the rate of deposition. Where the folds or fault blocks are only a few miles across, it appears that deposition is able to fill the potential depressions as fast as they are produced by subsidence. Where large areas subside rapidly, the sediments may not accumulate fast enough to fill the subsiding areas. The result is a starved basin, as described on pages

301–303.   Where starved basins occur, isopach maps do not give reliable indications of the time or amount of folding.

Facies Changes.   The manner in which facies changes may be used to date structural events has been described in Chap. 11.   Although this information is qualitative rather than quantitative, it is a welcome addition to the data furnished by angular unconformities and by variations in thickness.

Cross Sections.   Often cross sections show the time of formation of folds and the amount of folding during the deposition of the various formations shown.   Fig. 15-1 is a cross section of an ideal supratenuous fold.

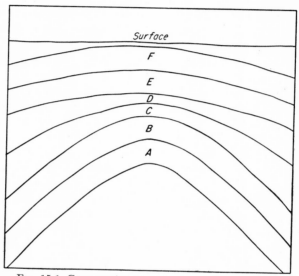

Surface

F

E

D

C

B

A

Fig. 15-1. Cross section of an ideal supratenuous fold.

During the deposition of formations *A* and *B* there was no folding of the anticline.   This is indicated by the uniform thickness of these formations as they pass over the crest of the fold.   On the other hand, the thinning of formations *C* and *D* as they pass over the crest of the anticline indicates that relative uplift of the crest of the anticline occurred during the time when they were deposited.   The uniform thickness of formations *E* and *F* shows that the anticline was quiescent during the time when they were deposited.   The folding of formations *E* and *F* indicates that after their deposition there was a further uplift of the crest of the anticline.   All that is indicated by the cross section about the time of deformation of this latest folding is that it is after the deposition of formation *F* and long enough ago so that erosion has had time to plane off the topographic high at the anticlinal crest.   Folds, uplifts, and depressions which have grown intermittently in this manner are of rather common occurrence.

Paleogeologic Maps. The nature and uses of paleogeologic or paleoareal maps have been discussed on pages 20–22. One important use of this type of map is to determine the time of origin of structural traps for the accumulation of oil or gas. For example, let it be supposed that in a region the structure of the outcropping beds or of key horizons at relatively shallow depth is known accurately. If a paleogeologic map is available which shows the areal distribution of the formations at some earlier geologic time, a glance at this map indicates whether each anticline found in the younger strata shows up. If it does, its prospects for deeper production are better than they would be if it were not expressed. There are two reasons for this. In the first place, the closure of each anticline which is expressed on a paleogeologic map is greater in the older formations by the amount of uplift indicated. Furthermore, if an anticline present in shallow formations shows up on a paleogeologic map of an older erosion surface, the trap for oil and gas accumulation must have been in existence longer than one which did not show up in this manner.

Value of Dating Geologic Structures

One use of the knowledge of the time of development of structures is in building up a conception of the geologic history. A knowledge of the geologic history of an area is useful for solving a number of geologic problems, including the location of the oil and gas fields. A knowledge of the time of origin of a fold or trap may aid in estimating its oil and gas prospects. A knowledge of the age of a trap is especially important if the time of oil accumulation is known. For example, if a number of traps of various ages are present in an area, but only those in existence in Devonian time are productive, this suggests that the oil and gas in the area ceased to accumulate at the end of Devonian time. If this is the case, untested traps known to have formed entirely after Devonian time will be dry, while those which were in existence in Devonian time will have good prospects. Even where the only available information about a structure is derived from surface exposures, it is sometimes possible to determine the age by the trend or other characteristics of the structure. If seismic surveys showing reflections from a number of horizons are available, the variations in the intervals between the reflecting beds may indicate the age of the structure.

ADDITIONAL REFERENCES

Baldwin, T. A.: San Ardo Field—A Geologic Case History, *Jour. Petroleum Technology*, vol. 5, no. 1, part 1, pp. 9–10, part 2, p. 5 (1953).

Ballard, N.: Stratigraphy and Structural History of East-central United States, *A.A.P.G. Bull.*, vol. 22, pp. 1519–1555 (1938).

Barton, J. M.: Pre-Permian Axes of Maximum Deposition in West Texas, *A.A.P.G. Bull.*, vol. 29, pp. 1336–1348 (1945).

Blackwelder, E.: The Valuation of Unconformities, *Jour. Geology*, vol. 17, pp. 289–299 (1909).

Bryan, F.: Evidence of Recent Movements along Faults of Balcones System in Central Texas, *A.A.P.G. Bull.*, vol. 20, pp. 1357–1371 (1936).

Cheney, M. G.: Stratigraphic and Structural Studies in North-central Texas, *Univ. Texas Bur. Econ. Geology Bull.* 2913 (1929).

Denison, A. R., Oldham, A. E., and Kisling, J. W., Jr.: Structure and Stratigraphy of Kelsey Anticline, Upshur County, Texas, *A.A.P.G. Bull.*, vol. 17, pp. 656–679 (1933).

DeSitter, L. U.: Pliocene Uplift of Tertiary Mountain Chains, *Am. Jour. Sci.*, vol. 250, pp. 297–307 (1952).

Gallup, W. B.: Geology of Turner Valley Oil and Gas Field, Alberta, Canada, *A.A.P.G. Bull.*, vol. 35, pp. 797–821 (1951).

Gilluly, J.: Distribution of Mountain Building in Geologic Time, *G.S.A. Bull.*, vol. 60, pp. 561–590 (1949).

Hiestand, T. C.: Regional Investigations, Oklahoma and Kansas, *A.A.P.G. Bull.*, vol. 19, pp. 948–970 (1935).

Hintze, F. F.: Oil Accumulation in Relation to Periods of Folding, *A.A.P.G. Bull.*, vol. 7, pp. 58–66 (1923).

Kay, M.: Development of Northern Allegheny Synclinorium and Adjoining Regions, *G.S.A. Bull.* vol. 53, pp. 1601–1658 (1942).

———: Paleogeographic and Palinspastic Maps, *A.A.P.G. Bull.*, vol. 29, pp. 426–450 (1945).

King, P. B.: Tectonic Framework of Southeastern United States, *A.A.P.G. Bull.*, vol. 34, pp. 635–671 (1950).

Koester, E. A.: Geology of Central Kansas Uplift, *A.A.P.G. Bull.*, vol. 19, pp. 1405–1426 (1935).

Lahee, F. H.: Lateral Migration of Oil at Van, Texas, *A.A.P.G. Bull.*, vol. 20, p. 615 (1936).

———: Oil and Gas Fields of the Mexia and Tehuacana Fault Zones, Texas, "Structure of Typical American Oil Fields," American Association of Petroleum Geologists, Tulsa, vol. 1, pp. 304–388 (1929).

Levorsen, A. I.: Convergence Studies in Mid-Continent Regions, *A.A.P.G. Bull.*, vol. 11, pp. 657–682 (1927).

———: Studies in Paleogeography, *A.A.P.G. Bull.*, vol. 17, pp. 1107–1132 (1933).

———: Time of Oil and Gas Accumulation, *A.A.P.G. Bull.*, vol. 29, pp. 1189–1194 (1945).

Liddle, R. A.: The Van Oil Field, Van Zandt County, Texas, *Univ. Texas Bur. of Econ. Geology Bull.* 3601, pp. 55–59 (1936).

Longwell, C. R.: Sedimentation in Relation to Faulting, *G.S.A. Bull.*, vol. 48, pp. 433–442 (1937).

———: Structure of the Northern Muddy Mountain Area, Nevada, *G.S.A. Bull.*, vol. 60, pp. 923–968 (1949).

McCoy, A. W.: An Interpretation of Local Structural Development in Mid-Continent Areas Associated with Deposits of Petroleum, "Problems of Petroleum Geology," American Association of Petroleum Geologists, Tulsa, pp. 581–627 (1934).

——— and Keyte, W. R.: Present Interpretations of the Structural Theory for Oil and Gas Migration and Accumulation, "Problems of Petroleum Geology," American Association of Petroleum Geologists, Tulsa, pp. 253–335 (1934).

Moore, R. C.: Stratigraphic Evidence Bearing on Problems of Continental Tectonics, *G.S.A. Bull.*, vol. 47, pp. 1785–1808 (1936).

Morgan, A. L.: A Structural Analysis of the Delta Farms Field, Lafourche Parish, Louisiana, with Notes on the Stratigraphy, *Second Ann. Meeting of Gulf Coast Geol. Societies*, pp. 129–163 (1952).

Powers, S.: Age of Folding of the Oklahoma Mountains, the Ouachita, Arbuckle and Wichita Mountains of Oklahoma and the Llano-Burnet and Marathon Uplifts of Texas, *G.S.A. Bull.*, vol. 39, pp. 1031–1072 (1928).

———: Structural Geology of Northeastern Oklahoma, *Jour. Geology*, vol. 39, pp. 117–132 (1931).

Pratt, W. E., and Lahee, F. H.: Faulting and Petroleum Accumulation at Mexia, Texas, *A.A.P.G. Bull.*, vol 7, pp. 226–236 (1923).

Schuchert, C.: Orogenic Times of the Northern Appalachians, *G.S.A. Bull.*, vol. 41, pp. 701–724 (1930).

Scott, E. R.: Quitman Field, Wood County, Texas, "Structure of Typical American Oil Fields," American Association of Petroleum Geologists, Tulsa, vol. 3, pp. 419–431 (1948).

Sharp, R. P.: Early Tertiary Fanglomerate, Big Horn Mountains, Wyoming, *Jour. Geology*, vol. 56, pp. 1–15 (1948).

Shelby, T. H., Jr.: The Talco Field, Franklin and Titus Counties, Texas, "Occurrence of Oil in Northeast Texas," published by Texas Bureau of Economic Geology, Austin, Texas, and East Texas Geological Society, pp. 372–378 (1951).

Teas, L. P., and Miller, C. R.: Raccoon Bend Oil Field, Austin County, Texas, *A.A.P.G. Bull.*, vol. 17, pp. 1459–1491 (1933).

Thomas, E. P.: Mississippi Structures and Their Relation to Oil Accumulation, *A.A.P.G. Bull.*, vol. 34, pp. 1502–1516 (1950).

Trask, P. D., and Wu, C. C.: Does Petroleum Form in Sediments at the Time of Deposition?, *A.A.P.G. Bull.*, vol. 14, pp. 1451–1463 (1930).

Twenhofel, W. H.: Marine Unconformities, Marine Conglomerates and Thicknesses of Strata, *A.A.P.G. Bull.*, vol. 20, pp. 677–703 (1936).

Van Tuyl, F. M., and Parker, B. H.: The Time of Origin and Accumulation of Petroleum, *Colorado School of Mines Quart.*, vol. 36, no. 2, pp. 1–180 (1941).

Ver Wiebe, W. A.: Ancestral Rocky Mountains, *A.A.P.G. Bull.*, vol. 14, pp. 765–788 (1930).

Weller, J. M., and Bell, A. H.: Illinois Basin, *A.A.P.G. Bull.*, vol. 21, pp. 771–788 (1937).

CHAPTER 16

CLASSIFICATION OF TRAPS FOR OIL AND GAS ACCUMULATION

A trap, in the sense in which the word is used in this chapter, is any condition which tends to cause oil or gas to accumulate in a reservoir. The essentials of a trap are a permeable reservoir to contain the oil and gas, an impervious cover rock to prevent their escape upward, and some variation in structure or in the lithology of the reservoir which tends to seal the oil and gas in, or to limit their freedom of escape through the reservoir. In structural traps the escape of oil or gas laterally through the reservoir is prevented by water at lower levels than the oil or gas. In stratigraphic (or lithologic) traps the escape of the oil or gas from the trap through the reservoir is prevented or limited by the termination of the reservoir, or by decreases in its porosity or permeability. The escape of the oil or gas downward across the strata is limited by their imperviousness or by the presence of water in them.

The classification of traps for oil and gas accumulation has been described by Russell[1] elsewhere. However, the subject appears to be of sufficient importance to justify a brief discussion here.

Stratigraphic Relations of Structural Traps

On Closed Anticlines. The nature of traps may be better understood if a distinction is made between structural traps and the structures which produce them. The structure determines where the structural traps of an area occur, if any are present. The structure also determines the area covered by the structural traps and gives some information about the maximum possible thickness of the producing zones. However, the presence or absence of actual traps, their number, and the actual thickness of the productive zones are all determined by stratigraphic and lithologic relations, even in the case of purely structural traps. Structure-contour maps are used to classify the purely structural traps, even though the structure-contour map does not indicate whether or not the purely structural traps are present. If an anticline with large closure and large

---

[1] William L. Russell, "Principles of Petroleum Geology," McGraw-Hill Book Company, Inc., New York, pp. 109–151 (1951).

closed area is not underlain by porous and permeable beds with suitable cover rocks, no trap is present in spite of the favorable structure.

Effect of Possible Escape of Oil and Gas through Faults. It has been pointed out previously that statements of the amount of closure of faulted structures do not have much meaning unless the manner in which the closure is determined is stated. It has also been mentioned that traps on closed anticlines are not favorable for oil or gas accumulation unless the reservoirs are overlain by impervious cover rocks. In the case of faulted structures, there is the additional problem of whether the fault plane is impervious to the passage of fluids. Even if the cover rock makes a perfect seal where it is not faulted, it may permit the oil and gas to escape where it is fractured by faulting.

The lithology of the rocks cut by a fault indicates whether the fault is likely to be sealed. Faults through thick shale, clay, bentonite, volcanic tuff, salt, gypsum, and anhydrite appear to be generally sealed. However, if the shales have been altered so that they are rather hard and brittle, they may not seal the fault planes even where they are very thick. Chert, limestone, and dolomite are likely to fracture so that faults through them are not well sealed. The pervious character of the fractures along fault planes is indicated by the occurrence along the faults of springs and oil or gas seeps, and by the production of oil, gas, and water from the fractures associated with faults. It is known that many fault planes are sealed because they cut the reservoir rocks of producing oil fields.

If a fault cuts the reservoir rock within the closed area, the altitude of the highest point on the reservoir cut by the fault may be important. If the fault is permeable and cuts a reservoir on the crest of a closed anticline, the fault would drain all the oil or gas from the reservoir. If the highest point of the reservoir cut by the fault is well below the highest part of the reservoir in the trap, whether or not the fault can drain the reservoir depends on the type of flow up through it. If the oil or gas seeps slowly up through the fault, the oil-water or water-gas contacts would be nearly level at all times, and the oil and gas would not drain from the portions of the reservoir higher than the point of outlet at the fault. If, on the other hand, the oil and gas rush violently through the fault, a pressure gradient may be established toward it, and the oil and gas in portions of the reservoir higher than the outlet might drain away. Although the information is not conclusive, it appears that the oil and gas escape through the faults slowly. Hence it seems that the oil and gas in portions of the reservoir higher than the outlet where the fault cuts it would not be drained by permeable fault planes.

If this assumption is correct, the conditions produced by a permeable fault plane cutting a closed reservoir should be as shown in Figs. 16-1 and 16-2. In Fig. 16-1 the dotted line surrounds the closed areas. These are the areas which would be sealed against the escape of the oil, assuming that the fault plane would permit movement of the oil horizontally across the fault plane, but not vertically up through it. The diagonal shading shows the areas which would still contain oil on the assumption that the fault did let the oil and gas escape vertically up through it. The left-hand fault cuts across the edge of the closed area of the anticline on the left. Thus no oil or gas is drained from the closed area of this structure. The fault cuts the middle closed anticline at its crest. Therefore all the

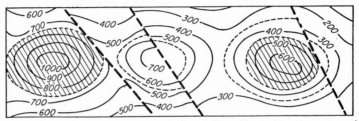

Fig. 16-1. Structure map of imaginary faulted anticlines, illustrating the manner in which faults with open fault planes may drain the oil and gas from closed structures.

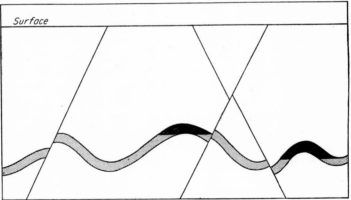

Fig. 16-2. Cross section along the axis of an anticline containing closed domes, showing the manner in which open faults may drain oil and gas from the closed areas.

oil is drained from the closed area of this pool. The fault cuts the right-hand structure part-way between the crest and the edge of the closed area. As a result the oil is drained from all portions of the closed area which are lower than the highest point at which the fault touches the reservoir.

Fig. 16-2 is a cross section along the axis of an anticline on which there are three domes. It is assumed that the oil and gas can escape along the fault plane to the surface. It is also assumed that each fault intersects the cross section at the highest point at which it cuts the reservoir on the anticline. The fault intersects the anticline at the left at its crest, with the result that all the oil and gas are drained from it. The fault inter-sects the middle structure part-way between the crest and the edge of the original closed area. The result is that the oil and gas are drained from the portion of the closed area that lies at a lower elevation than the highest point at which the fault intersects it. The fault intersects the dome on the right below the closed area, with the result that no oil or gas is drained from it.

Stratigraphic Control of the Sealing of Fault Traps. Two rocks are said to be in fault contact if they are separated only by a fault plane. Let it be assumed that a reservoir rock on a plunging anticline is cut by a transverse fault. If the fault plane is impervious to oil and gas, a trap will be formed on the anticline just downdip from the fault. However, where permeable reservoir rocks are in fault contact, oil and gas can generally migrate across the fault. Thus the potential trap on the down-dip side of the fault is sealed only where impervious rock is in contact with the reservoir on the updip side. Furthermore, if on the updip side of the trap impervious rock is in fault contact with the upper part of the reservoir, and permeable rock in fault contact with its lower portion, oil and gas will be drained from the reservoir up to the level of the highest point to which the permeable reservoir extends on the opposite side of the fault from the trap. Above this level, oil and gas should remain in the trap.

The principles involved in these relations are illustrated by Fig. 16-3, which shows a series of reservoir rocks cut by a fault. The dotted por-tions of the reservoirs contain salt water, and the black portions contain oil or gas. Where there is no permeable reservoir rock on the left-hand side of the fault, a trap is formed directly against the fault on its down-dip side. It is assumed that the cross section intersects the beds along the axis of an anticlinal nose which plunges to the right. Reservoir E intersects reservoir A at point J. All the oil or gas in reservoir A at a level lower than J drain out of A across the fault into reservoir E. It is assumed that the fault plane is too impervious to allow oil and gas to migrate along it, though they can move freely across it. Thus reservoir B is sealed at the fault, even though reservoir F is present a short dis-tance up the fault plane. Any oil or gas which accumulated in reservoir C before the faulting would drain out through reservoir H. Although reservoir I is in contact with reservoir D across the fault, the volume of reservoir I is so limited that after I has been filled with oil or gas, the accumulation may back up down the dip into reservoir D, as shown.

It is evident that the accumulation of oil under conditions such as those shown in Fig. 16-3 is dependent not only on the present distribu-tion of the permeable rocks on the opposite side of the fault from the trap, but also on the nature of the beds which have been across the fault from the reservoirs ever since the oil or gas began to accumulate.   The displacement along large faults generally takes place over a long interval of time by sudden movements of a few feet separated by hundreds or thousands of years of quiescence.   For example, let it be assumed that the strata cut by a fault are Upper Cretaceous, and that they are displaced by a fault which was active from the Eocene to the Miocene. It is further assumed that the trap is of the type shown in Fig. 16-3. Oil and gas could not have started to accumulate at the fault until the Eocene, because there was no trap.   After the accumulation started to form, the oil and gas in the trap could have been drained away by a permeable layer on the opposite side of the fault.   As the displacement

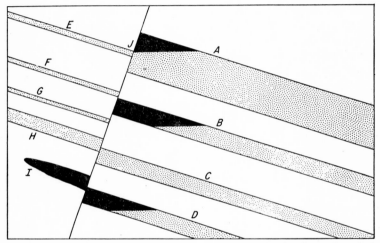

Fig. 16-3. Ideal cross section along axis of an anticline, showing how the relations of reservoirs on opposite sides of a fault control the sealing of the traps at the fault plane.

along the fault continued, each permeable layer would drain the reservoirs on the downdip side as it passed them.   Hence, if at present there is no permeable reservoir across a fault from the reservoir rock of a trap, this is no assurance that the oil on the downdip side of the fault has not been drained by a permeable stratum which is no longer opposite.

It should be noted that if the updip side of the fault moves down, a trap forms as soon as any appreciable displacement takes place along the fault.   If, on the other hand, the updip side of the fault moves up relative to the downdip side, the trap does not come into existence until the displacement is sufficient to disconnect the portions of the reservoir on opposite sides of the fault.   Where the dip is low, this means that the trap cannot produce an accumulation until the throw of the fault is greater than the thickness of the reservoir.   The fact that the traps come into existence earlier on the upthrown than on the downthrown sides of faults may be one reason why the traps on the upthrown sides are more likely to produce oil or gas.

Relations of Lithologic Variations in a Reservoir to Closure and Closed Area

It has been previously explained that the presence or absence of a trap in a closed anticline depends on the general stratigraphic section beneath the surface. The effect of variations in the lithology of a particular reservoir on the closure and closed area needs some explanation. The important point is that there are different aspects of closure, or different possible meanings of the word. Perhaps the term "closure" should not be applied to all these different meanings, but no other word is in general use to designate them. The meaning of "closure" is clearest when it applies to closed anticlines. This type of closure is purely structural, and the stratigraphic relations do not need to be considered at all. However, a closed trap exists in a closed anticline only where a suitable series of sediments is present. "Closure" may also have a purely structural meaning when applied to structures along faults. The lithology of the reservoir rock itself may have a very important bearing on the effective or actual closure of the trap. Since this meaning of the term is quite different from the purely structural use, it is advisable to state what is meant whenever the term is used.

The manner in which lithologic variations in the reservoir rock can cause variations in the effective closure of a trap is illustrated by Fig. 16-4. It is assumed that the horizon on which the structure contours are drawn is a few feet above the top of the reservoir rock. The diagonal shading indicates the area where the porous and permeable portion of the reservoir rock is missing. This could be caused by the entire absence of the reservoir rock, or by reduction in its porosity and permeability. In the area covered by the diagonal shading the reservoir rock, if present, is so lacking in porosity or permeability that oil and gas cannot migrate through it.

An anticline with 200 ft of structural closure is shown at A, and the dotted line B shows the boundary of the closed area of this anticline. The portion of the closed area covered by the diagonal shading cannot produce oil or gas. Here the size of the closed area which can produce oil or gas is lessened by the absence of the reservoir. An anticline with 300 ft of structural closure is shown at C, and the dotted line D shows the boundary of its closed area. Not only is the size of the portion of the closed area which can produce reduced by the absence of the reservoir on this anticline, but the effective amount of closure is also reduced. The highest point on the reservoir in the anticline is actually only 200 ft above the elevation of the top of the reservoir at the edge of the closed area.

The dashed line *EG* indicates the axis of an anticline which plunges toward the lower part of the figure. Oil or gas migrating up the dip near this axis would be trapped at the termination of the reservoir near *E*. If sufficient oil and gas continue to accumulate, it would eventually extend down the dip to the dotted line *F*. Any additional oil or gas which accumulated down the dip from the line *F* would tend to spill laterally to the right and escape past *H*. It is evident that the updip termination of the anticline has produced a stratigraphic or lithologic closure. Many

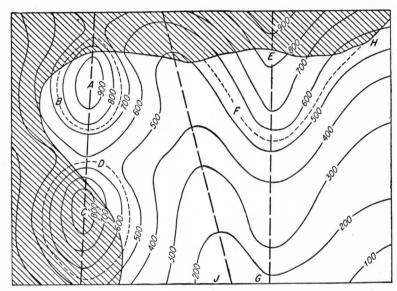

Fɪɢ. 16-4. Structure map of an imaginary area, showing the effects of lithologic variations on the effective closures of traps.

oil and gas fields occur on this type of trap, and consequently this type of closure is important. Since it is partly due to structure and partly due to the lithology of the reservoir, it may be called structural-lithologic closure. It may be defined as the difference in elevation between the top and the bottom of the producing zone when the trap is completely filled with oil or gas.

Unfortunately the complex relations of stratigraphy and structure in reservoir rocks make it difficult or impossible to use this term with a high degree of accuracy. For example, any oil or gas which migrates through the reservoir to the left of the synclinal axis *IJ* would be trapped in the general vicinity of anticlines *A* and *C* of Fig. 16-4. If oil and gas should continue to migrate into this area after the reservoir in the areas of structural closure was full of oil, the additional oil accumulation would extend down the dip to slightly below the 500-ft structure contour before spilling out. The whole area about the 500-ft structure contour in the vicinity of structures *A* and *C* could be considered to have structural-lithologic closure. However, whether such an area would be considered to be closed depends more or less on circumstances. Furthermore, information about the extent of the reservoir off the map would be needed to determine how far down the dip this trap would extend.

Definitions

Structural Trap. The terms "structural trap" and "stratigraphic trap" are frequently found in the literature dealing with oil exploration. A structural trap is produced by the combination of a reservoir rock, a suitable seal or cover rock above the reservoir rock, and a structural closure. Structural closure has already been defined. Where the reservoir and cover rocks are persistent, the locations and areas of structural traps are determined by the structure. It is customary in mapping and discussing these traps to illustrate them by structure-contour maps. However, a structure-contour map cannot indicate whether or not a reservoir is present unless the structure contours are drawn on the reservoir itself.

Stratigraphic Trap. A stratigraphic trap owes its existence to some variation in the characteristics of the reservoirs. Strictly speaking, a stratigraphic variation can arise only at the time the strata are deposited. Any characteristics of a reservoir which are acquired after deposition should be considered lithologic rather than stratigraphic. For this reason the term "lithologic trap" would be much better than "stratigraphic trap," in view of the fact that traps caused by both lithologic and stratigraphic variations are indicated. However, the term "stratigraphic trap" is so firmly fixed in the minds of geologists that it would doubtless be futile to attempt to change it.

The lithologic irregularities which cause stratigraphic traps consist in variations in porosity, permeability, or thickness. These irregularities may be original or stratigraphic, or they may have been produced by agencies which have affected the character of the sediments after deposition. Original or stratigraphic variations are in thickness, extent, shape of reservoir, lithologic nature, sorting, grain size, size of pores, interbedding of different lithologic types, and cementation. The agencies which cause changes in porosity or permeability after deposition are cementation, compaction, recrystallization, and solution. The trap lies just down the dip from the line or zone where the permeability decreases. Oil or gas rising up the dip through the water-saturated reservoir is stopped by the permeability barrier, and accumulates.

Structural-stratigraphic Trap. There are many types of traps which are caused partly by deformation and partly by lithologic changes in the reservoirs. Such traps are called "structural-stratigraphic" in this book. The term "stratigraphic trap" as commonly used in geologic literature covers both the "stratigraphic" and "structural-stratigraphic" traps of this book. In Table 16-1 traps due to truncation and overlap are

TABLE 16-1. CLASSIFICATION OF TRAPS FOR OIL AND GAS ACCUMULATION

Structural traps
    Closed anticlines
    Faulted anticlines
    Closures against faults
    Traps formed by the intersection or bending of faults
    Fractures produced by structural deformation
    Salt domes
    Anticlines on downdip sides of faults
Structural-stratigraphic traps
    Truncations
    Overlaps
    Truncated anticlines
    Bald-headed structures
    Intersections of the termination of a reservoir with plunging anticline
    Updip terminations of sheet reservoirs
    Reservoirs sealed near outcrops by asphalt
    Traps associated with buried hills and compaction
    Oil occurrences in synclines or in lower parts of reservoirs with gas updip
Purely stratigraphic traps
    Sand lenses, bars, channel deposits
    Porous zones filled with oil or gas
    Reefs
    Reservoirs in permeable organic solids, such as coal and bituminous shale

included among the structural-stratigraphic traps, though both the tilting and the truncation which produce these traps might be considered purely structural features. Confusion is likely to arise if traps of these types were classed as purely structural, for geologists are accustomed to think of them as stratigraphic. For example, the trap in the East Texas field is caused by truncation and tilting, but this field is generally said to be the best-known example of a stratigraphic trap. It seems advisable to make the distinction between structural and structural-stratigraphic traps on practical grounds. According to this criterion, traps which could be found by structure mapping would be classed as purely structural, while those which could be located only by subsurface data as well as by structure mapping would be classed as structural-stratigraphic. It should be noted that the structural factor in many of the types of structural-stratigraphic traps consists merely in the tilting which produces regional dip.

Recommended Classification

Table 16-1 gives the recommended classifications of traps for oil and gas accumulation.

Regional Variations in Types

It is a well-known fact that certain types of traps are relatively abundant in certain regions, and others absent or rare. Steeply dipping anticlines with large closure are naturally common in the vicinity of orogens or other strongly deformed areas and absent or relatively scarce in areas such as the central portion of the United States, where the strata are in most places flat-lying. Salt domes are confined to regions underlain by thick salt deposits. Stratigraphic traps are no doubt very common everywhere, but in some regions little production is found in them. Stratigraphic traps which have produced oil or gas are especially abundant in the Appalachian region. Fault traps are dominant in the oil fields of northwestern Peru.

These variations in the type of productive trap from one region to another are caused by variations in structure, stratigraphy, geological history, regional alteration, and sedimentation, by the volume of reservoir rock available, and by the quantities of oil and gas generated. It need hardly be said that one of the most important duties of a petroleum geologist is to learn thoroughly the types of traps which have been productive in the areas where he works, as well as the prospects for production from additional types of traps.

Relation to Age and Lithology of Rocks

The types of traps which produce oil and gas show some relation to the age and lithology of the rocks in which the traps occur. Although there are exceptions, the traps in Paleozoic strata tend to have gentler dips than those in younger formations. The clastic rocks of the Paleozoic era are in general harder, more consolidated, and of higher specific gravity and lower porosity than those of the Cenozoic. Therefore there is also some relation between the lithology of the rocks and the nature of the traps in them.

Cover Rocks

Petroleum geologists seem to have a tendency to take cover rocks for granted. In many discussions of oil and gas prospects there is no mention of cover rocks. In many large regions of the United States there are so many oil and gas fields that the general presence of adequate cover rocks is assumed. However, even in these areas there is a question as to whether the cover rocks would be adequate where there are unusual conditions, such as igneous intrusions or unusually sharp folds. Shales and clays generally make very good cover rocks, but information is needed as to what other rocks can serve as cover rocks, and under what conditions shales are not suitable. It is well known that fresh-water deposits are generally devoid of oil, and one would like to know whether this is because the source rocks of oil are not present in fresh-water deposits, or whether it is because the fresh-water shales do not make good cover rocks. All shales lose their property of making good cover rocks as they become highly altered. No shales are good cover rocks where they have become permeable to oil and gas because of fracturing. A certain minimum thickness of shales is probably needed, and this probably varies from place to place.

The best cover rocks are shales, clays, salt, gypsum, anhydrite, and probably bentonite and fine-grained altered volcanic tuff or ash. Nonporous limestone and dolomite may serve as cover rocks where they are not fractured. Limestones and dolomites which make good cover rocks in very gentle folds may be too fractured to serve as seals in sharp folds or along faults. Probably no limestones make satisfactory cover rocks in areas that are strongly folded or fractured.

ADDITIONAL REFERENCES

Adams, J. E.: Origin, Migration, and Accumulation of Petroleum in Limestone Reservoirs in the Western United States and Canada, "Problems of Petroleum Geology," American Association of Petroleum Geologists, Tulsa, pp. 347–364 (1934).

———: Oil Pool of Open Reservoir Type, *A.A.P.G. Bull.*, vol. 20, pp. 780–796 (1936).

Baker, N. E., and Henson, F. R. S.: Geological Conditions of Oil Occurrence in Middle East Fields, *A.A.P.G. Bull.*, vol. 36, pp. 1885–1901 (1952).

Baldwin, T. A.: San Ardo—A Stratigraphic Analysis of a California Oil Field, *A.A.P.G. Bull.*, vol. 34, pp. 1981–1989 (1950).

Bartram, J. G.: Summary of Rocky Mountain Geology, *A.A.P.G. Bull.*, vol. 23, pp. 1131–1152 (1939).

Bates, F. W., and Wharton, J. B., Jr.: Geology of West Tepetate Oil Field, Jefferson Davis Parish, Louisiana, *A.A.P.G. Bull.*, vol. 32, pp. 1712–1727 (1948).

Bauerschmidt, A. J., Jr.: West Ranch Oil Field, Jackson County, Texas, *A.A.P.G. Bull.*, vol. 28. pp. 197–216 (1944).

Billingsley, J. E.: Occurrence of Oil and Gas in West Virginia, Eastern Ohio and Eastern Kentucky, "Problems of Petroleum Geology," American Association of Petroleum Geologists, Tulsa, pp. 485–514 (1934).

Blixt, J. E.: Cut Bank Oil and Gas Field, Glacier County, Montana, "Stratigraphic Type Oil Fields," American Association of Petroleum Geologists, Tulsa, pp. 327–381 (1941).

Borger, H. D.: Case History of the Quiriquire Field, Venezuela, *A.A.P.G. Bull.*, vol. 36, pp. 2291–2330 (1952).

Caribbean Petroleum Co. Staff: Oil Fields of Royal Dutch–Shell Group in Western Venezuela, *A.A.P.G. Bull.*, vol. 32, pp. 517–628 (1948).

Carman, J. E., and Stout, W.: Relationship of Accumulation of Oil to Structure and Porosity in the Lima-Indiana Field, "Problems of Petroleum Geology," American Association of Petroleum Geologists, Tulsa, pp. 521–530 (1934).

Charles, H.: Bush City Field, Anderson County, Kansas, "Stratigraphic Type Oil Fields," American Association of Petroleum Geologists, Tulsa, pp. 43–56 (1941).

Clapp, F. G.: A Proposed Classification of Petroleum and Natural Gas Fields Based on Structure, *Econ. Geology*, vol. 5, pp. 503–521 (1910).

————: Revision of the Structural Classification of the Petroleum and Natural Gas Fields, *G.S.A. Bull.*, vol. 28, pp. 553–602 (1917).

————: Role of Geologic Structure in the Accumulation of Petroleum, "Structure of Typical American Oil Fields," American Association of Petroleum Geologists, Tulsa, vol. 2, pp. 667–716 (1929).

Clark, F. R.: Origin and Accumulation of Oil, "Problems of Petroleum Geology," American Association of Petroleum Geologists, Tulsa, pp. 309–338 (1934).

Dobbin, C. E.: Exceptional Oil Fields in Rocky Mountain Region of United States, *A.A.P.G. Bull.*, vol. 31, pp. 797–823 (1947).

————: Structural Conditions of Oil and Gas Accumulation in Rocky Mountain Region, United States, *A.A.P.G. Bull.*, vol. 27, pp. 417–478 (1943).

———— and Erdmann, C. E.: Geologic Occurrence of Oil and Gas in Montana, "Problems of Petroleum Geology," American Association of Petroleum Geologists, Tulsa, pp. 695–718 (1934).

Eggleston, W. S.: Summary of Oil Production from Fractured Rock Reservoirs in California, *A.A.P.G. Bull.*, vol. 32, pp. 1352–1355 (1948).

Freeman, J. C.: Strand-line Accumulation of Petroleum, Jim Hogg County, Texas, *A.A.P.G. Bull.*, vol. 33, pp. 1260–1270 (1949).

Fuller, M. L.: Appalachian Oil Field, *G.S.A. Bull.*, vol. 28, pp. 617–654 (1917).

Garlough, J. L., and Taylor, G. L.: Hugoton Gas Field, Grant, Haskell, Morton, Stevens and Seward Counties, Kansas, and Texas County, Oklahoma, "Stratigraphic Type Oil Fields," American Association of Petroleum Geologists, Tulsa, pp. 78–104 (1941).

Gibson, H. S.: Oil Production in Southwestern Iran, *World Oil*, vol. 128, no. 1, pp. 271–280; no. 2, pp. 217–226 (1948).

Heaton, R. L.: Stratigraphy versus Structure in Rocky Mountain Region, *A.A.P.G. Bull.*, vol. 21, pp. 1241–1246 (1937).

Hedberg, H. D., Sass, L. C., and Funkhouser, H. J.: Oil Fields of Greater Oficina Area, Central Anzoategui, Venezuela, *A.A.P.G. Bull.*, vol. 31, pp. 2089–2169 (1947).

Hintze, F. F.: Oil Accumulation in Relation to Periods of Folding, *A.A.P.G. Bull.*, vol. 7, pp. 58–66 (1923).

Krampert, E. W.: Geological Characteristics of Producing Oil and Gas Fields in Wyoming, Colorado, and Northwestern New Mexico, "Problems of Petroleum Geology," American Association of Petroleum Geologists, Tulsa, pp. 719–734 (1934).

Landes, K. K.: "Petroleum Geology," John Wiley & Sons, Inc., New York, pp. 207–210 (1951).

Lees, G. M.: The Geology of the Oil Field Belt of Iran and Iraq, "Science of Petroleum," Oxford University Press, New York, vol. 1, pp. 140–148 (1938).

Levorsen, A. I.: Stratigraphic versus Structural Accumulation, *A.A.P.G. Bull.*, vol. 20, pp. 521–530 (1936).

————: Time of Oil and Gas Accumulation, *A.A.P.G. Bull.*, vol. 29, pp. 1189–1194 (1945).

McClain, A. H.: Stratigraphic Accumulation in the Jackson-Kanawha Counties Area of West Virginia, *A.A.P.G. Bull.*, vol. 33, pp. 336–345 (1949).

McCoy, A. W.: An Interpretation of Local Structural Development in Mid-Continent Areas Associated with Deposits of Petroleum, "Problems of Petroleum Geology," American Association of Petroleum Geologists, Tulsa, pp. 581–628 (1934).

—— and Keyte, W. R.: Present Interpretations of Structural Theory for Oil and Gas Migration and Accumulation, "Problems of Petroleum Geology," American Association of Petroleum Geologists, Tulsa, pp. 253–308 (1934).

McCoy, A. W., III, and others: Types of Oil and Gas Traps in Rocky Mountain Region, *A.A.P.G. Bull.*, vol. 35, pp. 1000–1037 (1951).

Marshall, J. W.: Spraberry Reservoir of West Texas, *A.A.P.G. Bull.*, vol. 36, pp. 2189–2191 (1952).

Minor, H. E., and Hanna, M. A.: East Texas Oil Field, Rusk, Cherokee, Smith, Gregg and Upshur Counties, Texas, "Stratigraphic Type Oil Fields," American Association of Petroleum Geologists, Tulsa, pp. 600–640 (1941).

Muir, J. M.: Limestone Reservoir Rocks in the Mexican Oil Fields, "Problems of Petroleum Geology," American Association of Petroleum Geologists, Tulsa, pp. 377–398 (1934).

Olcott, D. P.: Amelia Field, Occurrence of Oil in Texas, *Univ. Texas, Bur. Econ. Geology, Progress Rept.* pp. 43–47 (1949).

Pack, R. W.: The Sunset-Midway Oil Field, Calif: I, Geology and Oil Resources, *U.S.G.S. Prof. Paper* 116 (1920).

Pratt, W. E., and Lahee, F. H.: Faulting and Petroleum Accumulation at Mexia, Texas, *A.A.P.G. Bull.*, vol. 7, pp. 226–236 (1923).

Reeves, F.: Outline for Classification of Oil Possibilities, *A.A.P.G. Bull.*, vol. 30, pp. 111–115 (1946).

Sanders, C. W.: Stratigraphic Type Oil Fields and Proposed New Classification of Reservoir Traps, *A.A.P.G. Bull.*, vol. 27, pp. 539–550 (1943).

Schneider, W. T.: Geology of Wasson Field, Yoakum and Gaines Counties, Texas, *A.A.P.G. Bull.*, vol. 27, pp. 479–523 (1943).

Selk, E. L.: Types of Oil and Gas Traps in Southern Oklahoma, *A.A.P.G. Bull.*, vol. 35, pp. 582–606 (1951).

Sherrill, R. E., Dickey, P. A., and Matteson, L. S.: Types of Stratigraphic Oil Pools in Venango Sands of Northwestern Pennsylvania, "Stratigraphic Type Oil Fields," American Association of Petroleum Geologists, Tulsa, pp. 507–538 (1941).

"Stratigraphic Type Oil Fields," American Association of Petroleum Geologists, Tulsa (1941).

"Structure of Typical American Oil Fields," American Association of Petroleum Geologists, Tulsa, vols. 1 and 2 (1929); vol. 3 (1948).

Summerford, H. E., Schieck, E. E., and Hiestand, T. C.: Oil and Gas Accumulation Controlled by Sedimentary Facies in Upper Cretaceous Newcastle Sandstone, Wyoming, *A.A.P.G. Bull.*, vol. 34, pp. 1850–1865 (1950).

Tomlinson, C. W.: Relation of Oil and Gas Accumulation to Geologic Structure in the Mid-Continent Region, "Problems of Petroleum Geology," American Association of Petroleum Geologists, Tulsa, pp. 571–580 (1934).

Wharton, J. B., Jr.: Isopachous Maps of Sand Reservoirs, *A.A.P.G. Bull.*, vol. 32, pp. 1331–1339 (1948).

Wilhelm, O.: Classification of Petroleum Reservoirs, *A.A.P.G. Bull.*, vol. 29, pp. 1537–1581 (1945).

Wilson, W. B.: Proposed Classification of Oil and Gas Reservoirs, "Problems of Petroleum Geology," American Association of Petroleum Geologists, Tulsa, pp. 433–446 (1934).

CHAPTER 17

STRUCTURAL FACTORS IN PETROLEUM PROSPECTING

A brief comment is needed on the way in which a knowledge of structure is put to practical use in wildcatting and in developing oil and gas fields. In the preceding portions of this book, descriptions have been given of the various structures present in sedimentary rocks, of the methods for discovering and mapping them, and of some of the processes connected with their development. The applications of this information to finding and producing oil and gas have been discussed briefly, but it has not been explained how this information is coordinated and used in a practical manner in prospecting and development. This chapter gives a summary of such applications, and discusses the relation of the structural information to the other factors which are important in the development of oil and gas fields.

Relative Importance of Structural Data

In applying structural techniques and data to problems of oil-field development, a geologist should keep in mind two important considerations. One is the economic aspect of the operations, and the other is that other factors besides structure affect the occurrence of oil and gas. The economic limitations to securing and applying structural information do not mean that this information is any less important, but they do condition and guide exploration activities related to structure. Stratigraphic traps are examples of occurrences of oil and gas which are not produced solely by structural effects. There appears to be a general opinion that stratigraphic traps will slowly grow in relative importance in the future. If this happens, it will increase somewhat the importance of stratigraphic methods of locating oil at the expense of the structural techniques. However, structure is very useful for finding traps which are partly stratigraphic in nature. Although the relative importance of stratigraphic studies is likely to grow larger in the later stages of the oil industry of the United States, a knowledge of structure will always be valuable also.

Practical Considerations in Wildcatting

The various practical problems involving the use of structure in wildcatting are related to the cost of acquiring structural information, the

373

cash value of the data, the chances of finding production in various traps, the ultimate production of oil and gas from each field which may be expected if production is found, the amount of oil or gas recovery per acre and per well which may be expected, the cost of leases, the cost of drilling wells and producing oil and gas, the cost of pipelines, the character of titles, taxes, the price of oil and gas, the demand for oil and gas, and variations in the price of materials and labor. Some of these problems belong in petroleum geology, and have been discussed or mentioned elsewhere by Russell.[1] A number of the others are related to petroleum engineering or to business procedures. Every petroleum geologist should know something about the bearing of these practical considerations on the use of structure in petroleum development. The sole function of some petroleum geologists is to describe the structure, letting others in the company take the responsibility of deciding on the practical problems. However, even in this case a knowledge of the values of the structures he finds and describes would help a geologist in his structural work. Moreover, if a geologist is promoted to executive positions, or becomes independent, he is certain to have to deal with the practical or economic aspects of structure. These practical aspects of structure are outside the scope of this book, and accordingly they are not treated here; however, the problem of estimating the chances for finding oil on various traps is so important that some discussion of it is given below.

CHANCES OF FINDING PRODUCTION ON UNTESTED TRAPS

The chief reason for structural work relating to oil and gas is the increase in chances for finding oil on structural traps over drilling at random. If the chances of finding production were the same for drilling at random as for drilling on structures, there would be no incentive for paying for structure mapping or geophysics. Since this difference in the chances of finding oil is so important, it is advisable to have some idea of what it is. The chances of finding production in a well located at random are the same as the ratio of productive to unproductive territory in the region on which the well is drilled. Thus if 400 square miles are productive in a region covering 10,000 square miles, at the beginning of development the chances of finding production in a well located at random would be 400/10,000, or 1 in 25. While a region is being developed, the total productive area is not known, but it may be estimated accurately in areas which have been extensively prospected and in which development has practically ceased, such as the Appalachian region and parts of Oklahoma and Kansas. Judging by the percentage of produc-

---

[1] William L. Russell, "Principles of Petroleum Geology," McGraw-Hill Book Company, Inc., New York (1951).

tive territory in such regions, it appears that the chances for success of a well located at random in an oil-producing region may vary from about 1 in 500 to 1 in 10. Where many productive stratigraphic traps occur close together, the chances of success in a wildcat well located at random may be greater than 1 in 10. Structure mapping not only shows where to locate the test, but indicates the area which the field is likely to cover if the trap is productive. Furthermore, structure maps are very useful for guiding the development of oil and gas fields after their discovery.

The best sources of information on the chances of finding oil or gas in wildcat wells are the statistics of exploration drilling which are written by F. H. Lahee and published annually in the *Bulletin of the American Association of Petroleum Geologists*. From these publications it is possible to estimate the chances for finding production under various conditions and in various areas. The chances of finding production in wildcat wells decrease with distance from producing fields. They are also much less if the formations to be tested have never before produced oil in the region. The chances of finding production in a well on an untested structure (that is, a prospect recommended as a result of geological or geophysical work) have been about 1 in 10 for the United States as a whole, and have not changed much for several years. However, the chances vary considerably in different parts of the United States.

A wildcat in these statistics is classed as successful if it produces oil. In many cases this production is not in sufficient volume to be profitable. Furthermore, if the field consists of only a few wells, it is likely to be unprofitable because a number of dry holes are drilled in defining it. Lahee[1] has discussed the percentage of successful wildcat wells which open up profitable pools. In areas where the depth of the producing horizons is only about 1,000 ft, operators might make a profit by finding oil pools which had an ultimate recovery of only 1 million bbl of oil. However, only an insignificant amount of production is being found by such shallow wells. In most of the important oil regions, oil companies would lose money in the end on oil fields which had an ultimate recovery of less than about 1 million bbl of oil. Lahee finds that only about 1 wildcat in 40 discovers an oil field with more than 1,000,000 bbl ultimate production. In a region where gas production is valuable, the chances for a wildcat being profitable might be a little better.

Many geologists and people with long experience in the oil business seem to have exaggerated ideas of the percentage of wildcat wells which are financially successful. Certainly many of those outside the oil business who invest money in wildcat wells would not do so if they knew these chances. This is clearly a subject which should be thoroughly

[1] F. H. Lahee, Degrees of Success in Wildcat Drilling, *A.A.P.G. Bull.*, vol. 35, pp. 138–140 (1951).

understood by all those who spend money on structural work or on investments based on it.

Nonstructural Factors

Whether a given structure produces oil or gas is determined by a number of factors, some structural, some not related to structure. The most important are the presence of reservoir rocks, cover rocks, and source rocks. The most reliable evidence as to whether these conditions are present is the actual occurrence of oil or gas. Accordingly, decisions as to whether to test structural traps are based largely on the nature of the production which has been obtained from the formations in the traps in other structures in the same region. Oil companies naturally hesitate to test traps if the prospective producing reservoirs in them have never produced oil in other traps. However, if this cautious policy were followed rigidly, no new regions or formations would be opened up to production.

Although the chances of finding production on a trap in an unproductive region are much smaller than in the case of a trap close to production, the rewards of discovering oil in a new region may in some cases be large enough to justify the extra risk. In unproductive regions the leases or concessions are generally easier and less expensive to obtain and can be secured in larger blocks. Furthermore, the chances of finding oil or gas fields of great size are likely to be better in a region which is relatively untested than in one that has been extensively prospected.

Regional Structural Conditions

Nature of Regional Structural Conditions. The prospects for production in a structural trap are affected by the regional structural conditions. These are the position on the regional structure, the amount of the regional dip, the nature, spacing, trend, and alignment of the folds and faults, the character and relations of the unconformities, and the effects of igneous intrusion and regional alteration. Any characteristic of folds or faults which is found over a wide area may be considered a regional characteristic. For example, the anticlines in certain regions may increase in closure downward, while in other regions there may be no increase in closure with depth.

Significance of Position. The position of any point in a series of sedimentary rocks may be described with reference to both the regional and the local structure. For example, a point may be located near the axis or on the flank of a local structure such as an anticline or a syncline, or of a regional structure such as a geanticline, a regional arch, or a geosyncline. Since the prospects of structural traps are affected by the position of the traps with reference to both regional and local structures, this information is generally given in the geological reports describing them.

A given structural trap is more likely to be located on the flank of a regional structure than close to its axis. This is because the flanks of these structures cover a larger area than the regions close to the axes. The position of a given anticline or other structural trap on the flank of a regional structure determines the position of the most critical dip. This is the dip in the direction opposite to the regional dip—in other words, it is the same as the reversal, defined previously. The position of the prospect on the flanks of regional structures also determines which side of the structural-stratigraphic traps can be open. The open side must be downdip. In general, a position on the flanks of regional structures is neither favorable nor unfavorable for the oil and gas prospects of traps. Probably at least two-thirds of all traps are on the flanks of some regional structure.

It was formerly supposed that a position near the bottom of a geosyncline, basin, or regional syncline was very unfavorable as regards oil and gas prospects. In fact, some of the worst mistakes which petroleum geologists have made in the past consisted in condemning such areas. Their reasoning was that since local synclines are unfavorable for oil and gas accumulation, regional synclines should also be unfavorable. Many of them also supposed that oil migrates great distances to reach the trap in which it accumulates, and that the size of the area downdip from which the oil could migrate was of considerable importance. The discovery of many prolific oil and gas fields near the lowest portions of these structural depressions has completely disproved this theory. A number of these fields occur on local anticlines, and their existence in no way discredits the anticlinal theory. What they do indicate is that the oil and gas in them did not migrate very far. Stratigraphic traps may also occur near the axes of regional synclines merely by chance. One factor in favor of oil and gas production from the lowest portions of regional structures is the greater thickness of sediments present in such areas. This generally means a larger number of possible reservoir rocks.

It appears that oil and gas fields tend to be concentrated along the crests of regional uplifts. Hence the location of a trap near the crest of a regional structure may be considered a point in its favor. On the other hand, the axial portions of some regional anticlines are unfavorable for oil and gas accumulation because the sedimentary section is too thin or because the oil and gas have been flushed from the sediments during periods of uplift and erosion.

Regional Alteration. The most reliable indication as to whether a formation at a given locality is too highly altered to produce oil or gas is furnished by actual production. The problem of whether regional alteration is too high therefore arises only in the case of regions which do not have oil or gas production, of formations deeper than those which produce, and of areas where the degree of alteration may change rapidly. Regional alteration is not discussed at length in this book, but it has been mentioned on pages 270–272 and has been discussed elsewhere by Russell.[1]

Other Regional Structural Relations. Several other regional structural relations have a bearing on oil and gas prospects. The presence of angular unconformities, cover rocks, and regional variations in thickness have been discussed previously. Another factor which may be important is the degree of artesian circulation in the reservoir rocks. Although opinions are divided on the effect of artesian circulation on oil accumulation, the relative scarcity of oil and gas fields in reservoirs which contain fresh water suggests that artesian circulation is in general unfavorable. However, it also seems probable that reservoirs which still contain salt water have generally not been subjected to an unfavorable degree of artesian circulation.

LOCAL STRUCTURAL CONDITIONS

Structural Position. The local structural conditions affecting oil and gas prospects are the type of local folding, the reversal, closure, and closed area of anticlines, the configuration, size, and throw of the faults, and the size, structural closure, and closed area of the prospects along faults. As previously mentioned, the prospects of production of each lease or well are affected by its position with reference to the local structures. An area lying on a homocline or regional dip with no signs of local structure at all could obviously not be described in this manner, but if local structures are present, the position with reference to them is important. The most unfavorable location is in the bottom of a syncline, and the situation from a structural viewpoint becomes increasingly unfavorable toward this position. As the crests of anticlines are approached, the prospects for production in general become brighter. However, there may not be much difference in the prospects of areas outside of the vicinity of the axes and closed areas of uplifts. In other words, all the other areas are unfavorable with respect to local structure, and the differences in oil and gas prospects between a location halfway down the flank of an anticline and all the way down in the bottom of the adjacent syncline may be slight. Moreover, a geologist should be very cautious about making positive statements condemning areas that are low with respect to local structure. In the first place, such areas may contain small structural traps, the existence of which is not disclosed by the structural information available in advance of drilling them. Stratigraphic traps may be productive in such areas. Furthermore, it should

[1] *Op. cit.,* pp. 238–261.

be kept in mind that the conclusion that structurally low areas are unfavorable is based on the assumption that the reservoir rocks are generally saturated with water. In some areas the pore space in the reservoirs generally contains gas, and the oil is found in the synclines. Such areas are rare, but the geologist should take into consideration the information as to the relative amount of oil, gas, and water in the sands, as revealed by drilling. If the gas is found in the crests of anticlines or the upper portions of reservoirs, oil may occur in the lower portions. Since oil is generally much more valuable than gas, the best leases in such cases are located down the structure from the crest. This relation is especially important where a closed area is very large. An oil company which leases only the part of the closed area near the structural crest of such large uplifts may find that it owns only gas-producing leases, while its rivals own the oil production.

The area along the axes of anticlines outside the closed areas is favorable for oil and gas accumulation, though not nearly as promising as the closed areas themselves. This favorable nature of the regions near the anticlinal axes is due primarily to the fact that structural-stratigraphic traps are more likely to exist along the axes of anticlines than in localities that are more remote from them. The possibility of the occurrence of such traps may be estimated to some extent from the knowledge of the occurrence of truncations and of the lack of persistence of reservoirs. Such structural-stratigraphic traps are much more likely to occur in regions where the reservoirs are nonpersistent than where they extend over great distances without interruption.

Relation of Oil and Gas Production to Closure and Closed Area. The closures and closed areas of anticlines are their most important characteristics for determining their prospective value for oil and gas production. In advance of the drill, a geologist does not know the relative proportions of oil, gas, and water in a reservoir, though he may be able to make rough estimates from conditions found in drilling other structures in the region. If the amount of oil or gas is very small compared with the volume of the reservoir, only the highest part of the reservoir in the closed area may contain oil or gas. If relatively large volumes of oil or gas reach the reservoir, the whole of the closed area may be filled. Since it is possible that the whole of the closed area may produce, it is generally advisable to lease it in advance of drilling, provided that the leases can be obtained on reasonable terms.

In general, the promise and value of a structure increases with the amount of closure. One reason why a structure with large closure is better than one with small closure is that there is more chance that it persists to great depths. Possibly the steep dips associated with large closures are better traps for oil or gas than the gentle dips associated with small closures.   However, the most important factor in making the closure so important is the relation between the closure and the thickness of the producing zone.   Where the reservoir dips at a low angle, a given producing zone cannot be thicker than the reservoir in which it occurs, but it may be much thinner.   If a reservoir is 200 ft thick, only the upper 10 ft of it may produce oil or gas in a given well, the remaining portion being filled with water.   The terms "oil column," "gas

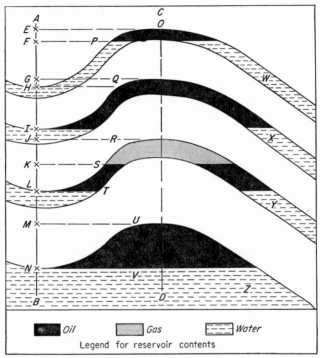

Fig. 17-1. Cross section along the anticlinal axis through a closed dome on an anticline.

column," and "productive relief" have been introduced to describe the difference in elevation between the top and bottom of the producing zones. These terms are used where the producing zones are underlain by water in part of the reservoir, and where the reservoir contains water down the dip.   They are illustrated by Fig. 17-1, which is a cross section showing a series of four reservoir rocks, W, X, Y, and Z, folded into an anticline. It is assumed that the vertical cross section coincides with the axial plane of the fold.   The closure is determined in the saddle along the line AB. The amount of closure is the difference in elevation of the top of the various reservoir rocks along the line AB and at the crest of the anticline along the line CD. The elevation of each of the reservoir rocks at the crest of the anticline and the elevation of each of the fluid contacts have been projected horizontally to the left to the line AB, and the points at which these lines intersect the line AB are designated by letters. Thus the top of the reservoir W is at point O on the crest of the anticline, and this point has been projected horizontally along the line OE to point E on line AB. Similarly, point F is the horizontal projection of the fluid contact at P on line AB. The height of the oil zones in reservoirs W, X, Y, and Z is respectively FE, IG, LK, and NM, and the height of the gas zone in reservoir Y is KJ. It is evident from this figure that the height of the oil zone plus the height of the gas zone may equal the closure, but would not exceed it. Where the closure is greater than the thickness of the reservoir rock, and where the closed area is all productive, the thickness of the producing zone in any well is limited by the thickness of the reservoir rock. On the other hand, where the reservoir rock is thicker than the amount of closure, and the closed area is completely filled with oil or gas, the maximum thickness of the producing zone is limited by the amount of closure, as in reservoir Z, Fig. 17-1.

Other Factors Affecting Prospects for Production on Local Structural Traps. Among the local structural conditions which affect the oil and gas prospects of a structural trap are its persistence or the changes in its character downward, the shifting of the axes of structures with depth, the changes in the throws of faults with depth, the shifting of the positions of faults with depth (in the case of faults which are not vertical), and the age of the trap in relation to the time of migration of oil and gas. These have all been discussed previously.

COMBINATION OF STRUCTURAL AND STRATIGRAPHIC METHODS IN PROSPECTING

Swann[1] has described the use of a combination of structural and stratigraphic methods to find oil in an area in southern Illinois. This example is important because it illustrates the final stage toward which prospecting trends in oil regions. By the time this stage has been reached, the general nature of the structure is known quite accurately from seismograph surveys or from subsurface data. The more promising structural traps have been drilled, and much subsurface information is available regarding the stratigraphic variations of the producing horizons. Figs. 17-2 and 17-3, from Swann's paper, show conditions in the area discussed. Fig. 17-2 shows the structure of a limestone just above the Waltersburg sandstone, and Fig. 17-3 is an isopach map showing the thickness of permeable Waltersburg sandstone. The structure shown by

[1] David H. Swann, Waltersburg Sandstone Oil Pools of Lower Wabash Valley Area, Illinois and Indiana, *A.A.P.G. Bull.*, vol. 35, pp. 2561–2581 (1951).

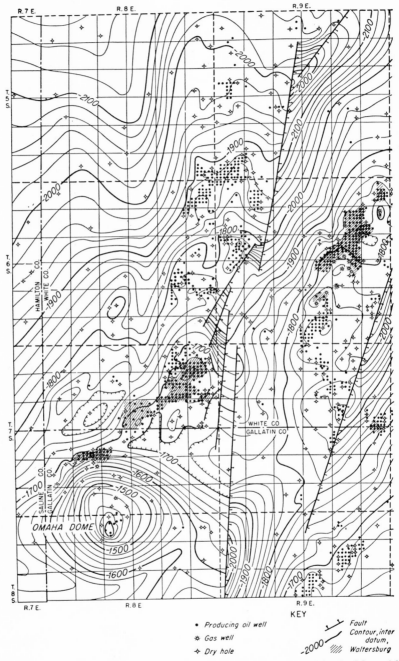

KEY

•   Producing oil well
✳   Gas well
✢   Dry hole

⌐⌐⌐ Fault
⟋   Contour, inter
         datum,
-2000 ▨ Waltersburg

Fig. 17-2. Structure map of an area in southern Illinois on a key bed in the Menard lime-stone (upper Mississippian) a short distance above the Waltersburg sandstone. (*After Swann, published by permission of the American Association of Petroleum Geologists.*)

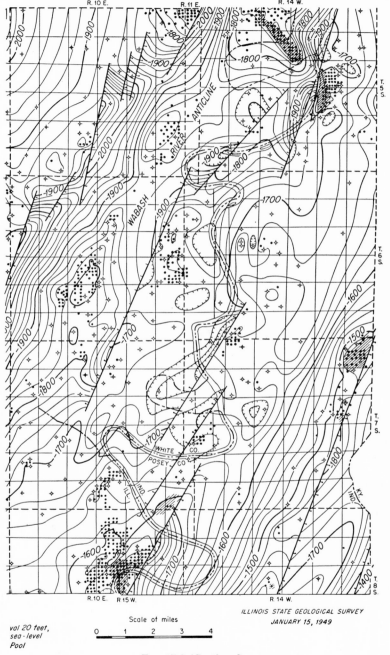

ILLINOIS STATE GEOLOGICAL SURVEY
JANUARY 15, 1949

Scale of miles

0   1   2   3   4

*vol 20 feet,
sea-level
Pool*

Fig. 17-2 (*Continued*)

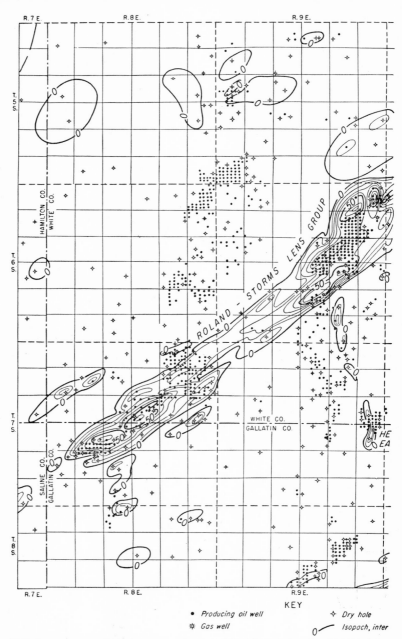

KEY

• Producing oil well   ✦ Dry hole

✳ Gas well   ◦⌒ Isopach, inter

Fig. 17-3. Isopach map of the same area shown in Fig. 17-2, giving the thickness of permeable Waltersburg sandstone. (*After Swann, published by permission of the American Association of Petroleum Geologists.*)

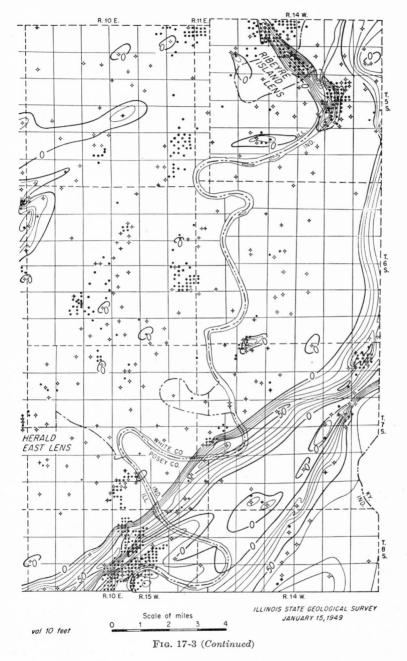

val 10 feet

Scale of miles
0   1   2   3   4

ILLINOIS STATE GEOLOGICAL SURVEY
JANUARY 15, 1949

FIG. 17-3 *(Continued)*

Fig. 17-2 consists chiefly in a series of anticlines and normal faults trending slightly east of north and superimposed on a general northward regional dip. The strata on the downthrown sides of the faults dip into them at an angle which is steeper than normal for the region. This suggests that these steep dips are reverse drag. The area has been so closely drilled that no oil field covering a very large area is likely to be found in the formations tested. Furthermore, these wells represent a large investment. The producing area already found is roughly about 5 per cent of the total area of about 525 square miles.

The production in this region is obtained chiefly from rather non-persistent sandstones of the upper Mississippian Chester series. There is a pronounced tendency for the pools to occur on anticlines, but there is also a marked stratigraphic or lithologic control. The latter is indicated by the dry areas between the pools on the anticlines, and by the large unproductive areas on the most favorable structures.

A comparison of Figs. 17-2 and 17-3 reveals the reason for the distribution of the Waltersburg production. The permeable Waltersburg sand lies in long, narrow lenses, which appear to be beaches or near-shore bars. Oil production is obtained from the Waltersburg sandstone where these sand bodies pass over anticlines.

It is important to consider how the geologist can aid in finding production in areas where the conditions are like those shown in Figs. 17-2 and 17-3. One way is to project the known trends of favorable sand conditions and recommend tests where they cross anticlines. Swann mentions that several Waltersburg pools have been found in this manner in the area illustrated. However, it is not to be expected that most sand bodies would show as regular trends as those shown in Fig. 17-3.

In general, the best the geologist can do under such conditions is to try to predict where the highest portions of each sand body occur. These are the areas in which to drill tests or secure leases. Even if oil pools are present in such areas, it is likely to take a number of wildcat wells to find them. It is possible that the oil development in a region will never reach this stage because of the high cost of drilling so many wells. In general, this stage is not reached unless there are a number of oil fields to encourage further development. As the wildcat wells become more closely spaced, the size of the oil pools which are found declines. When the pools become so small that it does not pay to find them, wildcatting ends unless it is revived by the discovery of deeper production.

Use of Structure in Developing Fields after Discovery

Many more geologists are engaged in developing oil and gas fields after discovery than are employed in finding them. Consequently the use of structure in developing fields is of great importance. The object of much of the intensive stratigraphic work which goes on concurrently with the development of a field is the accurate mapping of the structure. A knowledge of the structure is a great aid in development. If an accurate structure map is available at the beginning of the drilling in a field, the drilling of a number of dry holes is probably eliminated. Without such a map, these dry holes would probably have to be drilled in defining the structure as development proceeds. Structure maps made in advance of development would have to be made by surface mapping, core drilling, geophysics, or subsurface data on shallower horizons.

DIFFICULTY OF FINDING OIL

Descriptions of how oil is discovered are likely to give the impression that it is easy to find. The reader might assume that all that is necessary is to hire some geologists and geophysicists and drill a few of the structures they locate. Actually, finding oil production is very difficult, even with the best technical advice. There are several reasons for this. In the first place, the odds are very much against obtaining valuable production in any wildcat, even in the case of wildcats located where the geological conditions are most promising. It should be kept in mind that according to Lahee's figures, only 1 wildcat in 40 opens up a profitable oil field. Another difficulty is that it is necessary not only to discover oil, but to make a profit. A third is the time factor. It may be only the first company to locate a trap that profits by the discovery.

The statement made above applies only to wildcatting. The geologist who is engaged in developing oil fields after their discovery may encounter many very difficult problems, but his task is much simpler than that of the wildcatter. This is because many of the baffling problems and uncertainties have been automatically eliminated by the discovery of oil. Among them are the problems relating to the presence of source rocks and reservoir rocks, the effects of regional alteration and artesian circulation, and the uncertainties as to depths. Certainly after a field has been discovered there is much more definite and accurate information to rely on than in wildcatting.

MENTAL FACTORS IN WILDCATTING

In recent years a number of geologists have issued statements as to the qualifications needed by geologists to be successful in finding oil. Most of these statements have included imagination as one of the important mental attributes, and it is of interest to consider just what is meant by "imagination" in these statements. It appears that the initial idea which results in drilling a geologically located wildcat is based on two mental processes. One is the recognition that there is a favorable condition at a given locality. The other is the testing in the imagination of the evidence for the supposed favorable condition.   The first recognition may come about as a sudden flash of insight, though it can be more gradual.   The criticism of this idea consists in carefully weighing all the factors for and against it, in visualizing the relations which would be expected if the idea is correct and noting whether these relations are actually found, in testing the assumptions, and in eliminating preconceived ideas and prejudices not supported by what is known.   All this might be considered as imagination because it may be entirely mental.   Evidently the term "imagination" is used with a rather broad meaning in the statements mentioned.

FUTURE OF STRUCTURAL GEOLOGY IN THE OIL INDUSTRY

The future of structural geology in the oil industry is much the same as the future of petroleum geology.   As time goes on there should be a gradually increasing emphasis on stratigraphic and lithologic factors in prospecting, but no doubt petroleum geologists will always use structure. As long as the production of petroleum in the United States continues to rise, the number of petroleum geologists will also rise, and those entering the profession will be promoted rapidly.   On the other hand, when the development of new oil production in the United States diminishes over a long period of time, the number of petroleum geologists employed will also diminish, advancement will be slow, and it will be difficult for those who lose their positions to find employment again.   It is certain that eventually the development of new production will slacken off, but no one knows exactly when this will commence.   The duration of the period of expansion depends on the total reserves of undiscovered oil, the amount of foreign oil imported, and the demand for oil.   The first two of these factors are extremely difficult to estimate accurately.   About all that can be done at present is to call the attention of those entering the profession to this problem, and to list some of the important factors affecting it.

The old fields of the United States are in a more advanced state of development than the oil fields of the rest of the world.   Accordingly, it is likely that when the development of new oil fields is declining in the United States, it will still be increasing in foreign countries.   One would therefore expect that the number of petroleum geologists employed in foreign fields would continue to increase after the number employed in the United States had begun to decrease.   Under such conditions no doubt some geologists from the United States would find employment in foreign fields.   However, there is a tendency to replace geologists from the United States with geologists who are citizens of the country in which the oil fields occur.

ADDITIONAL REFERENCES

Abreau, S. F.: Brazilian Oil Fields and Oil-shale Reserves, *A.A.P.G. Bull.*, vol. 33, pp. 1590–1599 (1949).

Adams, J. E.: Oil Pool of Open Reservoir Type, *A.A.P.G. Bull.*, vol. 20, pp. 780–796 (1936).

————: Origin, Migration, and Accumulation of Petroleum in Limestone Reservoirs in the Western United States and Canada, "Problems of Petroleum Geology," American Association of Petroleum Geologists, Tulsa, pp. 347–364 (1934).

————: Paleogeography and Petroleum Exploration, *Jour. Sedimentary Petrology*, vol. 13, pp. 108–111 (1943).

Anderson, J. L.: Petroleum Geology of Colombia, South America, *A.A.P.G. Bull.*, vol. 29, pp. 1065–1142 (1945).

Applin, P. L., and Applin, E. R.: Regional Subsurface Stratigraphy and Structure of Florida and Southern Georgia, *A.A.P.G. Bull.*, vol. 28, pp. 1673–1753 (1944).

Baker, N. E., and Henson, F. R. S.: Geological Conditions of Oil Occurrence in Middle East Fields, *A.A.P.G. Bull.*, vol. 36, pp. 1885–1901 (1952).

Baldwin, H. L.: Tupungate Field, Mendoza, Argentina, *A.A.P.G. Bull.*, vol. 28, pp. 1455–1484 (1944).

Barb, C. F., and Ball, J. O.: Hydrocarbons of the Uinta Basin of Utah and Colorado, *Colorado School of Mines Quart.*, vol. 39, no. 1, pp. 1–115 (1944).

Bartram, J. G.: Summary of Rocky Mountain Geology, *A.A.P.G. Bull.*, vol. 23, pp. 1131–1152 (1939).

———— Imbt, W. C., and Shea, E. F.: Oil and Gas in Arbuckle and Ellenburger Formations, Mid-Continent Region, *A.A.P.G. Bull.*, vol. 34, pp. 682–700 (1950).

Bates, F. W., and Wharton, J. B., Jr.: Geology of West Tepetate Oil Field, Jefferson Davis Parish, Louisiana, *A.A.P.G. Bull.*, vol. 32, pp. 1712–1727 (1948).

Bates, R. L.: The Oil and Gas Resources of New Mexico, 2d ed., *New Mexico School of Mines Bull.* 18, 320 pp. (1942).

Beal, C. H.: Reconnaissance of the Geology and Oil Possibilities of Baja California, Mexico, *G.S.A. Memoir* 31 (1948).

Becker, C. M.: Structure and Stratigraphy of Southwestern Oklahoma, *A.A.P.G. Bull.*, vol. 14, pp. 37–56 (1930).

Beckwith, R. H.: Structure of the Southwest Margin of the Laramie Basin, Wyoming, *G.S.A. Bull.*, vol. 49, pp. 1515–1544 (1938).

Bell, A. H.: Role of Fundamental Geologic Principles in the Opening of the Illinois Basin, *Econ. Geology*, vol. 36, pp. 774–785 (1941).

Billingsley, J. E.: Occurrence of Oil and Gas in West Virginia, Eastern Ohio and Eastern Kentucky, "Problems of Petroleum Geology," American Association of Petroleum Geologists, Tulsa, pp. 485–514 (1934).

Bohdanowicz, C.: Geology and Mining of Petroleum in Poland, *A.A.P.G. Bull.*, vol. 16, pp. 1061–1091 (1932).

Borger, H. D.: Case History of the Quiriquire Field, Venezuela, *A.A.P.G. Bull.*, vol. 36, pp. 2291–2330 (1952).

Bornhauser, M.: Oil and Gas Accumulation Controlled by Sedimentary Facies in Eocene Wilcox to Cockfield Formations, Louisiana Gulf Coast, *A.A.P.G. Bull.*, vol. 34, pp. 1887–1896 (1950).

———— and Bates, F. W.: Geology of the Tepetate Oil Field, Acadia Parish, Louisiana, *A.A.P.G. Bull.*, vol. 22, pp. 285–305 (1938).

Caribbean Petroleum Co. Staff: Oil Fields of Royal Dutch–Shell Group in Western Venezuela, *A.A.P.G. Bull.*, vol. 32, pp. 517–628 (1948).

Carman, J. E., and Stout, W.: Relationship of Accumulation of Oil to Structure and Porosity in the Lima-Indiana Field, "Problems of Petroleum Geology," American Association of Petroleum Geologists, Tulsa, pp. 521–530 (1934).

Clapp, F. G.: The Fundamental Criteria of Oil Occurrence, A.A.P.G. Bull., vol. 11, pp. 683–703 (1927).

————: A Proposed Classification of Petroleum and Natural Gas Fields Based on Structure, Econ. Geology, vol. 5, pp. 503–521 (1910).

————: Role of Geologic Structure in the Accumulation of Petroleum, "Structure of Typical American Oil Fields," American Association of Petroleum Geologists, Tulsa, vol. 2, pp. 667–716 (1929).

Clark, F. R.: Origin and Accumulation of Oil, "Problems of Petroleum Geology," American Association of Petroleum Geologists, Tulsa, pp. 309–338 (1934).

Coffin, R. C.: Recent Trends in Geological-geophysical Exploration and Methods of Improving Use of Geophysical Data, A.A.P.G. Bull., vol. 30, pp. 2013–2033 (1946).

Cooper, H. H.: Occurrence and Accumulation of Oil in Laredo District, Texas, A.A.P.G. Bull., vol. 21, pp. 1422–1438 (1937).

Cottingham, K.: Structural Conditions in Portions of Eastern Ohio, A.A.P.G. Bull., vol. 11, pp. 945–958 (1927).

Cram, I. H.: Geology Is Useful, A.A.P.G. Bull., vol. 32, pp. 1–10 (1948).

Davies, H. F.: Structural History and Its Relation to the Accumulation of Oil and Gas in the Rocky Mountain District, "Problems of Petroleum Geology," American Association of Petroleum Geologists, Tulsa, pp. 679–694 (1934).

De Blieux, C.: Photogeology in Gulf Coast Exploration, A.A.P.G. Bull., vol. 33, pp. 1251–1259 (1949).

De Cizancourt, H.: Geology of Oil Fields of Polish Carpathian Mountains, A.A.P.G. Bull., vol. 15, pp. 1–41 (1931).

DeGolyer, E.: Oil Associated with Igneous Rocks in Mexico, A.A.P.G. Bull., vol. 16, pp. 799–807 (1932).

Denison, A. R.: Deeper Drilling Prospects in the Mid-Continent, A.I.M.M.E. Tech. Pub. 1650, pp. 2–8 (1944).

Deussen, A., and Owen, K. D.: Correlation of Surface and Subsurface Formations in Two Typical Sections of the Gulf Coast of Texas, A.A.P.G. Bull., vol. 23, pp. 1603–1634 (1939).

Dix, C. H.: "Seismic Prospecting for Oil," Harper & Brothers, New York, pp. 281–323 (1952).

Dobbin, C. E.: Exceptional Oil Fields in Rocky Mountain Region of United States, A.A.P.G. Bull., vol. 31, pp. 797–823 (1947).

————: Structural Conditions of Oil and Gas Accumulation in Rocky Mountain Region, United States, A.A.P.G. Bull., vol. 27, pp. 417–478 (1943).

———— and Erdmann, C. E.: Geologic Occurrence of Oil and Gas in Montana, "Problems of Petroleum Geology," American Association of Petroleum Geologists, Tulsa, pp. 695–718 (1934).

Driver, H. L.: Genesis and Evolution of Los Angeles Basin, California, A.A.P.G. Bull., vol. 32, pp. 109–125 (1948).

Eardley, A. J.: "Aerial Photographs, Their Use and Interpretation," Harper & Brothers, New York (1942).

————: Petroleum Geology of Aquitaine Basin, France, A.A.P.G. Bull., vol. 30, pp. 1517–1545 (1946).

Echols, D. J., and Malkin, D. S.: Wilcox (Eocene) Stratigraphy, a Key to Production, A.A.P.G. Bull., vol. 32, pp. 11–33 (1948).

Eggleston, W. S.: Summary of Oil Production from Fractured Rock Reservoirs in California, *A.A.P.G. Bull.*, vol. 32, pp. 1352–1355 (1948).

Emmons, W. H.: "Geology of Petroleum," McGraw-Hill Book Company, Inc., New York, 2d ed. (1931).

Evans, P., and Sansom, C. A.: The Geology of British Oil Fields: III, The Oil Fields of Burma, *Geol. Mag.*, vol. 78, pp. 321–350 (1941).

Fettke, C. R.: The Bradford Oil Field, Pennsylvania and New York, *Pennsylvania Geolog. Survey Bull.* M21 (1938).

Finn, F. H.: Geology and Occurrence of Natural Gas in Oriskany Sandstone in Pennsylvania and New York, *A.A.P.G. Bull.*, vol. 33, pp. 303–335 (1949).

Fohs, F. J.: Oil-reserve Provinces of Middle East and Southern Soviet Russia, *A.A.P.G. Bull.*, vol. 31, pp. 1372–1383 (1947).

———: Petroliferous Provinces of Union of Soviet Socialist Republics, *A.A.P.G. Bull.*, vol. 32, pp. 317–350 (1948).

Freeman, J. C.: Strand-line Accumulation of Petroleum, Jim Hogg County, Texas, *A.A.P.G. Bull.*, vol. 33, pp. 1260–1270 (1949).

Fuller, M. L.: The Appalachian Oil Field, *G.S.A. Bull.*, vol. 28, pp. 617–654 (1917).

Gallup, W. B.: Geology of Turner Valley Oil and Gas Field, Alberta, Canada, *A.A.P.G. Bull.*, vol. 35, pp. 797–821 (1951).

Garlough, J. L., and Taylor, G. J.: Hugoton Gas Field, Grant, Haskell, Morton, Stevens and Seward Counties, Kansas, and Texas County, Oklahoma, "Stratigraphic Type Oil Fields," American Association of Petroleum Geologists, Tulsa, pp. 78–104 (1941).

"Geology of Natural Gas," American Association of Petroleum Geologists, Tulsa (1935).

"Geology of the Tampico Region, Mexico," American Association of Petroleum Geologists, Tulsa (1936).

"Geophysical Case Histories," Society of Exploration Geophysicists (1948).

Gester, G. C.: World Petroleum Reserves and Petroleum Statistics, *A.A.P.G. Bull.*, vol. 28, pp. 1485–1505 (1944).

Gibson, H. S.: Oil Production in Southwestern Iran, *World Oil*, vol. 128, No. 1, pp. 271–280; vol. 128, no. 2, pp. 217–226 (1948).

Goodman, A. J.: The Structure of the Turner Valley Gas Field, Alberta, *Canadian Inst. Min. Metallurgy Trans.*, vol. 34, pp. 307–356 (1932).

Goubkin, I. M.: Tectonics of Southeastern Caucasus and Its Relation to the Productive Oil Fields, *A.A.P.G. Bull.*, vol. 18, pp. 603–671 (1934).

Green, C. H.: Integration in Exploration, *A.A.P.G. Bull.*, vol. 32, pp. 1216–1220 (1948).

"Gulf Coast Oil Fields," American Association of Petroleum Geologists, Tulsa (1936).

Guzman, E. J.: New Petroleum Development by Petroleos Mexicanos in Northeastern Mexico, *A.A.P.G. Bull.*, vol. 33, pp. 1351–1384 (1949).

Hager, D.: "Fundamentals of the Petroleum Industry," McGraw-Hill Book Company, Inc., New York (1939).

Halse, G. W.: Oil Fields of West Buchivacoa, Venezuela, *A.A.P.G. Bull.*, vol. 31, pp. 2170–2192 (1947).

Hanna, M. A.: Geology of Gulf Coast Salt Domes, "Problems of Petroleum Geology," American Association of Petroleum Geologists, Tulsa, pp. 629–678 (1934).

Heaton, R. L.: Stratigraphy versus Structure in Rocky Mountain Region, *A.A.P.G. Bull.*, vol. 21, pp. 1241–1246 (1937).

Hedberg, H. D., Sass, L. C., and Funkhouser, H. J.: Oil Fields of Greater Oficina Area, Central Anzoategui, Venezuela, *A.A.P.G. Bull.*, vol. 31, pp. 2089–2169 (1947).

Hemsell, C. C.: Geology of Hugoton Gas Field of Southwestern Kansas, *A.A.P.G. Bull.*, vol. 23, pp. 1054–1067 (1939).

Hennen, R. V.: Tertiary Geology and Oil and Gas Prospects in Dakota Basin of North Dakota, *A.A.P.G. Bull.*, vol. 27, pp. 1567–1594 (1943).

Herald, F. A., Ed.: Occurrence of Oil and Gas in Northeast Texas, *Univ. Texas Bur. Econ. Geology Pub.* 5116, 449 pp. (1951).

Heroy, W. B.: Oil for the Future, *Econ. Geology*, vol. 39, pp. 593–599 (1944).

Hiestand, R. C.: Regional Investigations, Oklahoma and Kansas, *A.A.P.G. Bull.*, vol. 19, pp. 948–970 (1935).

Hoffman, M. G.: Structural History of Billings Field, Noble County, Oklahoma, Interpreted in Terms of Isostasy, *A.A.P.G. Bull.*, vol. 24, pp. 2006–2018 (1940).

Howard, W. V.: Accumulation of Oil and Gas in Limestone, "Problems of Petroleum Geology," American Association of Petroleum Geologists, Tulsa, pp. 365–376 (1934).

Hume, G. S.: The Geology of British Oilfields: II, The Geology of the Oilfields and Some Prospective Oil Areas in Canada, *Geol. Mag.*, vol. 78, pp. 1–36 (1941).

———: Petroleum Geology of Canada, *Canada Geol. Survey Bull.* 98, Econ. Geology ser. 14, 64 pp. (1944).

Hunt, C. B.: New Interpretation of Some Laccolithic Mountains and Its Possible Bearing on Structural Traps for Oil and Gas, *A.A.P.G. Bull.*, vol. 26, pp. 197–203 (1942).

Illing, V. C.: Role of Stratigraphy in Oil Discovery, *A.A.P.G. Bull.*, vol. 29, pp. 872–884 (1945).

Jacobsen, L.: Structural Relations on East Flank of Anadarko Basin, Cleveland and McClain Counties, Oklahoma, *A.A.P.G. Bull.*, vol. 33, pp. 695–719 (1949).

Jakosky, J. J.: Whither Exploration, *A.A.P.G. Bull.*, vol. 31, pp. 1118–1124 (1947).

Kay, M.: Paleogeographic and Palinspastic Maps, *A.A.P.G. Bull.*, vol. 29, pp. 426–450 (1945).

Kellum, L. B.: Geologic History of Northern Mexico and Its Bearing on Petroleum Exploration, *A.A.P.G. Bull.*, vol. 28, pp. 301–376 (1944).

Krampert, E. W.: Geological Characteristics of Producing Oil and Gas Fields in Wyoming, Colorado, and Northwestern New Mexico, "Problems of Petroleum Geology," American Association of Petroleum Geologists, Tulsa, pp. 719–734 (1934).

Krumbein, W. C.: Lithofacies Maps and Regional Sedimentary-stratigraphic Analysis, *A.A.P.G. Bull.*, vol. 32, pp. 1909–1923 (1948).

———: Some Relations among Sedimentation, Stratigraphy and Seismic Exploration, *A.A.P.G. Bull.*, vol. 35, pp. 1505–1522 (1951).

——— and Sloss, L. L.: Principles of Correlation, "Stratigraphy and Sedimentation," W. H. Freeman and Co., San Francisco, chap. 10, pp. 287–316 (1951).

Lahee, F. H.: A Study of the Evidences for Lateral and Vertical Migration of Oil, "Problems of Petroleum Geology," American Association of Petroleum Geologists, Tulsa, pp. 399–428 (1934).

Landes, K. K.: "Petroleum Geology," John Wiley & Sons, Inc., New York (1951).

Lees, G. M.: Foreland Folding, *Geol. Soc. London Quart. Jour.*, vol. 108, pp. 1–34 (1952).

———: The Geology of the Oil Field Belt of Iran and Iraq, "Science of Petroleum," Oxford University Press, New York, vol. 1, pp. 140–148 (1938).

——— and Richardson, F. D. S.: The Geology of the Oil-field Belt of Southwest Iran and Iraq, *Geol. Mag.*, vol. 77, pp. 227–252 (1940).

——— and Taitt, A. H.: The Geological Results of the Search for Oil Fields in Great Britain, *Geol. Soc. London Quart. Jour.*, vol. 101, pp. 255–317 (1945).

Leet, L. D.: Elastic Rebound, "Practical Seismology and Seismic Prospecting," Appleton-Century-Crofts, Inc., New York, pp. 330–333 (1938).

Levorsen, A. I.: Convergence Studies in the Mid-Continent Region, *A.A.P.G. Bull.*, vol. 11, pp. 657–682 (1927).

———: Discovery Thinking, *A.A.P.G. Bull.*, vol. 27, pp. 887–928 (1943).

———: Our Petroleum Resources, *G.S.A. Bull.*, vol. 59, pp. 283–300 (1948).

———: Petroleum Geology, *A.A.P.G. Bull.*, vol. 24, pp. 1355–1360 (1940).

———: The Petroleum Prospect, *Mines Mag.*, vol. 41, no. 10, pp. 24–29 (Oct., 1951).

———: Stratigraphic versus Structural Accumulation, *A.A.P.G. Bull.*, vol. 20, pp. 521–530 (1936).

———: Studies in Paleogeography, *A.A.P.G. Bull.*, vol. 17, pp. 1107–1132 (1933).

———: Trends in Petroleum Geology, *Econ. Geology*, vol. 36, pp. 763–773 (1941).

Liddle, R. A.: "The Geology of Venezuela and Trinidad," Paleontological Research Institute, Ithaca, N.Y., 2d ed., (1946).

Lilley, E. R.: "The Geology of Petroleum and Natural Gas," D. Van Nostrand Company, Inc., New York (1928).

Link, T. A.: Interpretations of Foothills Structures, Alberta, Canada, *A.A.P.G. Bull.*, vol. 33, pp. 1475–1501 (1949).

Link, W. K.: Significance of Oil and Gas Seeps in World Oil Exploration, *A.A.P.G. Bull.*, vol. 35, pp. 1505–1540 (1952).

Lockett, J. R.: General Structure of Producing Sands in Eastern Ohio, *A.A.P.G. Bull.*, vol. 11, pp. 1023–1033 (1927).

Loveley, H. R.: Geological Occurrence of Oil in United Kingdom, with Reference to Present Exploratory Operations, *A.A.P.G. Bull.*, vol. 30, pp. 1444–1516 (1946).

McClain, A. H.: Stratigraphic Accumulation in the Jackson-Kanawha Counties Area of West Virginia, *A.A.P.G. Bull.*, vol. 33, pp. 336–345 (1949).

McClellan, H. W.: Subsurface Distribution of Pre-Mississippian Rocks of Kansas and Oklahoma, *A.A.P.G. Bull.*, vol. 14, pp. 1535–1556 (1930).

McCollough, E. H.: Structural Influence on Accumulation of Petroleum in California, "Problems of Petroleum Geology," American Association of Petroleum Geologists, Tulsa, pp. 735–760 (1934).

McCoy, A. W.: An Interpretation of Local Structural Development in Mid-Continent Areas Associated with Deposits of Petroleum, "Problems of Petroleum Geology," American Association of Petroleum Geologists, Tulsa, pp. 581–628 (1934).

——— and Keyte, W. R.: Present Interpretations of Structural Theory for Oil and Gas Migration and Accumulation, "Problems of Petroleum Geology," American Association of Petroleum Geologists, Tulsa, pp. 253–308 (1934).

McCoy, A. W., III, and others: Types of Oil and Gas Traps in Rocky Mountain Region, *A.A.P.G. Bull.*, vol. 35, pp. 1000–1037 (1951).

Mansfield, G. R.: Geography, Geology and Mineral Resources of Part of Southeastern Idaho, *U.S.G.S. Prof. Paper* 152 (1929).

Marshall, J. W.: Spraberry Reservoir of West Texas, *A.A.P.G. Bull.*, vol. 36, pp. 2189–2191 (1952).

Meholin, G. L.: Recent Geological Developments in Western Anadarko Basin, Texas and Oklahoma Panhandles, *A.A.P.G. Bull.*, vol. 34, pp. 1530–1539 (1950).

Mellen, F. F.: Black Warrior Basin, Alabama and Mississippi, *A.A.P.G. Bull.*, vol. 31, pp. 1801–1816 (1947).

Miller, B. L.: Geological Significance of Geophysical Data, *G.S.A. Bull.*, vol. 48, pp. 803–812 (1937).

Miller, W.: The Relationship of Structure to Petroleum Production in Eastern Venezuela, *Econ. Geology*, vol. 34, pp. 524–536 (1939).

Minor, H. E., and Hanna, M. A.: East Texas Oil Field, Rusk, Cherokee, Smith, Gregg and Upshur Counties, Texas, "Stratigraphic Type Oil Fields," American Association of Petroleum Geologists, Tulsa, pp. 600–640 (1941).

Moody, C. L.: Petroleum Geology, *A.A.P.G. Bull.*, vol. 35, pp. 1499–1504 (1951).

Moore, E. L., and Shields, J. A.: Chimire Field, Anzoategui, Venezuela, *A.A.P.G. Bull.*, vol. 36, pp. 857–877 (1952).

Morgan, F. A.: Oil Finding, *A.A.P.G. Bull.*, vol. 36, pp. 1297–1304 (1952).

Muir, J. M.: Limestone Reservoir Rocks in the Mexican Oil Fields, "Problems of Petroleum Geology," American Association of Petroleum Geologists, Tulsa, pp. 377–398 (1934).

National Petroleum Council: "Productive Capacity," National Petroleum Council, Washington, D.C., 102 pp. (1952).

Nettleton, L. L.: Geophysics, Geology and Oil Finding, *A.A.P.G. Bull.*, vol. 49, pp. 1154–1160 (1949).

Newcombe, R. B.: Oil and Gas Fields of Michigan, *Michigan Geol. and Biol. Survey Pub.* 38, Geol. Ser. 32 (1932).

———: Structure and Accumulation in the Michigan "Basin" and Its Relation to the Cincinnati Arch, "Problems of Petroleum Geology," American Association of Petroleum Geologists, Tulsa, pp. 531–556 (1934).

Noble, E. B.: Geological Masks and Prejudices, *A.A.P.G. Bull.*, vol. 31, pp. 1109–1117 (1947).

Notestein, F. B., Hubman, C. W., and Bowler, J. W.: Geology of Barco Concession, Republic of Colombia, South America, *G.S.A. Bull.*, vol. 55, pp. 1165–1218 (1944).

Nugent, L. E., Jr.: Aerial Photographs in Structural Mapping of Sedimentary Formations, *A.A.P.G. Bull.*, vol. 31, pp. 478–494 (1947).

Olcott, D. P.: Amelia Field, Occurrence of Oil in Texas, *Univ. Texas Bur. Econ. Geology, Progress Rept.*, pp. 43–47 (1949).

Pack, R. W.: The Sunset-Midway Oil Field, Calif.: I, Geology and Oil Resources, *U.S.G.S. Prof. Paper* 116 (1920).

Phinney, A. J.: The Natural-gas Field of Indiana, *U.S.G.S. Ann. Rept.* 11, part 1, pp. 579–742 (1891).

Pirtle, G. W.: Michigan Structural Basin and Its Relationship to Surrounding Areas, *A.A.P.G. Bull.*, vol. 16, pp. 145–152 (1932).

Possible Future Oil Provinces of the United States and Canada, by various authors, *A.A.P.G. Bull.*, 25, pp. 1433–1586 (1941).

Possible Future Petroleum Provinces of North America, a Symposium Edited by M. W. Bell and others, *A.A.P.G. Bull.*, vol. 35, pp. 141–498 (1951).

Pratt, W. E.: Distribution of Petroleum in the Earth's Crust, *A.A.P.G. Bull.*, vol. 28, pp. 1506–1509 (1944).

———: Geology in the Petroleum Industry, *A.A.P.G. Bull.*, vol. 24, pp. 1209–1213 (1940).

———: Toward a Philosophy of Oil Finding, *A.A.P.G. Bull.*, vol. 36, pp. 2231–2236 (1952).

——— and Good, D., Eds.: "World Geography of Petroleum," American Geographical Society, Special Publication 31, Princeton University Press, Princeton, N.J. (1951).

Pressler, E. D.: Geology and Occurrence of Oil in Florida, *A.A.P.G. Bull.*, vol. 31, pp. 1851–1862 (1947).

"Problems of Petroleum Geology," American Association of Petroleum Geologists, Tulsa (1934).

Pugh, W. E., and Preston, B. G., Eds.: "Bibliography of Stratigraphic Traps," Seismograph Service Corp., Tulsa (1951).

Reed, J. C.: Recent Investigations by United States Geological Survey of Petroleum Possibilities in Alaska, *A.A.P.G. Bull.*, vol. 30, pp. 1433–1443 (1946).

Reed, R. D.: "Geology of California," American Association of Petroleum Geologists, Tulsa (1933).

—— and Hollister, J. S.: Structural Evolution of Southern California, *A.A.P.G. Bull.*, vol. 20, pp. 1529–1721 (1936).

Reeves, F.: Australian Oil Possibilities, *A.A.P.G. Bull.*, vol. 35, pp. 2479–2525 (1951).

——: Outline for Classification of Oil Possibilities, *A.A.P.G. Bull.*, vol. 30, pp. 111–115 (1946).

——: Status of German Oil Fields, *A.A.P.G. Bull.*, vol. 30, pp. 1546–1584 (1946).

—— and Price, P. H.: Early Devonian Gas in Northern West Virginia and Pre-Devonian Oil Prospects, *A.A.P.G. Bull.*, vol. 34, pp. 2095–2132 (1950).

Rich, J. L.: Oil Possibilities of South America in the Light of Regional Geology, *A.A.P.G. Bull.*, vol. 29, pp. 495–563 (1945).

——: Problems of the Origin, Migration and Accumulation of Oil, "Problems of Petroleum Geology," American Association of Petroleum Geologists, Tulsa, pp. 337–346 (1934).

Richardson, G. B.: Geologic Structure and Occurrence of Gas in Part of Southwestern New York: II, Subsurface Structure of Part of Southwestern New York and Mode of Occurrence of Gas in the Medina Group, *U.S.G.S. Bull.*, 899(b) (1941).

Rojas, A. G.: Mexican Oil Fields, *A.A.P.G. Bull.*, vol. 33, pp. 1336–1350 (1949).

Russell, R. D.: Future of Field Geology, Discussion, *A.A.P.G. Bull.*, vol. 25, pp. 324–326 (1941).

——: Trends in Sedimentology, *A.A.P.G. Bull.*, vol. 33, pp. 1145–1153 (1949).

Russell, W. L.: Geology of the Oil and Gas Fields of Western Kentucky, *A.A.P.G. Bull.*, vol. 16, pp. 231–254 (1932).

——: Oil and Gas Accumulation in the Clinton Sand of Ohio, *Econ. Geology*, vol. 21, pp. 538–559 (1926).

——: The Origin of Artesian Pressure, *Econ. Geology*, vol. 13, pp. 132–157 (1928).

Rutherford, R. L.: Structural Interpretation of Loci of Petroliferous Parts of Devonian Reefs in Edmonton Area, Alberta, Canada, *A.A.P.G. Bull.*, vol. 35, pp. 844–853 (1951).

Sale, H. M., and Evans, P.: The Geology of British Oil Fields: I, The Geology of the Assam-Arakan Oil Region (India and Burma), *Geol. Mag.*, vol. 77, pp. 337–363 (1940).

Sanders, C. W.: Stratigraphic Type Oil Fields and Proposed New Classification of Reservoir Traps, *A.A.P.G. Bull.*, vol. 27, pp. 539–550 (1943).

Schneegans, D.: Gas Bearing Structures of Southern France, *A.A.P.G. Bull.*, vol. 32, pp. 198–214 (1948).

Schneider, W. T.: Geology of Wasson Field, Yoakum and Gaines Counties, Texas, *A.A.P.G. Bull.*, vol. 27, pp. 479–523 (1943).

Schuppli, H. M.: Geology of Oil Basins of East Indian Archipelago, *A.A.P.G. Bull.*, vol. 30, pp. 1–22 (1946).

Selk, E. L.: Types of Oil and Gas Traps in Southern Oklahoma, *A.A.P.G. Bull.*, vol. 35, pp. 582–606 (1951).

Sellards, O. H.: Oil Fields in Igneous Rocks in Coastal Plain of Texas, *A.A.P.G.Bull.*, vol. 16, pp. 741–768 (1932).

Shanazarov, D. A.: Petroleum Problem of Siberia, *A.A.P.G. Bull.*, vol. 32, pp. 153–197 (1948).

Sherrill, R. E., Dickey, P. A., and Matteson, L. S.: Types of Stratigraphic Oil Pools in Venango Sands of Northwestern Pennsylvania, "Stratigraphic Type Oil

Fields," American Association of Petroleum Geologists, Tulsa, pp. 507–538 (1941).

Smith, H. T. U.: "Aerial Photographs and Their Applications," Appleton-Century-Crofts, Inc. (1943).

Stach, L. W.: Petroleum Exploration and Production in Western Pacific during World War II, A.A.P.G. Bull., vol. 31, pp. 1384–1403 (1947).

Stamp, L. D.: The Conditions Governing the Occurrence of Oil in Burma, Jour. Inst. Petroleum (London), vol. 13, pp. 21–70 (1927).

Stewart, J. S.: Petroleum Possibilities in Mackenzie River Valley, N.W.T., Canadian Inst. Min. Metallurgy Trans., vol. 47, pp. 152–171 (1944).

"Stratigraphic Type Oil Fields," American Association of Petroleum Geologists, Tulsa (1941).

"Structure of Typical American Oil Fields," American Association of Petroleum Geologists, Tulsa, vols. 1 and 2, (1929); vol. 3 (1948).

Summerford, H. E., Schieck, E. E., and Hiestand, T. C.: Oil and Gas Accumulation Controlled by Sedimentary Facies in Upper Cretaceous Newcastle Sandstone, Wyoming, A.A.P.G. Bull., vol. 34, pp. 1850–1865 (1950).

Suter, H. H.: Relative Role of Some Geological Tools in Oil Exploration, A.A.P.G. Bull., vol. 32, 2127–2139 (1948).

Sutton, F. A.: Geology of Maracaibo Basin, Venezuela, A.A.P.G. Bull., vol. 30, pp. 1621–1741 (1946).

Swesnik, R. M., and Wheeler, R. R.: Stratigraphic Convergence Problems in Oil Finding, A.A.P.G. Bull., vol. 31, pp. 2021–2029 (1947).

Taylor, E. F.: Geology and Oil Fields of Brazil, A.A.P.G. Bull., vol. 36, pp. 1613–1626 (1952).

Thomas, C. R.: Geology and Petroleum Exploration in Magallanes Province, Chile, A.A.P.G. Bull., vol. 33, pp. 1553–1578 (1949).

Thomas, E. P.: Mississippi Structures and Their Relation to Oil Accumulation, A.A.P.G. Bull., vol. 34, pp. 1502–1516 (1950).

Thomas, H. D.: Changing Concepts in Wyoming Petroleum Exploration, Mines Mag., vol. 41, pp. 57–60 (1951).

Tomlinson, C. W.: Relation of Oil and Gas Accumulation to Geologic Structure in the Mid-Continent Region, "Problems of Petroleum Geology," American Association of Petroleum Geologists, Tulsa, pp. 571–580 (1934).

Van Tuyl, F. M., and Parker, B. H.: The Time of Origin and Accumulation of Petroleum, Colorado School of Mines Quart., vol. 36, no. 2, pp. 1–180 (1941).

Wagoner, G. E.: Geophysical Frontiers, A.A.P.G. Bull., vol. 35, pp. 1523–1528 (1951).

Walters, R. P.: Oil Fields of Carpathian Region, A.A.P.G. Bull., vol. 30, pp. 319–336 (1946).

Weaver, C. E.: Geology of Oregon and Washington and Its Relation to Occurrence of Oil and Gas, A.A.P.G. Bull., vol. 29, pp. 1377–1415 (1945).

Weaver, P.: Geological Interpretation of Exploratory Wells, A.A.P.G. Bull., vol. 33, pp. 1135–1144 (1949).

Weeks, L. G.: Concerning Estimates of Oil Reserves, A.A.P.G. Bull., vol. 34, pp. 1947–1953 (1950).

———: Factors of Sedimentary Basin Development That Control Oil Occurrence, A.A.P.G. Bull., vol. 36, pp. 2071–2124 (1952).

———: Paleogeography of South America, A.A.P.G. Bull., vol. 31, pp. 1194–1241 (1947).

Wegemann, C. H.: The Salt Creek Oil Field, Wyoming, U.S.G.S. Bull., 670 (1917).

Weller, J. M.: Outline of Chinese Geology, A.A.P.G. Bull., vol. 28, pp. 1417–1429 (1944).

Wharton, J. B., Jr.: Isopachous Maps of Sand Reservoirs, *A.A.P.G. Bull.*, vol. 32, pp. 1331–1339 (1948).

Willard, B., and Stevenson, R. E.: Northeastern Pennsylvania and Central New York Petroleum Probabilities, *A.A.P.G. Bull.*, vol. 34, pp. 2269–2283 (1950).

Willis, R.: Structural Development and Oil Accumulation in Texas Permian, *A.A.P.G. Bull.*, vol. 13, pp. 1033–1043 (1929).

Wilson, W. B.: Proposed Classification of Oil and Gas Reservoirs, "Problems of Petroleum Geology," American Association of Petroleum Geologists, Tulsa, pp. 433–446 (1934).

Workman, L. E.: Subsurface Geology of Chester Series in Illinois, *A.A.P.G. Bull.*, vol. 24, pp. 209–224 (1940).

LABORATORY PROBLEMS

Value for Training Students.   Laboratory work has a very important role in training beginning students in structural geology.   In fact, many students probably derive more insight into the true nature of the common geologic structures from the laboratory work of their first course in structural geology than from the lectures.   One does not get a thorough understanding of geologic structures from memorizing verbal descriptions.   On the other hand, anyone who can visualize the structures in three dimensions may be said to have this understanding.   The chief purpose of the laboratory work given on the succeeding pages is to train the student in this visualization.   The aim is to give a basic training in the fundamentals, rather than to concentrate on some special technique, such as structure contouring.   Many students can learn best by studying their own work, and benefit greatly by having their corrected laboratory problems returned for study.

Classification.   The classification of the laboratory problems is given in Table L-1.

General Instructions Regarding Problems Involving Geometry or Trigonometry.   Problems 1 to 14 involve geometrical relationships and may be solved by geometrical or trigonometrical methods.   One procedure which is helpful in solving such problems is to construct a cross section at right angles to the strike, with the various points and lines projected on this cross section.   Another helpful procedure is to project the points and lines to a horizontal plane.   This is what is done when a map is made.   Accordingly, distances measured between points projected on a horizontal plane are called map distances.   The relations between slope distance and map distance may be readily perceived if a vertical cross section is made which comprises the line along which the slope is measured.

PROBLEMS

1. In an area the strike is N. 15° W., and the dip 23° NE.   Bed *A* outcrops at point *B* at an elevation of 1,100 ft, and bed *C* outcrops at point *D* at an elevation of 1,600 ft.   Point *D* is N. 75° E. of point *B*, and the distance between *B* and *D* is 1,500 feet.   This distance is measured along the slope, which is at a uniform angle from *B* to *D*.   What is the thickness of the stratigraphic interval *AC*?   What is the depth of bed *A* at point *C*?

TABLE L-1. SUBJECT MATTER OF LABORATORY PROBLEMS

Subject	Problem numbers
Areal geologic maps, geologic maps, or outcrop maps	13, 18, 19, 20, 29, 30, 31, 32, 33, 34, 43, 46, 47, 48
Faults	29, 30, 31, 32, 33, 34, 46
Folds	18, 19, 20, 46
Unconformities	43
Block diagrams	21, 22
Convergence	48, 49
Cross sections	11, 12, 16, 26, 27, 28, 41, 42, 44, 45, 46
Dips	11
Faults and related structures	26, 27, 45
Folds	16, 17, 45
Salt domes and related features	45
Sedimentary structures relating to thickness	42, 12
Unconformities	41, 42
Dating structural events	50, 51
Depth	1, 2, 3, 5
Dip	1, 2, 3, 4, 5, 6, 7, 8, 9, 10, 11, 12, 39, 40
Depth in relation to dip	1, 2, 3, 5
Local dips from structure contours	39
Outcrops in relation to dip	4
Structure contours from local dips	40
Three-point problem	8, 9
Thickness in relation to dip	1, 2, 3, 5, 6, 7, 12
True dip from component dips	10, 11
Faults and related structures	13, 14, 26, 27, 29, 30, 31, 32, 33, 34, 45
Geologic maps (*See* Areal maps)	
Folds	16, 17, 19, 22, 23, 24, 25, 28, 30, 43, 46, 48, 49, 50, 51
Intersections	
Plane with curved surface	15
Two curved surfaces	47, 48
Two planes	13
Inlier	28
Isopach maps	49, 50
Outlier	28
Outcrops	1, 2, 3, 4, 15, 46
Outcrop maps (*See* Areal maps)	
Overlap	42
Sedimentary structures	44
Structure contours	14, 23, 24, 25, 35, 36, 37, 38, 39, 40, 47, 48, 49
Areal and topographic maps	48
Elevations at known points	35, 36, 37, 38
Folds	23, 24, 25
Local dips	40
Thickness	1, 2, 3, 5, 6, 7, 48, 49
Truncation	41, 42, 43, 51
Unconformities	41, 42, 43, 51
Width of outcrop	1, 2, 3, 4, 31, 32, 33, 34

2. The base of a formation crops out at point *A*. Point *B* is down the slope at right angles to the strike from point *A*. By sighting on point *B* from point *A* with a clinometer, it was determined that the straight line of sight from *A* to *B* slopes downward at an angle of 5°. The distance along this straight line from *A* to *B* is 1,500 ft. The top of the formation crops out at point *B*, and its base was encountered in a vertical borehole at a depth of 1,000 ft. What is the angle of dip (in degrees) and the thickness of the formation?

3. In an area where the strike and dip are uniform, the dip is known to be 26° in a general southeasterly direction. Point 1 is on bed *A* at an elevation of 2,310 ft, point 2 is on bed *A* at an elevation of 2,310 ft, and point 3 is on bed *B* at an elevation of 2,550 ft. Point 2 is 1,200 ft N. 55° E. of point 1. Point 3 is 1,350 ft N. 80° E. (measured along the uniform slope) from point 2. What is the strike and the stratigraphic interval between beds *A* and *B*? What is the depth of bed *A* at point 3?

4. In a certain region the land surface is level and the stratigraphic thickness of formation *A* does not change. Formation *A* is 100 ft thick. At area *B* in this region the width of the outcrop of formation *A*, measured at right angles to the strike, is 900 ft. At area *C* the width of the outcrop of formation *A*, measured in the same manner, is 200 ft. If the dip is expressed in percentage, what is the ratio of the dip at *C* to the dip at *B*? Would the ratio be the same if the dips were expressed in degrees?

5. In an area where the dip is 68°, a vertical borehole encounters the top of a formation at a depth of 112 ft and the base at a depth of 612 ft. What is the true thickness of the formation?

6. In what might be termed the step method for measuring the thickness of a stratigraphic interval, the clinometer of a Brunton is set at the angle of dip, and the observer sights in the direction of the dip. Starting at the base of the interval to be measured, he sights through the Brunton at a point on the ground. He then stands on this point and repeats this process, until his line of sight touches the top of the interval. Each step is equal to the height of the observer's eyes above the ground, and the thickness is assumed to be the height of each step times the number of steps. Where the dip is only a few degrees, there is no appreciable trigonometric error in this method, but where the dips are high there is an error. Let it be assumed that the line along which the sights are taken is at right angles to the strike. What is the true thickness of a formation if the dip is 32° and the thickness as measured by the step method is 500 ft?

7. The true thickness of a hard limestone is 1,000 ft, its strike N. 10° E., and its dip 50° W. A horizontal tunnel penetrates the limestone in a direction N. 30° E. What is the distance along the central axis of the tunnel between the top and bottom of the limestone?

8. A bed is at an elevation of 312 ft at point *A*, 132 ft at point *B*, and 199 ft at point *C*. Point *B* is N. 12° E. 2,200 ft from point *A*, and *C* is 1,700 ft N. 60° W. of point *B*. These distances are map distances. What are the strike and the dip in per cent? Per cent dip between two points is equal to 100 times the difference in elevation of the two points divided by the horizontal or map distance between them.

9. All the conditions are the same as in Prob. 8 except that the elevation of point *C* is 80 ft instead of 199 ft. What are the strike and the dip in per cent?

10. A vertical rock face in a quarry trends due north. The apparent dip in this rock face is 12° N. Another vertical rock face in the same quarry trends N. 60° W. The apparent dip along this rock face is 9° NW. What are the true dip and strike in degrees?

11. In an area the strata strike north and dip 50° E. What would be the apparent dip in vertical cross sections under the following conditions: (*a*) The plane of the cross

section strikes east and west?   (b) The plane of the cross section strikes north?
(c) The plane of the cross section strikes N. 40° E.?

12. In an area the strata strike N. 40° W. and dip 70° NE.   In each of two vertical
cross sections the apparent thickness of a formation on the cross section is 1,000 ft.
This apparent thickness is the distance between the top and bottom of the formation
in the plane of the cross section.   What is the true thickness of the formation under
the following conditions: (a) The cross section strikes N. 50° E.?   (b) The cross section strikes N. 40° W.?

13. A fault plane strikes N. 70° W. and dips 65° N.   Another fault plane strikes
N. 60° E. and dips 35° SE.   What is the direction on a map of the line formed by
the intersection of the two faults?

A simple method for solving this problem is to draw structure contours on the two
planes.   Let a line be drawn on a map parallel to the strike of each of the two planes.
These two lines may be considered to be structure contours on the two planes.   Let
it be assumed that the two structure contours have the same elevation.   Then the
two planes would intersect at the point where the two structure contours intersect.
Let two other structure contours be drawn one structure-contour interval higher or
lower than the two previously drawn.   The scale of the map and the structure-
contour interval should be chosen so that the two structure contours are several
inches apart.   The distance between the two successive structure contours on the
same plane is determined by the angle of dip.   These two additional structure contours of the same elevation also meet at a point on the line where the two planes
intersect.   Consequently the line connecting the points where the two sets of structure contours intersect is the line of intersection of the two planes.

14. What is the actual distance in inches on a map surface between successive
100-ft structure contours under the following conditions: (a) The scale of the map is
1,000 ft per in. and the dip is 2 per cent?   (b) The scale of the map is 100 ft per in.
and the dip is 20°?

In each case the structure-contour interval is 100 ft.

15. In Fig. L-1 the lines represent topographic contours.   The land surface is intersected by three planes, each of which has the same strike and dip throughout the area
shown.   These planes could be considered to represent stratigraphic horizons, fault
planes, dikes, sills, or veins.   The strikes and dips of these planes are as follows:
plane A, strike N. 20° W., dip 3 per cent NE.; plane B, strike N. 45° E., dip 5° NW.;
plane C, strike E-W, dip 25° S.

Draw the outcrop pattern for each of the three planes.   All these planes crop out
at point D at an elevation of 1,900 ft.

Note: The best method for solving this problem is to determine how far apart the
structure contours would be on each of the planes with the scale of the map and a
100-ft structure-contour interval.   Draw contours on each plane and make a dot
where each structure intersects the topographic contour of the same elevation.   Lines
connecting these dots are the outcrop patterns.

It should also be noted that the same method could be used to plot on a map the
intersection of a fault plane with a key horizon the structure of which is given by a
structure-contour map.   In this case the lines used in plotting the intersection would
be structure contours and not topographic contours.

16. Make cross sections showing the following parts of folds: (a) axial plane;
(b) trough plane; (c) crestal plane.

17. Make cross sections showing the following types of folds:

(a) Anticline   (b) Syncline
(c) Symmetrical anticline   (d) Asymmetrical anticline

(*e*) Overturned anticline

(*g*) Isoclinal folds

(*i*) Basin

(*k*) Geanticline

(*m*) Supratenuous anticline

(*o*) Homocline

(*q*) Anticlinorium

(*s*) Disharmonic folds

(*u*) Folds produced by slumping during deposition

(*f*) Recumbent anticline

(*h*) Fan folds

(*j*) Geosyncline

(*l*) Diapir or piercing folds

(*n*) Monocline

(*p*) Terrace

(*r*) Synclinorium

(*t*) Drag folds

(*v*) Folds produced by solution

In all problems involving areal maps assume that the land surface is flat, and that any structural relief produced by deformation has been completely beveled off by erosion. Letter the formations on the areal maps, and show beside the areal maps geologic columns. Each formation should be designated by the same letter in the geologic columns and the areal maps.

18. Make an areal geologic map showing an asymmetrical closed anticline.

19. The area to be shown on the map is square and the diagonals of the square are 8 miles long. The regional dip is northeast, and an anticline extends across the area from the southwest to the northeast corner. This anticline plunges northeast from the center of the square to its northeast corner, and from the southwest corner to a point 2 miles northeast of this corner. From this point to the center of the square the anticlinal axis plunges southwest. Hence there is a closed area on the anticline at the center of the square. Show these conditions by an areal map.

20. The area to be mapped is square, with a diagonal 8 miles long. The regional dip is north, and a syncline extends across the square from the southwest corner to the northeast corner. The synclinal axis plunges northeast from the southwest corner of the area to its center, and from the northeast corner to a point 2 miles southwest. From this point to the center of the square the axis of the syncline plunges southwest. Show these conditions by an areal geologic map.

21. Make a cabinet-type block diagram showing a closed anticline. Letter the formations shown on the top and sides of the block.

22. Make an isometric-type block diagram of a closed syncline. Letter the formations shown on the top and sides of the block.

23. Show the following by structure contours: (*a*) homocline; (*b*) monocline; (*c*) structural terrace; (*d*) saddle; (*e*) anticline with 60 ft of closure, using a 10-ft structure-contour interval; (*f*) anticline with 400 ft of reversal and no closure, using a 100-ft structure-contour interval.

24. Show the structural conditions of Prob. 19 by structure contours. Use a 100-ft structure-contour interval and show 400 ft of closure on the anticline.

25. Show the structural conditions of Prob. 20 by structure contours. Use a 100-ft structure-contour interval and show 300 ft of closure in the syncline.

26. In parts (*a*) to (*h*) let the plane of the cross sections be at right angles to the strike of the fault planes. Show the following by cross sections:

(*a*) Hade and dip of the fault plane

(*c*) Dip slip

(*e*) Heave

(*g*) Normal and reverse drag

(*i*) Bedding fault

(*k*) Omission and repetition of beds in wells because of faulting

(*b*) Hanging and foot walls

(*d*) Throw

(*f*) Stratigraphic throw

(*h*) Normal and reverse faults

(*j*) Omission and repetition of outcrops of beds at surface because of faulting

27. Make cross sections showing the following features or structures associated with faults:

(a) Horst
(c) Horse
(e) Imbricate structure
(g) Resequent and obsequent erosional fault scarps

(b) Graben
(d) Slice
(f) Decollement
(h) Klippe and fenster

28. (a) Make a cross section showing an outlier and an inlier produced as a result of folding.

(b) Make a cross section showing an outlier produced by erosion and topographic variations in an area of uniform dip.

Compare the klippe and fenster with the outlier and inlier, and note resemblances and differences.

29. Show the following features by areal maps:

(a) Horst
(c) Transverse fault
(e) Strike fault

(b) Graben
(d) Longitudinal fault
(f) Dip fault

30. In an area where the regional dip is northeast, an anticline plunges northeast. This anticline is cut by a fault striking northwest, with its downthrown side on the southwest. Show these features by an areal geologic map.

31. In a certain area the formations dip due north at a uniform rate of 20 ft per mile, except where faulted. These strata are cut by a fault with a north-south strike, no strike slip, and a throw of 80 ft, the downthrown side being on the east. Make an areal geologic map showing how the outcrops of a formation 10 ft thick would be affected by the fault. Indicate north and give a graphic scale. Make the scale of the map 1 in. per mile. Assume that the land surface is flat and that any topographic relief produced by the structural deformation has been completely beveled off by erosion.

32. All the conditions are exactly the same as in Prob. 29 except that the fault has 4 miles of strike slip and no dip slip. The east side of the fault has moved south relative to the west side. Make an areal geologic map showing these features. Compare this areal map with that of Prob. 31.

33. In an area the exposed formations have the following thicknesses: formation *A*, 50 ft, *B*, 100 ft, *C*, 200 ft, *D*, 300 ft, and *E*, 400 ft. The strata dip uniformly due north at a rate of 1°. They are cut by a vertical fault with no strike slip which strikes due north. Make an areal map showing that the throw of the fault is 100 ft.

34. The conditions are the same as in Prob. 33 except that the formations dip 50° due north. Make an areal map showing that the throw of the fault is 300 ft.

Problems 35 to 38 involve drawing structure contours around points at which the elevations of the key horizons are known. The positions of these points are given on the location maps, Figs. L-2 to L-5. The numbers given in Probs. 35 to 38 are the elevations at which the key horizons were encountered in the boreholes at the locations indicated. These elevations are in feet, and the minus sign indicates depth below sea level. It should be noted that in a number of cases there is no figure for the elevation of a key horizon at a particular location. This indicates that there is no information about the elevation of the key horizon at this particular location.

In solving Probs. 35 to 38 the following procedure should be followed: (*1*) Place the figure indicating the elevation of the key horizon beside each well location. Leave these figures on the maps when they are handed in. (*2*) Draw the structure contours. (*3*) Number each structure contour. (*4*) Show by diagonal lines the areas which are promising for oil and gas accumulation. (*5*) If faults are shown, assume that the dip of the fault planes is 60° and show by horizontal lines the areas in which the key horizon is cut out by the fault. *M* indicates that the key horizon is missing because of faulting at the location indicated.

35. Draw structure contours, using a 100-ft structure-contour interval.

1	580	11	380	21	440	31	290	40	330	51	705	61	490
3	540	12	570	23	340	32	390	42	60	52	725	63	270
4	510	13	540	24	260	33	250	43	710	53	570	64	280
5	430	14	450	25	350	35	130	44	770	55	360	65	180
6	480	15	460	26	320	36	620	45	620	57	290	66	240
7	380	17	280	28	290	37	470	46	520	58	360	67	380
8	480	18	240	29	510	38	550	48	270	59	500	68	470
9	410	19	460	30	380	39	460	50	270	60	620	69	370
												70	280

36. Draw structure contours, using a 200-ft structure-contour interval.

1	−425	11	−300	21	−440	29	−10	39	−550	49	175	59	−400
3	100	13	480	22	−50	30	420	40	−400	50	0	61	240
5	620	15	−880	23	−470	31	−310	41	−100	52	−190	62	450
7	700	16	−370	24	−120	32	−330	42	200	53	−250	63	310
8	−680	17	20	26	0	34	30	44	280	54	100	64	−400
9	−220	19	225	28	375	36	45	46	−80	55	430	66	−450
						37	420	47	100	56	30	68	240
						38	300	48	−195	58	−180	70	150

37. Draw structure contours, using a 100-ft structure-contour interval.

3	−2680	18	M	29	−3050	39	−2140	56	−3010
7	−2500	19	−2750	30	M	42	−2895	57	−2490
8	−2800	21	−2670	31	−2090	43	M	59	−2420
10	−2740	22	−2960	32	−2060	45	−2255	61	−2380
11	−2720	23	−2910	33	M	47	−2190	63	M
12	−2670	24	M	34	−2850	48	M	64	−2570
15	−2880	25	M	36	−3130	49	−2950	67	−2480
17	−2810	27	−2780	37	−2200	50	−2400	70	−2410
						52	−2340		
						55	−2250		

38. Draw structure contours, using a 200-ft structure-contour interval.

1	−6180	12	M			35	−6070	47	−5650	59	−6480
2	−6030	13	−6090	23	−5350	36	−5530	48	−5900	60	−5920
3	−5970	14	−6300	24	M	37	−5180	49	−6160	61	−6090
4	−6580	15	−5780	25	−6280	38	−6230	50	−5820	62	−6250
5	−6630	16	−5590	26	−5470	39	−6210	51	M	63	−6370
6	−6290	17	−5480	27	−5810	40	−5460	52	−6380	64	−6180

7	−6500	18	−6380	28	−6100	41	−5790	53	M	65	−6590
8	−5940	19	M	29	−5500	42	−6100	54	−5850	66	−6560
9	−5810	20	−5920	30	−5160	43	−5600	55	−6080	67	−6160
10	−5720	21	−6170	31	−6170	44	−5380	56	−6250	68	−6290
11	−6480	22	−5600	32	−6200	45	−6310	57	−5980	69	−6380
				33	−5470	46	M	58	−6500	70	−6500
				34	−5770						

39. Fig. L-6 is a structure-contour map. Indicate the dip and strike at each point marked x. Give the dip in per cent.

40. Fig. L-7 is a map showing local dips and strikes. The dips are in per cent. Show the anticlinal and synclinal axes on this map by dashed lines. Draw structure contours, using a 100-ft structure-contour interval. The key horizon to be contoured is at an elevation of 2,000 ft at point A. Number each structure contour.

41. Make cross sections showing the following types of unconformities: (a) disconformity; (b) angular unconformity; (c) nonconformity.

42. Make a cross section showing truncation and overlap at an angular unconformity.

43. Make an areal map showing two angular unconformities intersecting near the center of the map. Assume that the land surface is flat and give a geologic column showing the relations of the various formations.

44. Make cross sections showing the following: (a) limestone reef; (b) buried channel; (c) offshore sand bar; (d) cross-bedding; (e) top-set, fore-set, and bottom-set beds of a delta; (f) buried hill, with overlying anticline due to compaction.

45. Make cross sections showing the following features related to salt domes: (a) arrangement of overlying faults; (b) overlying uplift; (c) overhang; (d) cap rock, showing three zones; (e) marginal upturning; (f) rim syncline; (g) residual high.

46. Fig. L-8 is a geologic map of an area where the ground surface is level. Make cross sections along the lines LM and NO. Make the horizontal scale of the cross section 1,000 ft per in., and the vertical scale 100 ft per in. Assume that all fault planes are vertical. Indicate the direction of movement along the faults. Show the position of the formation contacts down to a depth of 200 ft below the surface.

47. Fig. L-9 is a map showing both topographic contours and structure contours. Show on the map the outcrop of the key horizon contoured.

48. Fig. L-10 is a combined areal and topographic map. Make a structure map on bed A, using a 20-ft structure-contour interval. Number all structure contours. The first stage in solving this problem is to draw structure contours on beds A and B. Then select three localities where the dip appears from the structure contours to be fairly uniform between beds A and B. Determine for each of these localities what stratigraphic interval between beds A and B produces the least irregularity in dip between the outcrops of beds A and B. Take the average of these three measurements of interval, and use it for converting the structure contours on bed B to structure contours on bed A.

49. Fig. L-11 is a structure map on bed A. Bed B is below bed A. The interval between beds A and B at the location of the four wells near the corners of the map is given by the figures beside them. Except for the tilting necessary to produce the changes in interval between beds A and B, there was no structural deformation during the time when the strata in the interval between beds A and B were being deposited.

(a) Shade in the closed areas shown by the structure contours on bed A.

(b) Make an isopach map of the interval between beds A and B, using an interval of 100 ft between successive isopach lines.

(c) Draw structure contours on bed *B*, using a 100-ft structure-contour interval and numbering all structure contours.

(d) Shade in the closed areas shown by structure contours on bed *B*, using a different pattern or color from that used to show the closed areas on bed *A*.

50. Fig. L-12 shows a structure map on bed *A*. The interval between bed *A* and bed *B*, which is below bed *A*, in general increases toward the west at a rate of 20 ft per mile. There was 100 ft of local uplift on the closed anticline shown during the time between the deposition of beds *A* and *B*. This uplift did not affect the area outside of this anticline. Make an isopach map of the interval between beds *A* and *B*, using an interval of 20 ft between successive isopach lines.

51. Fig. L-13 is a structure section. Make a cross section showing conditions as they were at the beginning of the deposition of formation *I*.

Fig. L-1.

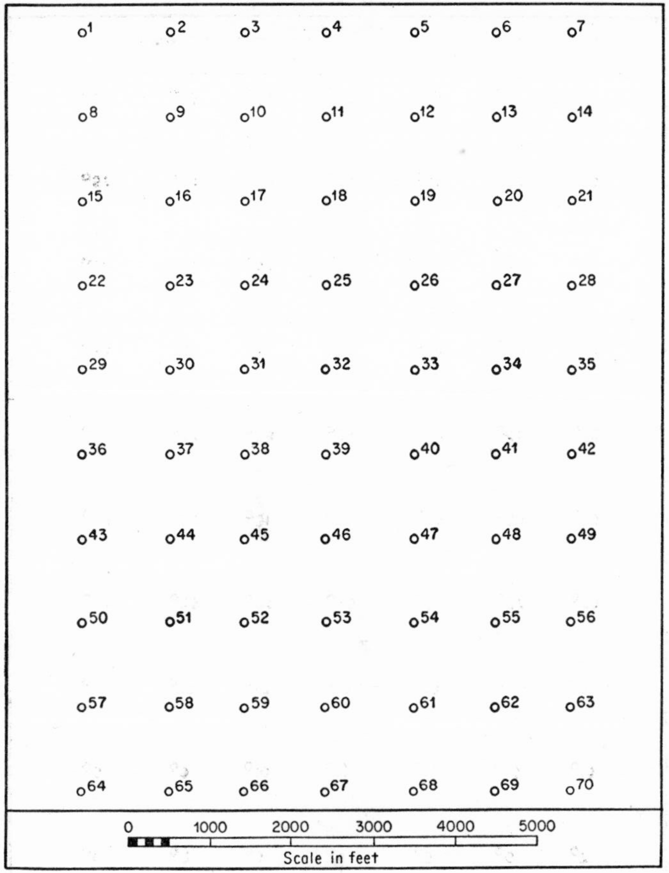

o1 o2 o3 o4 o5 o6 o7
o8 o9 o10 o11 o12 o13 o14
o15 o16 o17 o18 o19 o20 o21
o22 o23 o24 o25 o26 o27 o28
o29 o30 o31 o32 o33 o34 o35
o36 o37 o38 o39 o40 o41 o42
o43 o44 o45 o46 o47 o48 o49
o50 o51 o52 o53 o54 o55 o56
o57 o58 o59 o60 o61 o62 o63
o64 o65 o66 o67 o68 o69 o70

0   1000   2000   3000   4000   5000

Scale in feet

FIG. L-2.

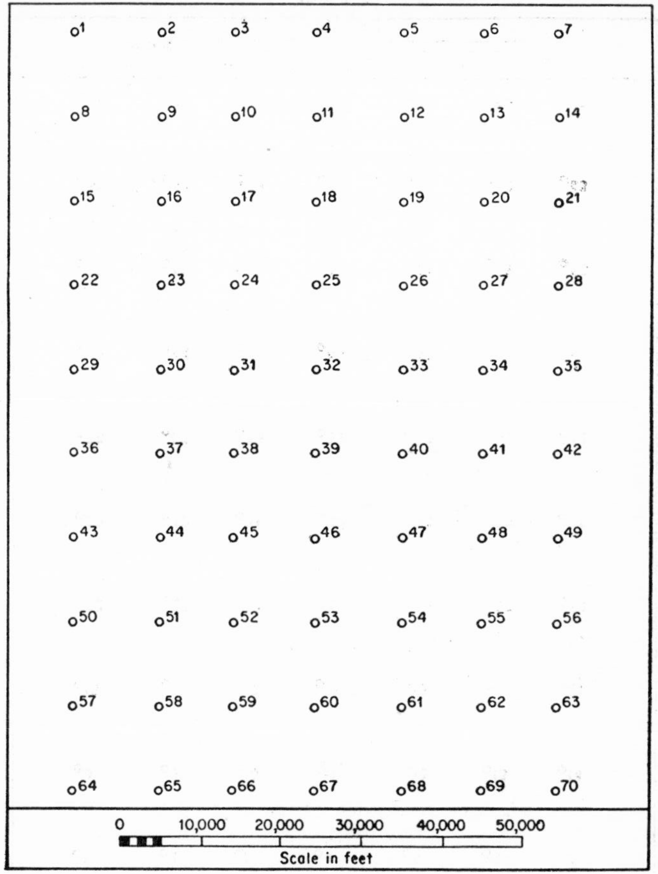

o1 o2 o3 o4 o5 o6 o7
o8 o9 o10 o11 o12 o13 o14
o15 o16 o17 o18 o19 o20 o21
o22 o23 o24 o25 o26 o27 o28
o29 o30 o31 o32 o33 o34 o35
o36 o37 o38 o39 o40 o41 o42
o43 o44 o45 o46 o47 o48 o49
o50 o51 o52 o53 o54 o55 o56
o57 o58 o59 o60 o61 o62 o63
o64 o65 o66 o67 o68 o69 o70

0   10,000   20,000   30,000   40,000   50,000

Scale in feet

FIG. L-3.

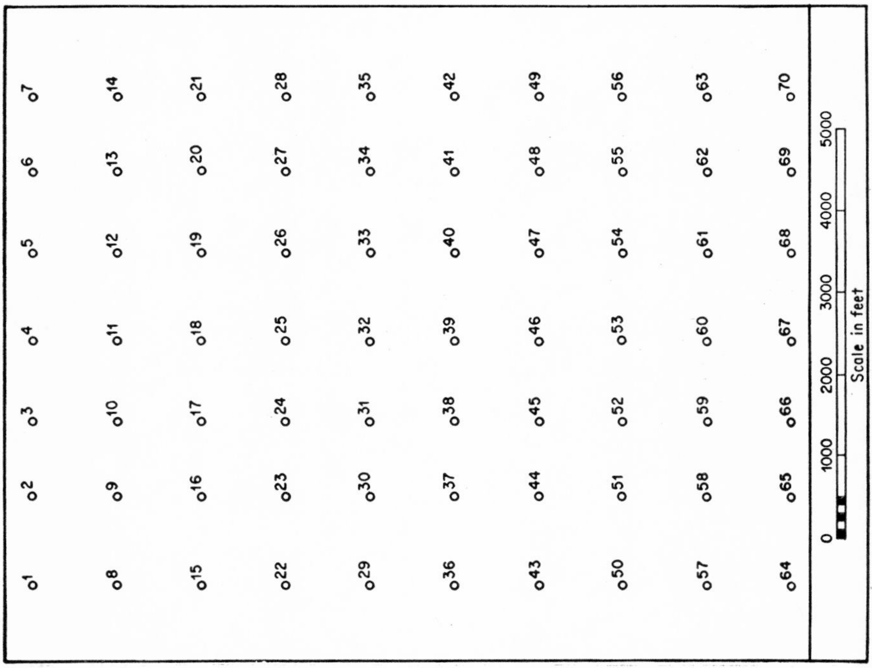

Scale in feet

FIG. L-5.

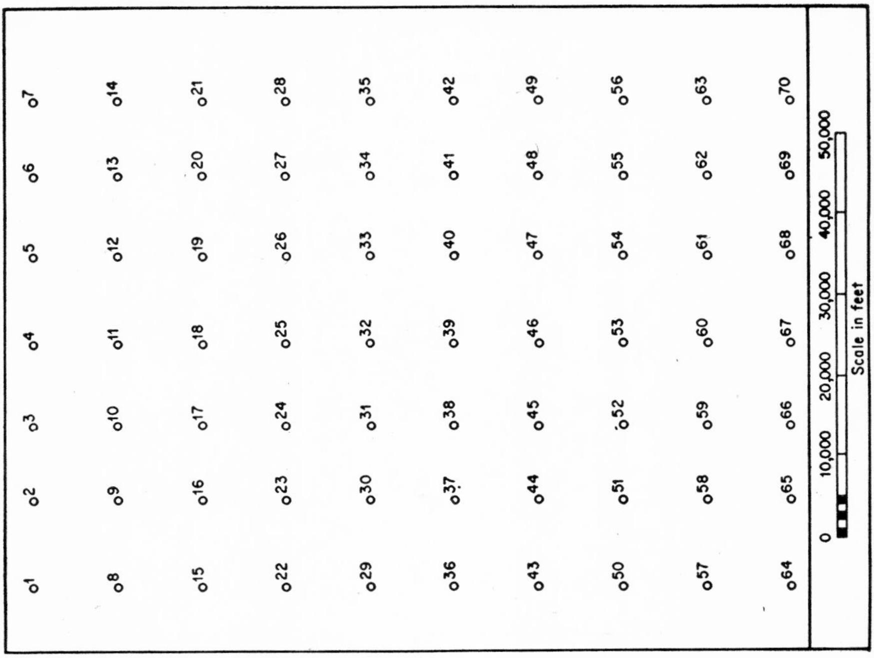

Scale in feet

FIG. L-4.

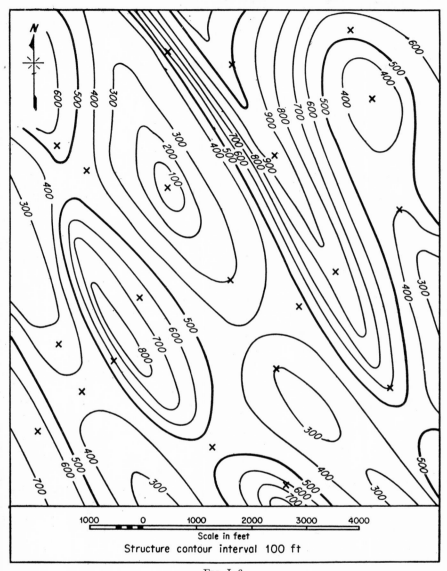

Scale in feet

Structure contour interval 100 ft

Fɪɢ. L-6.

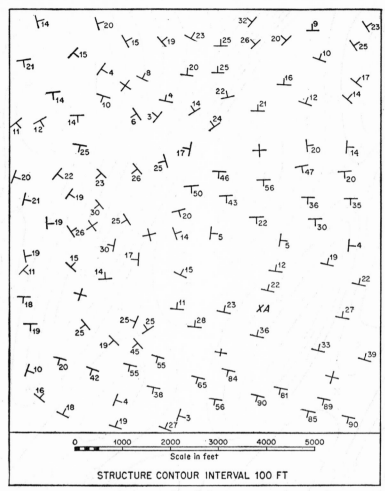

STRUCTURE CONTOUR INTERVAL 100 FT

Fig. L-7.

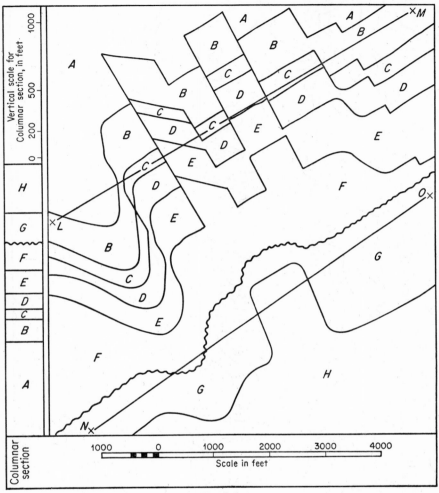

Fig. L-8.

Fig. L-9.

Fig. L-10.

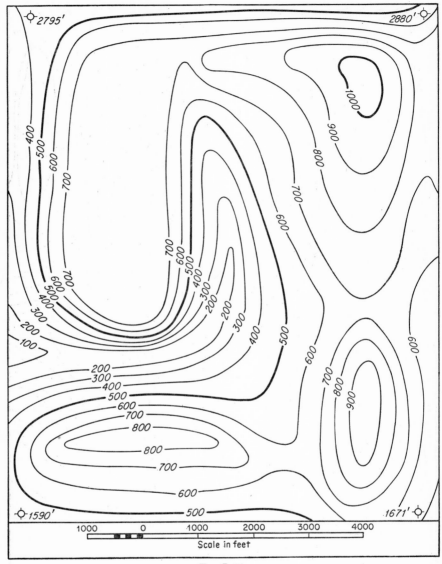

Fɪɢ. L-11.

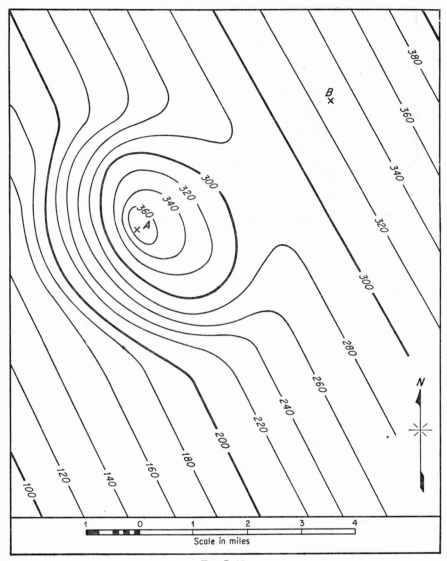

Fig. L-12.

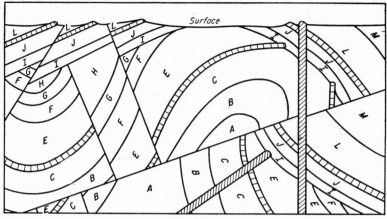

Fig. L-13.

INDEX